THERMOPHYSICS

A Series of Books in Physics
EDITORS: Henry M. Foley, Malvin A. Ruderman

Concepts of Classical Optics
  John Strong

Thermophysics
  Allen L. King

Introduction to Electromagnetic Field and Waves
  Dale R. Corson and Paul Lorrain

Modern Quantum Theory
  Behram Kurşunoğlu

X-Ray Diffraction in Crystals, Imperfect Crystals, and Amorphous Bodies
  A. Guinier

On the Interaction Between Atomic Nuclei and Electrons (*A Golden Gate Edition*)
  H. B. G. Casimir

THERMOPHYSICS

by ALLEN L. KING, *Dartmouth College*

W. H. FREEMAN AND COMPANY

SAN FRANCISCO AND LONDON

(C2)

To my wife

    NANCY TESSIENE KING

and our children

    NANCY MARIBETH

    ALLEN ANTHRON

    FERN TESSIENE

PREFACE

Thermophysics is not a separate well-defined discipline, nor is it simply a sequence of related subjects. Rather it is a broad area of physics which is pervaded by the temperature concept. I have adopted the generic term Thermophysics* as a title for this book, instead of listing several of the subjects touched upon, as is so often done (for example, thermodynamics, kinetic theory, statistical mechanics). By so doing I suggest that there is a certain unity and coherence in the subject matter and at the same time avoid the ambiguity and confusion which has arisen as a result of attempts to appropriate the long-established term "thermodynamics" for essentially the same purpose.

This text and reference book is designed for serious students who have had excellent courses in elementary college physics and mathematics, including the calculus, and who wish to learn more about the thermophysical foundations of modern science. The level of difficulty increases as the student progresses in the subject. Chapters are so arranged that an adequate short course in heat and thermodynamics may be built around the first ten chapters or a somewhat longer course, including kinetic theory and classical statistical mechanics, around the first thirteen chapters. With additional selected material from topical Chapters 14–21 the book may be used in a full year course. Furthermore, with a minimum of guidance it should be suitable for self-study by honor students, especially if reference is made to other sources as suggested in the bibliographies in Chapter 1 and in Chapters 14–21.

Several topics of unusual significance which are discussed only briefly in the early part of the book are expanded and developed more fully in Chapters 14–21. Each of these chapters is self-contained and may be studied in almost any order, although occasionally some reference is made to earlier

---

* Guggenheim writes: "We have now seen what might be reasonably called *thermo-mechanics* (or *thermo-dynamics*), *thermo-hydrodynamics*, *thermo-electrostatics*, *thermo-electrodynamics* (or *thermo-magnetics*) and *thermo-chemics*. These examples are not exhaustive. . . . The natural and obvious name for the science which embraces all these classes is *thermophysics*." (*Thermodynamics*, North-Holland Publishing Company, Amsterdam, 1957, p. 5.)

discussions. On the other hand, none should be considered more than an introduction to a selected topic.

The problems at the end of the chapters are integral parts of the text; frequently they extend and illuminate the formal developments. No attempt has been made to list them in the order of their difficulty. The student sometimes will find it helpful to consult a suitable handbook, such as the *American Institute of Physics Handbook* or a recent edition of the *Handbook of Chemistry and Physics*.

For the most part symbols in this book are from the Final Report of the Committee on Letter Symbols and Abbreviations of the American Association of Physics Teachers (1948) as they are published in the *Handbook of Chemistry and Physics*. Intensive thermophysical quantities are distinguished from extensive ones by being printed sans-serif. Script symbols are used for a few other quantities.

A book such as this contains few, if any, original contributions. Nevertheless, it is very personal, for it embodies my interpretations of what I have learned from my teachers, from my colleagues, and from other authors whose books I have consulted. To all these people I am greatly indebted. In addition, special recognition is extended to former students whose inquisitive minds and youthful insight frequently have suggested new ways of presenting involved or abstruse parts of thermophysics.

March, 1962   A. L. KING

CONTENTS

CHAPTER 1

INTRODUCTION   1

1.1.   What Is Temperature?   1
1.2.   The Thermometer and Early Scales of Temperature   2
1.3.   Heat   4
1.4.   Internal Energy and the First Law of Thermodynamics   5
1.5.   Units of Energy   8
1.6.   Kinetic Theory and Statistical Thermophysics   9

CHAPTER 2

TEMPERATURE AND THERMOMETRY   13

2.1.   Thermal Equilibrium   14
2.2.   Temperature Concept   14
2.3.   Standards of Temperature   16
2.4.   The Triple-point Cell   17
2.5.   Comparison of Liquid-in-glass and
       Resistance Thermometers   18
2.6.   Gas Thermometers and the Standard
       Scale of Temperature   21
2.7.   Thermocouples and Pyrometers   26
2.8.   The International Temperature Scale   28
2.9.   Comparison of Temperature Scales   29

CHAPTER 3

EQUATIONS OF STATE AND THERMODYNAMIC 33 PROCESSES

3.1.   Equations of State for Fluid Systems   34
3.2.   Equations of State for Other Systems   36
3.3.   Reversible Quasistatic Process   38
3.4.   Thermodynamic Processes   39
3.5.   Thermophysical Coefficients   40
3.6.   Relations Among Partial Derivatives   42

CHAPTER 4

WORK AND HEAT   46

4.1.   Work   46
4.2.   Graphical Representation of Work   47
4.3.   Heat   49
4.4.   Heat Capacity   50
4.5. C_v and C_p 52
4.6.   Measurement of C_p 53
4.7.   Latent Heat and Heat of Reaction   55
4.8.   Work and Heat Reservoirs   57

CHAPTER 5

HEAT-WORK CYCLIC PROCESSES   61

5.1.   A Simple Heat-to-work Converter   61
5.2.   The Carnot Cycle   63
5.3.   Heat Engines and Refrigerators   65
5.4.   The Four-stroke Gasoline Engine   66
5.5.   The Diesel Engine   69
5.6.   The Gas Turbine and Jet Engine   71
5.7.   The Vapor-compression Refrigerator   72
5.8.   The Vapor-absorption Refrigerator   74

CHAPTER 6

THE SECOND LAW OF THERMODYNAMICS   78

6.1. Two Equivalent Statements of the Second Law of   78
      Thermodynamics
6.2. Carnot's Theorem   81
6.3. A Corollary to Carnot's Theorem   82
6.4. The Kelvin Temperature   82
6.5. The Kelvin Temperature Scale   83
6.6. Equality of the Kelvin and the Ideal Gas Temperature   84
6.7. General Form of the Clapeyron Equation   85
6.8. The Common Phase-transformations   86
6.9. Liquid Surfaces   88

CHAPTER 7

THERMODYNAMIC ENTROPY   91

7.1. The Clausius Theorem   91
7.2. Thermodynamic Entropy   93
7.3. The Third Law of Thermodynamics   94
7.4. Total Entropy Change of the Local Universe During   96
      Reversible Processes
7.5. Total Entropy Change of the Local Universe During   96
      Irreversible Processes
7.6. The Second Law of Thermodynamics Restated   99
7.7. The Degradation of Energy   101
7.8. Irreversibility in Thermodynamics   102
7.9. Entropy and Disorder   103

CHAPTER 8

GAS SYSTEMS   106

8.1. Free Expansion of a Gas under Adiabatic Conditions   107
8.2. The Experiments of Rossini and Frandsen   109

8.3. The Joule-Thomson Porous-plug Experiment   111

8.4. Thermodynamic Equation for the Joule-Thomson   114
      Coefficient

8.5. Thermal Effusion   116

8.6. The Difference $C_p - C_v$ 117

8.7. Second Equation of State for an Ideal Gas   119

8.8. Direct Measurement of γ for Gases   120

8.9. Mixtures of Ideal Gases   123

8.10. Isothermal Interdiffusion of Two Ideal Gases   124

CHAPTER 9

APPLICATIONS OF THERMODYNAMIC 128
METHODS TO OTHER SYSTEMS

9.1. State Functions   128

9.2. The Maxwell Identities   130

9.3. Pressure in Blackbody Radiative Systems   131

9.4. Internal Energy of an Ideal Paramagnetic Substance   132

9.5. Elastomers   133

9.6. Heat Capacities and Compressibilities of   135
      Solids and Liquids

CHAPTER 10

PHASE TRANSFORMATIONS 138

10.1. P-V Diagram for Liquid-vapor Systems   139

10.2. Explanation of the Liquid-vapor Isotherms for Real 140
       Substances

10.3. P-V-T Surfaces   144

10.4. Thermodynamic Equations for Phase Transformations   148

10.5. Thermodynamic Potentials   151

CHAPTER 11

MOLECULAR THERMOPHYSICS 155

11.1. The Kinetic Theory 155
11.2. The Ideal Gas 156
11.3. Number of Molecules Striking a Unit Area 157
Per Unit Time
11.4. Gas Pressure 159
11.5. The Avogadro Number and Boltzmann Constant 160
11.6. Temperature in Kinetic Theory 160
11.7. Equipartition of Energy and Specific Heats 161
11.8. Molecular Effusion and Thermal Transpiration 162
11.9. Maxwell's Derivation of $f(v)$ 163
11.10. Values of β, $\bar{v}$, v_{rms} and the Most Probable Speed 166
11.11. Experimental Verification of the Maxwellian Distribution 167
11.12. Thermionic Emission 171
11.13. Maxwellian Distribution of Speeds in the Electron Gas 173

CHAPTER 12

MEAN FREE PATH AND TRANSPORT 176
PROCESSES

12.1. Mean Free Path and Collision Cross-section 177
12.2. Viscosity in Gases 179
12.3. Values of Average Speeds, Mean Free Paths, and 181
Collision Diameters
12.4. Thermal Conductivity in Gases 183
12.5. Diffusivity in Gases 184
12.6. Results from the Chapman-Enskog Theory 185
12.7. Distribution of Free Paths and Mean Collision Frequency 186
12.8. Attenuation in a Molecular Beam 188

CHAPTER 13

STATISTICAL THERMODYNAMICS 191

13.1. Thermophysical Probability 193
13.2. Accessibility of Microstates 196

13.3.   Partition Function of a Monatomic Ideal Gas   199
13.4.   The Liouville Theorem and Equal Probability in   201
        Phase Space
13.5.   The Maxwell Distribution of Speeds in a Gas   201
13.6.   Harmonic Oscillators   202

CHAPTER 14

BROWNIAN MOTION AND RANDOM   205
FLUCTUATIONS

14.1.   Energy and Momentum Fluctuations   206
14.2.   Theory of Brownian Motion   207
14.3.   Rotational Brownian Motion   210
14.4.   Current Fluctuations and Johnson Noise   212
14.5.   Theory of Fluctuations about an Average   215
14.6.   The Shot Effect   217
14.7.   Density Fluctuations in a Gas   218
14.8.   Density Fluctuations Near the Critical Point   220

CHAPTER 15

THEORIES OF SPECIFIC HEAT AND   224
DIPOLE MOMENT

15.1.   The Ideal Crystalline Solid   225
15.2.   Einstein's Theory of Specific Heat   226
15.3.   Debye's Theory of Specific Heat   227
15.4.   Remarks on Theories of Specific Heat   229
15.5.   Classical Theory of Dipole Moment   230
15.6.   Quantum Theory of Dipole Moment   233

CHAPTER 16

THERMAL RADIATION   237

16.1.   Intensity of Radiation   238

16.2. The Fourth Power Law of Radiation 239

16.3. Pyrometry 240

16.4. Temperatures of the Sun and Planets 241

16.5. Spectral Energy Distributions for Blackbody Radiation 243

16.6. Wien's Displacement and Distribution Laws 244

16.7. Classical Forms of $f(\lambda T)$ 245

16.8. Planck's Law 247

16.9. Verification of Planck's Law 248

16.10. Maxwell's Sorting Demon 250

16.11. Negative Entropy and Information 251

16.12. Laboratory Observations 253

CHAPTER 17

QUANTUM STATISTICS 256

17.1. The Uncertainty Principle 257

17.2. Bose-Einstein Statistics 258

17.3. Condensation of an Ideal Bose-Einstein Gas 260

17.4. Fermi-Dirac Statistics 262

17.5. The Electronic Specific Heat of a Metal 264

17.6. Probability in Classical and Quantum Statistics 266

CHAPTER 18

VERY LOW TEMPERATURES 269

18.1. Production of Low Temperatures 269

18.2. Thermometry at Low Temperatures 274

18.3. The Thermodynamic Scale Below 1°K 276

18.4. Negative Temperatures 278

CHAPTER 19

SUPERFLUIDITY AND SUPERCONDUCTIVITY   284

19.1.   Helium I and Helium II   285
19.2.   Superfluidity   289
19.3.   Super Heat Conduction   292
19.4.   The Two-fluid Model of Helium II   292
19.5.   Heat Transfer in Helium II   295
19.6.   Phonons and Rotons   299
19.7.   Superconductors   301
19.8.   Magnetic Properties of Superconductors   305
19.9.   Thermodynamics of Superconducting Systems   309
19.10. Theories of Superconductivity   312

CHAPTER 20

IRREVERSIBLE FLOW PROCESSES   316

20.1.   Thermal Conduction   317
20.2.   Thermal Convection   320
20.3.   Temperature and Entropy of Conductors   324
        During Flow Processes
20.4.   Creation of Entropy During Flow Processes   326
20.5.   Energy Transfer During Flow Processes   328
20.6.   Secondary Flow Processes   329
20.7.   Thermo-osmosis   331
20.8.   Thermo-electricity   334
20.9.   The Thermocouple   335

CHAPTER 21

VERY HIGH TEMPERATURES   341

21.1.   Thermodynamic and Kinetic Temperatures   341
21.2.   The Law of Mass Action   343

21.3.   The Equilibrium Constant   345
21.4.   Determination of High Gas Temperatures   346
21.5.   Plasma Temperatures   347
21.6.   Ionic Composition of Plasmas   350
21.7.   Transport Phenomena in Plasmas   352
21.8.   The Production of High-temperature Plasmas   355

INDEX   360

CHAPTER 1

Introduction

THERMOPHYSICS deals with transfers of energy between a system and its surroundings and with transformations of energy from one form to another. In thermophysics a system is a limited and clearly recognized region of the universe which is singled out for study. The adjoining regions with which a system exchanges energy and matter are called near-surround; more remote regions which are not affected by the system are called far-surround. Thermophysics, then, embraces those fundamental laws and principles governing energy transformations and exchanges between a system and its near-surround and between one part of a system and another.

A system is said to occupy a physical state which may be steady or may vary from instant to instant. As we develop the subject of thermophysics we shall find that many variables and functions are needed for the complete description of the state of a system. Temperature is one; in addition, there are such quantities as pressure, volume, force, charge, magnetic field intensity, surface tension, and internal energy. Usually only a few of these are required for an adequate description of any one system. The quantities which are considered independent are variables of state; the others are dependent and are called state functions.

1.1. What Is Temperature?

According to Bridgman,[1] "it appears that the temperature concept is not a clear cut thing, which can be made to apply to all experience, but that it

---

[1] Bridgman, P. W., *Logic of Modern Physics* (Macmillan, New York, 1927), p. 121.

is more or less arbitrary, involving the scale of our measuring instruments." On the other hand, Worthing[2] writes: "At present we know of no purely mechanical quantity—that is, one expressible in terms of mass, length and time only—which can be used, however inconveniently, in place of temperature. We are inclined to conclude that temperature probably is itself a basic concept."

The most common and perhaps the most inaccurate definition of temperature is that which involves the physiological sensations of hotness and coldness. We know from experience that a piece of iron may *feel* colder than a block of wood even though the two are at the same temperature as determined by any one thermometer. Furthermore, it is easy to vary the sensation noted, when using the finger or any other part of the body for testing, by subjecting that part of the body to different treatments immediately before the test. For these reasons the usual physiological definitions are utterly unreliable.

In order for a definition to be acceptable today it must be operational. An operational definition clearly states or implies the operation or series of operations by which the quantity being defined can be established. In Chapter 2 we shall set up criteria for the recognition of thermal equilibrium between systems, and then we shall be able to formulate this operational definition: *Temperature is that property of a system which determines whether the system is in thermal equilibrium with other systems.*

1.2. The Thermometer and Early Scales of Temperature

It is now generally agreed that temperature may be considered a basic concept, as are mass, length, and time. From our everyday experience we know that temperature is measured in degrees on a thermometer, but hidden behind this simple device and the quantity it measures is a truly remarkable story in the development of thermophysics.

No thermal measurements were possible, and therefore the science of thermophysics could not develop, until after the invention of the thermometer near the beginning of the seventeenth century. Galileo commonly is credited with its invention in 1593, but Drebbel of Holland made one independently at about the same time. These instruments were not thermometers as we know them today but rather thermobaroscopes; they were open to the

---

[2] Worthing, A. G., "The Temperature Concept," *Am. J. Phys.*, **8**, 28 (1940).

atmosphere and therefore responded to changes in atmospheric pressure as well as to temperature. It must be remembered, however, that the pressure of the atmosphere had yet to be discovered. In 1641 the Grand Duke of Tuscany sealed his alcohol-in-glass thermoscopes in order to prevent evaporation of the alcohol, and he attached to them scales having arbitrary graduations. These devices were the prototypes of modern thermometers.

Hooke and his contemporaries had observed that the level of the liquid in a thermometer always came to the same position whenever the thermometer was immersed in a mixture of ice and water. It was reasonable to assume that there exists a characteristic temperature for the freezing of water. In 1664 Hooke utilized the freezing point of water for standardizing thermometers, and thirty years later Renaldini adopted both the freezing and boiling points of water for this purpose.

A few years after, Roemer (1702) and Fahrenheit (1717) proposed the temperature scales which in modified form serve to this day. Meanwhile Elvins (1710), and seemingly Linnaeus independently (1740), suggested the centigrade or centismal scale. However, by the vagaries of historical accident the latter scale became associated with the name of Anders Celsius.[3] The story of the early development of the thermometer and temperature scales may be found in Bolton's *Evolution of the Thermometer 1592–1743*. This and other sources are listed in the bibliography at the end of this chapter.

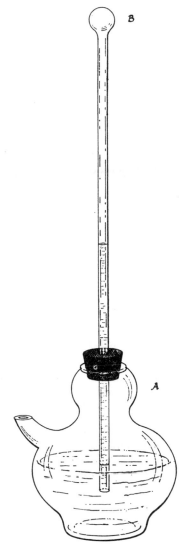

Figure 1.1. A thermoscope, precursor of the thermometer.

---

[3] In 1954 the Tenth International Conference on Weights amd Measures formally adopted the name *Celsius* for the old centigrade scale. The symbol °C then is read "degree Celsius."

1.3. Heat

From their writings we learn that early scientist philosophers and investigators, such as Locke, Bacon, Boyle, and Hooke, considered heat to be a microscopic manifestation of the motion of "small parts" or particles within a body; thus they were the first to recognize heat as a mechanical phenomenon. Unfortunately, the caloric theory, which arose in the eighteenth century, displaced these early speculations. In this theory heat was regarded as an all-pervading elastic and self-repellant fluid which flows readily from hot into cold bodies. The story of the rise and fall of the caloric theory provides us with an excellent illustration of the interplay of experimental observation, speculation, and theoretical developments. Out of it have come many of our current terms in thermophysics: specific heat, latent heat, heat capacity, calorie, calorimeter, and so on. The theory did not fall into disfavor until well into the nineteenth century.

Until the middle of the eighteenth century little or no distinction was made between heat and temperature. About that time Black clearly distinguished between *quantity* of heat and *intensity* of heat. He observed that the amount of heat required to raise the temperature of a unit mass of substance through a given interval is constant and, furthermore, he found that when ice melts, heat is "absorbed and concealed within the water so as not to be discoverable by the application of a thermometer."[4] Thus Black conceived bodies to have heat capacities and discovered latent heats.

As a result of the experiments of Davy and Thompson (Count Rumford) near the close of the eighteenth century, the theory that heat is "a mode of motion," to use Tyndall's phrase, was revived. Davy demonstrated that ice melts when two pieces are rubbed together, even though the ambient temperature is below freezing, and concluded that the heat for melting came from the work done against friction. Thompson showed that heat can be produced almost indefinitely by the rubbing action of a dull boring tool on a cannon in sufficient quantity to boil water. He concluded rightly that heat is not an all-pervading fluid, but rather that it must arise from the motion of the boring tool. This mechanical theory of heat was given firm support by the experiments of Joule, fifty years later. He showed conclusively in many ways that a given amount of work can be converted completely into an equivalent amount of heat. But, as happens so frequently in physics, the

[4] Black, J., *Lectures on the Elements of Chemistry*, Vol. 1 (Longman and Rees, London, 1803), p. 119.

meaning of a term becomes restricted and sharpened as the phenomenon described by it becomes better understood. So here, the meaning of the word "heat" has changed until today the phrase "a mode of motion" hardly applies. *Heat now is the name for energy as it is transferred from one region to another by the thermal processes of conduction, convection, and radiation.* The agitation or random motions of the small parts (molecules) of a body, hitherto associated with the word "heat," are more closely related to the internal energy of the body.

1.4. Internal Energy and the First Law of Thermodynamics

The potential energy acquired by a system when it is placed in a gravitational or an electric field and the kinetic energy it has from its translational and rotational motions arise from external factors. These energies are not part of the internal energy of the system, for internal energy is the name given all those energies associated with the random motions and relative positions of the small parts within the system. A rigorous operational definition for it will be developed later. Energies arising from external factors may be transformed to internal energy through the medium of frictional and viscous forces, electrical resistance, and other dissipating agents. The internal energy of a system is changed, on the other hand, by mechanical, thermal, and chemical transfer processes between the system and its near-surround.

Any energy transfer process resulting from the action of an agent which can be replaced by the raising and lowering of a weight, by the winding and unwinding of a spring, or by any other equivalent simple frictionless mechanism is a mechanical process. A process in which energy is transferred by thermal conduction, convection, radiation, or a combination of these, is a thermal process. If a process involves a change in mass or chemical constituency of the system, it is a chemical process. Several mechanical, thermal, and chemical processes are illustrated in Fig. 1.2.

A change in internal energy often is accompanied by a change in temperature. That the temperature of a system may be increased by mechanical and chemical processes, as well as by thermal processes, is demonstrated in a simple experiment. A closed cylinder with a piston in one end is filled with a mixture of dry hydrogen and oxygen gases in the ratio of two parts by volume of hydrogen to one of oxygen. Initially the system is at room temper-

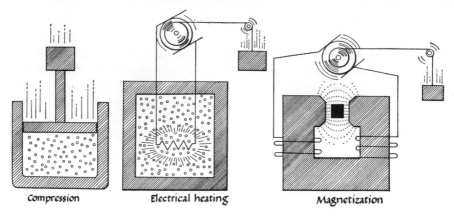

Compression   Electrical heating   Magnetization

Figure 1.2.   (a) Mechanical processes.

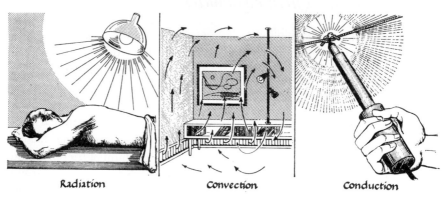

Radiation   Convection   Conduction

Figure 1.2.   (b) Thermal processes.

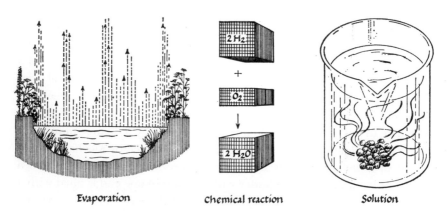

Evaporation   Chemical reaction   Solution

Figure 1.2.   (c) Chemical processes.

6

ature, but the walls of the cylinder are diathermic; that is, heat can readily flow through them into the system. If the cylinder is immersed in a warm bath and the volume of gas in it is held constant, the temperature of the system is observed to rise by purely thermal processes. Suppose now that the cylinder is thoroughly insulated to prevent heat exchanges with the near-surround, that is, is made adiabatic. (In practice, metal walls are diathermic, whereas walls of asbestos, rock or glass wool, and other similar lagging materials are approximately adiabatic. Perhaps one of the best practical adiabatic walls is an evacuated space enclosed by highly reflecting surfaces, as in a Thermos bottle.) When the gas in the insulated cylinder is compressed by means of the piston, again the temperature of the system is observed to increase, this time by a purely mechanical process. Finally, suppose the cylinder is not only thermally insulated but also has its piston held immovable to prevent any work exchange with the near-surround. By means of an electrical spark or a suitable catalyst such as platinized asbestos the gases are induced to react and form water, and the temperature of the system increases by a purely chemical process. Clearly temperature is a physical property of the system which can be changed by any one or more of the energy transfer processes, not just by heating alone. It is one of the fundamental thermophysical variables of state.

A change in internal energy of a system is set equal to the total energy influx by mechanical, thermal, and chemical processes. In symbols,

$$U_f - U_i = W + Q + E, \qquad (1.1)$$

where U_i and U_f are the initial and final values of internal energy for the system, W represents the work input by mechanical processes, Q represents the heat inflow by thermal processes, and E represents the added energy by chemical processes.[5] (In America W often represents work output of the system, so a negative sign would appear before W in the equation. However, I shall adopt the more consistent European convention of considering energy input, whatever its form, as positive and energy output as negative.)

In 1842 Mayer, a physician in Heilbrunn, wrote: "I therefore hope that I may reckon on the reader's assent when I lay down as an axiomatic truth that, just as in the case of matter, so also in the case of force [the then current term for energy], only a transformation but never a creation takes place." This is a translation of the original statement of the general principle of

---

[5] No simple monosyllabic word exists as a name for the energy which we have represented by E. Perhaps the Anglo-Saxon word *sawl*, meaning the spirit or essence of a substance, is suitable. Then sawl, like work and heat, is one form of energy during its transfer between a system and the near-surround.

conservation of energy. Equation (1.1) is one statement of this principle called *the first law of thermodynamics.*

1.5. Units of Energy

One common unit of energy is the joule, which is equivalent to ten million ergs. Other units of energy are the foot-pound of engineering, the kilowatt-hour of electricity, the calorie and British Thermal Unit of heat, the electron-volt of atomic and nuclear physics, and the liter-atmosphere of chemistry. Definitions of these units may be found in elementary textbooks and handbooks of physics and chemistry. The equivalent number of absolute joules for each of these units is as follows:

1 foot-pound	$= 1.35582$ joules
1 kilowatt-hour	$= 3.6000 \times 10^6$ joules
1 calorie (15°C)	$= 4.1858$ joules
1 electron-volt	$= 1.5921 \times 10^{-19}$ joule
1 liter-atmosphere	$= 101.328$ joules
1 BTU (mean)	$= 1054.8$ joules

The 15°C calorie and the mean BTU are classical units of heat. The 15°C calorie equals the amount of heat required to raise the temperature of one gram of pure water from 14.5° to 15.5° Celsius at a pressure of one standard atmosphere (101,325 newtons per square meter). The mean BTU equals one hundred eightieth of the amount of heat required to raise the temperature of one pound of pure water from 32° to 212° Fahrenheit at a pressure of one standard atmosphere. These units belong to none of the accepted systems of units and are superfluous. In 1948 the Ninth International Conference on Weights and Measures adopted the joule as the basic unit of heat and asked only that "those who still use the calorie shall give with their results all the information necessary to convert their results to joules," *Science,* **109,** 99 (1949).

The number of joules in one calorie is known as the mechanical equivalent of heat or simply the Joule constant. The history of its determination constitutes a long chapter in the development of thermophysics. As early as 1839 the French engineer Seguin had estimated a value for the amount of work required to raise the temperature of a unit mass of water one degree. In his 1842 paper Mayer calculated a value for this work independently from existing data on gases. The experimental evidence for both results was meager, and the assumptions made in obtaining them were questionable at that time. It remained for Joule, an English brewer, to carry out the necessary extensive and carefully controlled experiments which established this constant beyond doubt. His first results were published in 1843, and subsequently he refined his measurements over a period of nearly forty years. Although Joule's investigations exerted a tremendous influence on the downfall of the caloric theory and the development of the mechanical theory of heat, it is clear that the constant he measured is no more than the ratio of two units of energy, one of which is arbitrary.

From another point of view, and perhaps a preferable one, accurate determinations of Joule's constant are simply careful measurements of the specific heat of water at 15°C in joules per gram-degree Celsius. This is called the gram heat capacity of water at 15°C.

1.6. Kinetic Theory and Statistical Thermophysics

Long before Mayer had enunciated the energy conservation principle and before Thompson and Joule had performed their crucial experiments which undermined the caloric theory, the Democritian idea that all matter consists of small parts or molecules in rapid motion was stated by many outstanding philosophers and scientists. Although Boyle held that bodies consist of small parts in a "vehement and variously determined agitation" when he published the law relating pressure and volume of a gas in 1660, the first explanation of the law in terms of a molecular kinetic theory, including the notion that the average speed of the molecules remains constant for a given temperature, was not made until nearly eighty years later by D. Bernoulli. Hooke, who was at one time Boyle's assistant, observed that fluidity is due to "nothing else but a certain pulse or shake of heat; for heat being nothing else but a very brisk and vehement agitation of the parts of a body (as I have elsewhere made probable), the parts of a body are thereby made so loose from one another, that they may easily move any way and become fluid." The relation between "heat," or internal energy in our terminology, and molecular energy was more clearly stated by Lavoisier and Laplace in 1780 when they wrote: ". . . heat is the *vis viva* resulting from the insensible movements of the molecules of a body. It is the sum of the products of the mass of each molecule by the square of its velocity." During the next few decades other qualitative and semiquantitative applications of the kinetic theory of matter were made, as in explaining phase transformations and the law of multiple proportions for chemical combinations.

The first direct observation of the chaotic motions experienced by molecules as manifested in the random movements of suspended pollen grains and soot particles was made by Brown in 1827 but was not understood. The correct explanation of these movements came some fifty years later. By midcentury, however, the time was ripe for the development of a rigorous general theory of molecular chaos. Many of the fundamental ideas of kinetic theory and statistical thermophysics were formulated between 1850 and 1880 by Clausius, Maxwell, and Boltzmann. Not long afterward these ideas were applied by Einstein to the problem of Brown's chaotic motions and were verified by the classical experiments of Perrin.

The nineteenth century also was a time of change in radiation concepts. Young's experiments on diffraction and interference had demonstrated the wave nature of light. During the first half of the century Wollaston, Fraunhofer, and Kirchhoff laid the groundwork for the study of spectra and the identification of elements by means of them. In 1864 Maxwell showed that radiation is an electromagnetic phenomenon. But by the end of the century several observations had been made which defied explanation. In 1887 Hertz discovered the photoelectric effect. Early in 1896 Roentgen observed x-rays for the first time, and a few months later Becquerel discovered the penetrating radiation emanating from uranium. Finally, in the years 1897–1899, Lummer and Pringsheim made careful measurements of the spectral distribution of energy in blackbody radiation. Then, in 1899, Planck made the radical suggestion that atomic vibrators could absorb or emit radiant energy only in incremental amounts or quanta. With this new concept the foregoing inexplicable observations were to be explained! Thus the nineteenth century was witness to the growth and transformation of the concepts of radiation from its wave nature, through its electromagnetic characteristics, to its quantum aspects.

The kinetic molecular structure of matter and the quantum properties of radiant energy were amalgamated during the first half of the twentieth century into a consistent and fruitful theory of great beauty. At the heart of it is the concept that natural laws are statistical and that events represent the maximization of thermophysical probability under given boundary conditions.

Bibliography

GENERAL

Allen, H. S., and R. S. Maxwell, *A Text-Book of Heat*, Parts I and II (Macmillan, London, 1939).

American Institute of Physics, *Temperature, its Measurement and Control in Science and Industry* (Reinhold, New York, Vol. I, 1941; Vol. II, 1955).

Bolton, H. C., *Evolution of the Thermometer 1592–1743* (Chemical Publishing Co., Easton, Pa., 1900).

Bridgman, P. W., *The Physics of High Pressure* (Macmillan, New York, 1931).

McKie, D., and N. H. de V. Heathcote, *The Discovery of Specific and Latent Heats* (Arnold, London, 1935).

Penman, H. L., *Humidity* (Institute of Physics, London, 1955).

Planck, M., *The Theory of Heat Radiation* (Blakiston's, Philadelphia, 1914).

Roller, D., *Case 3, the Early Development of the Concepts of Temperature and Heat* (Harvard University Press, Cambridge, 1950).

Saha, M. N., and B. N. Srivastava, *A Text-Book of Heat* (Indian Press, Allahabad, India, 1931).

Sears, F. W., *An Introduction to Thermodynamics, the Kinetic Theory of Gases and Statistical Mechanics*, 2nd ed. (Addison-Wesley, Reading, Mass., 1953).

Slater, J. C., *Introduction to Chemical Physics* (McGraw-Hill, New York, 1939).

Smithsonian Physical Tables, 9th ed. (Smithsonian Institution, Washington, D.C., 1954).

Taylor, L. W., *Physics, the Pioneer Science* (Houghton Mifflin, New York, 1941).

Tyndall, J., *Heat Considered as a Mode of Motion* (Appleton, New York, 1863).

THERMODYNAMICS

Ames, J. S., *The Free Expansion of Gases, Memoirs of Gay-Lussac, Joule, and Joule and Thomson* (Harper, New York, 1898).

Bridgman, P. W., *The Thermodynamics of Electrical Phenomena in Metals* (Macmillan, New York, 1934).

———, *The Nature of Thermodynamics* (Harvard University Press, Cambridge, 1941).

———, *A Condensed Collection of Thermodynamic Formulas* (Harvard University Press, Cambridge, 1925).

Cork, J. M., *Heat* (Wiley, New York, 1942).

Guggenheim, E. A., *Thermodynamics*, 3rd ed. (North-Holland, Amsterdam, 1957).

Keenan, J. H., and J. Kaye, *Thermodynamic Properties of Air* (Wiley, New York, 1945).

Keenan, J. H., and F. G. Keyes, *Thermodynamic Properties of Steam* (Wiley, New York, 1936).

Landsberg, P. T., *Thermodynamics* (Interscience, New York, 1961).

Lee, J. F., and F. W. Sears, *Thermodynamics* (Addison-Wesley, Reading, Mass., 1955).

Magie, W. F. (ed.), *The Second Law of Thermodynamics, Memoirs of Carnot, Clausius and Thomson* (Harper, New York, 1899).

Pippard, A. B., *Elements of Classical Thermodynamics* (The University Press, Cambridge, 1957).

Planck, M., *Treatise on Thermodynamics* (Longmans, Green, London, 1903).

Worthing, A. G., and D. Halliday, *Heat* (Wiley, New York, 1948).

Zemansky, M. W., *Heat and Thermodynamics*, 4th ed. (McGraw-Hill, New York, 1957).

KINETIC THEORY AND STATISTICAL MECHANICS

Guggenheim, E. A., *Boltzmann's Distribution Law* (North-Holland, Amsterdam, 1955).

Jeans, J. H., *The Dynamical Theory of Gases*, 3rd ed. (The University Press, Cambridge, 1921).

Kennard, E. H., *Kinetic Theory of Gases*, 1st ed. (McGraw-Hill, New York, 1938).

Knudsen, M., *Kinetic Theory of Gases*, 3rd ed. (Methuen, London, 1950).

Loeb, L. B., *Kinetic Theory of Gases* (McGraw-Hill, New York, 1927).

Rice, J., *Introduction to Statistical Mechanics for Students of Physics and Physical Chemistry* (Constable, London, 1930).

Schroedinger, E., *Statistical Thermodynamics* (The University Press, Cambridge, 1952).

Additional sources are listed at the ends of Chapters 14–21.

CHAPTER 2

Temperature and Thermometry

A CLOSED system may be described at any instant by specifying instantaneous values of such macroscopic variables as length, volume, electric charge, and dipole moment. In addition, to complete the description usually there are other specified variables such as force, pressure, electromotive force, and magnetic field intensity, which have meaning for the system as a whole only if they are uniform throughout the system. All these quantities can be measured fairly directly with laboratory apparatus, or they are simply related to other such quantities; they are suggested more or less immediately by our senses; and their existence does not require a special microstructure. In this sense they are macroscopic and are suitable for specifying the thermophysical state of a system.

Often only two macroscopic variables are needed to specify the state of a system. For a rubber filament the length and applied force are sufficient. Either the length may be kept constant and the applied force varied over a wide range of values, or the applied force may be kept constant and the length varied. The length and force are independent variables. Similarly, for a confined gas, volume and pressure are independent variables; for an iron bar within a current-bearing coil, dipole moment and magnetic field intensity are independent variables; for an electric cell, charge and electromotive force are independent variables.

2.1. Thermal Equilibrium

Imagine a system of constant mass and composition for which only one pair of independent variables X and Y is needed to specify its state. If X and Y have definite values which remain unchanged and there is no exchange of energy with the near-surround, the system is said to occupy an equilibrium state. Let system A (coordinates X and Y) be separated from another system B (coordinates X' and Y') by an adiabatic wall. Then equilibrium states for A exist independent of equilibrium states for B; that is, values of the coordinates X, Y and X', Y' are completely independent of one another. However, if the adiabatic wall is replaced by a diathermic one, and the coordinates X and Y are given arbitrary values, then X' and Y' are observed to change spontaneously until an equilibrium state for both systems is reached. The two systems in their final states are said to be in thermal equilibrium with each other. During the approach to thermal equilibrium, energy as heat is transmitted from one system to the other through the diathermic wall.

Consider systems A and B each in thermal equilibrium with a third system C. If now A and B are placed in contact through a diathermic wall, no changes take place in their coordinates. Thus A and B are in thermal equilibrium with each other. The expression "two systems are in thermal equilibrium" shall then mean that the two separate systems are in states such that, if the two systems *were* to communicate through a diathermic wall, they *would* be in thermal equilibrium.

The foregoing observations are summarized in another principle: *Two systems in thermal equilibrium with a third system are in thermal equilibrium with each other*. R. H. Fowler called this the *zeroth law of thermodynamics*.[1] It is basic to all temperature measurements.

2.2. Temperature Concept

We now find experimentally that there exist many states of A which are in thermal equilibrium with one specific state of B and, by the zeroth law of thermodynamics, therefore they are in thermal equilibrium with one another. If values for X and Y of all these states are plotted as a graph, they lie on an isotherm, such as a in Fig. 2.1.

For another specific state of B a series of equilibrium states of A may be found to describe a second isotherm. Thus a family of isotherms may be

[1] See, however, Turner, L. A., *Am. J. Phys.*, **29**, 71 (1961).

obtained for system *A* as shown in Fig. 2.1. Suppose now that a specific state of *A* on isotherm *a* is selected for test. The series of states for *B* which are in thermal equilibrium with this test state of *A* determines an isotherm for *B* (*a'* in Fig. 2.1). Every state on *a'* is in thermal equilibrium with every state on *a*, and therefore *a'* and *a* are corresponding isotherms. Isotherms of system *B* corresponding to isotherms *b*, *c*, and others of *A* also may be found.

All states of corresponding isotherms for *A*, *B*, and other systems too have this in common: they are states of thermal equilibrium. We now ascribe to the systems themselves a physical property, called *temperature*, which characterizes this common condition; that is, systems which are in thermal equi-

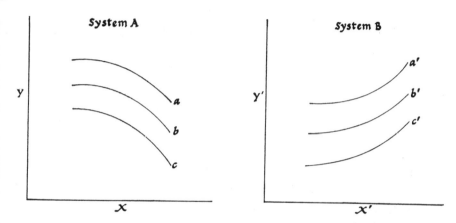

Figure 2.1.   Families of isotherms for two systems.

librium have the same temperature. Analytically this means that the family of isotherms may be described by the parametric equation

$$f(X, Y) = \theta, \tag{2.1}$$

in which θ represents temperature and has a different constant value for each isotherm in the family. We now see that temperature is a fundamental concept which strictly has meaning only for systems in thermal equilibrium. Applications of the concept to nonequilibrium situations can be made; but they must be examined critically to avoid absurdities.

Evidently temperature θ is another macroscopic variable. For the simple closed system *A* the variables X, Y, and θ are sufficient to specify every available state of the system. These variables are related by the foregoing parametric equation, which is called the equation of state for the system. Explicit forms of this equation ordinarily are found by experiment over limited ranges of values for the variables; these will be discussed in Chapter 3.

Here we shall apply the general equation to the problem of devising a temperature scale. For this purpose let Y equal a constant Y_0, so

$$\theta = f(X, Y_0). \qquad (2.2)$$

Because this function is completely arbitrary we are at liberty to select its form for any *one* system such as A. Once the selection is made the arbitrariness disappears, and system A becomes a thermometer with a temperature scale. For convenience, therefore, *assume* $f(X, Y_0)$ equals kX, in which k is a constant coefficient to be evaluated by an appropriate standardizing procedure. If θ is assigned the value θ_0 for X equal to X_0, so that k equals θ_0/X_0, then any other temperature may be obtained by means of the relation

$$\theta = \theta_0(X/X_0), \qquad (2.3)$$

where X is the thermometric property of system A when it is employed as a thermometer.

2.3. Standards of Temperature

The transition of any pure substance from one phase to another, such as from solid to liquid or from liquid to vapor, takes place at a characteristic temperature called in thermometry a fixed point. Many of these fixed points have been given special names. The normal melting point (NMP) of ice, namely the temperature of a mixture of flaked ice and air-saturated water at one standard atmosphere (101,325 newton/m^2), is the ice point. Likewise the normal boiling point (NBP) of water, namely the temperature of condensing steam over boiling pure water at one standard atmosphere, is the steam point. Prior to 1954 these two points were the standard fixed points of thermometry. The ice point was assigned the value 0.00°C, and the steam point was assigned the value 100.00°C. Hereafter we shall call them the standard pair of fixed points.

In 1854 Joule and Thomson pointed out that only *one* fixed point is needed for calibration purposes. Giauque revived this suggestion in 1939, and in 1954 the Tenth International Conference on Weights and Measures adopted it. The triple point of water was chosen as the primary standard fixed point and was assigned the value 273.16°K.[2] The triple point of water is that temperature at which ice, liquid water, and water vapor coexist in thermal equilibrium. On the Celsius scale the temperature of the triple

---

[2] The symbol °K is read "degree Kelvin." The Kelvin scale of temperature is identical to the ideal gas scale, as described in Section 2.6. On this scale the ice point is at 273.15°K and the steam point at 373.15°K.

point is 0.01°C; the value of 273.16°K was chosen so as not to alter the old values of temperatures for the standard pair of fixed points on the Kelvin scale and therefore for other fixed points as well. We should recognize that the old and new methods of standardization define two independent scales; the sizes of the degree on them probably are different, but the difference is at present undetectable. Sometimes it will be more convenient to evaluate the coefficient k by means of the standard pair instead of the primary fixed point.

The manner in which the numerical values of the standard pair and other fixed points are determined from the primary standard cannot be described without examining actual thermometers and their thermometric properties. This we shall do in the following sections.

2.4. *The Triple-point Cell*

After a long painstaking investigation the Bureau of Standards developed the apparatus and technique for obtaining the triple-point temperature with high precision. The apparatus consists of a cylindrical Pyrex glass tube about 5 cm in diameter, which is closed at one end and has a re-entrant coaxial wall at the other, of sufficient length to hold the thermometers under test. After the tube is blown and annealed it is cleaned thoroughly with acid, distilled water, and steam until the condensed steam runs down the inner walls in a continuous unbroken film. It is then evacuated and filled to within a couple of centimeters from the top with distilled water from which nearly all the dissolved gases have been removed. Then it is sealed off. A side tube below the sealing-off point serves as a handle, or as a support when it is hung inside a Dewar flask. This apparatus is called a triple-point cell (Fig. 2.2).

To prepare the cell for measurements it is first cooled by immersing it in a bath of flaked ice and water. Then crushed

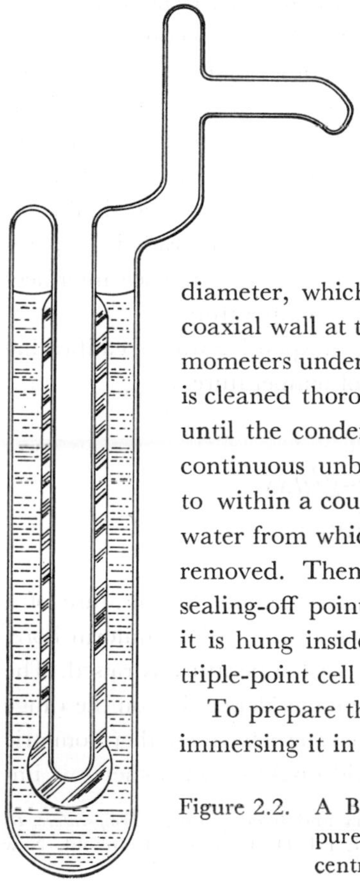

Figure 2.2.   A Bureau of Standards triple-point cell containing pure water, water vapor, and an ice mantle around the central well.

dry ice or a freezing mixture is kept in the thermometer well until a clear glasslike mantle of ice 3–10 mm thick freezes around it. The dry ice or freezing mixture is removed, and the triple-point cell is immersed in the ice bath once again. A warm tube now is inserted into the well for a few seconds until enough ice next to the well wall melts to free the mantle and provide a thin layer of pure water. If the mantle is free, it will rotate around the well when the cell is given a quick twist about its axis. The equilibrium temperature of the water layer, ice mantle, and water vapor above them is the standard triple-point temperature for calibration purposes. To make better thermal contact between thermometers under test and the cell wall the well is filled with ice water.

According to Stimson[3] of the Bureau of Standards, the procedure of inner melting is very valuable for obtaining reproducibility of temperature. As the water freezes, impurities are left behind in the liquid; thus water from the melted ice is purer than the water outside the mantle. Experience at the Bureau of Standards has shown that the inner melting procedure "provides temperatures which are as identical to each other and as reproducible as we are now able to differentiate temperatures, namely, within about 0.00008°C." The temperature of the water outside the mantle is likely to be lower, owing to impurities both initially in the distilled water and added to it from the cell walls. This lower temperature introduces no significant error, however, because any small transfer of heat due to a radial temperature gradient merely causes freezing or melting at the water-ice interfaces without a measurable effect on the triple-point temperature.

With this apparatus we have a convenient, inexpensive way of calibrating thermometers against the primary standard of temperature.

2.5. Comparison of Liquid-in-glass and Resistance Thermometers

Perhaps the most common method of measuring the temperature of a fluid is to place in it a glass bulb and capillary tube with a uniform bore, containing a liquid that expands readily as the temperature is raised. The liquid may be mercury, alcohol, toluol, or pentane, depending on the range of temperatures to be measured. Approximate ranges for these thermometric fluids are given in Table 2.1. When a liquid-in-glass thermometer is im-

---

[3] H. F. Stimson, "Precision resistance thermometry and fixed points," *Temperature, Its Measurement and Control in Science and Industry*, Vol. II, Ed. H. C. Wolfe (Reinhold, New York, 1955).

TABLE 2.1.   *Approximate Ranges for a Few Liquid-in-Glass Thermometers in Degrees Celsius.*

Liquid	Mercury	Alcohol	Toluol	Pentane
Low limit	−38	−80	−95	−196
High limit	550	100	100	30

mersed in a fluid the column of liquid is observed to change its length at first rapidly and then, as thermal equilibrium is approached, more and more slowly until finally its surface comes to a stationary level. Ordinarily, the equilibrium level of the surface is read off a scale which may be etched on the glass stem or placed alongside it. Suppose the reading on a certain mercury-in-glass thermometer is 40.00. We say that the thermometer and the fluid in which it is immersed are at a temperature of 40.00°. Just what does this statement mean?

Assume for the moment that the thermometer has only three marks etched on it at 0.00, at 40.00, and at 100.00. These marks are located on the stem in the following manner. First the thermometer is calibrated at the ice and steam points, and the equilibrium levels of the mercury surface are marked 0.00 and 100.00 on the stem. At a point exactly two-fifths of the distance between these marks a third mark is etched and labeled 40.00. The reading 40.00° means, therefore, that the surface of the mercury stands exactly two-fifths of the distance along the stem between the marks for the ice point and the steam point on this particular mercury-in-glass thermometer.

Instead of observing variations in the length of a mercury column we may measure changes in its electrical resistance. To satisfy the requirements of durability, simplicity, stability, and ease of handling, resistance thermometers often are made of metal wires or ribbons (platinum, copper, nickel, or an alloy such as phosphor bronze). At very low temperatures carbon-composition resistors, germanium, and other semiconductors, have been found satisfactory.

For highest precision of measurement resistance thermometers are connected into suitable bridge or potentiometer circuits. Figure 2.3 shows two forms of three-lead thermometers in bridge circuits. Leads A and B should have identical resistance values at all temperatures. This is accomplished by making them of the same material and dimensions and by bringing them out of the thermometer side by side. On the other hand, by connecting a four-lead thermometer in a potentiometer circuit, as shown in Fig. 2.4, the effect of lead resistance is eliminated, and high precision can be obtained.

If a platinum resistance thermometer is calibrated first at the ice point and then at the steam point by one of the foregoing circuits, its resistance is found to change from an equilibrium value R_i to another value R_s. Let R_i and R_s be labeled 0.00° and 100.00°. A resistance value two-fifths of $R_s - R_i$ above R_i then is set equal to 40.00° on this scale. Do the *scales* of the platinum resistance thermometer and the mercury-in-glass thermometer agree numerically when the two thermometers are in thermal equilibrium?

The two scales have been made to agree at the ice and steam points. Nevertheless, in a fluid for which the mercury-in-glass thermometer reads 40.00°, the platinum resistance thermometer reads 40.25°, as stated in Table 2.2. Inasmuch as both types of thermometers may be constructed to read to one-hundredth of a degree or better, the difference of one-quarter of a degree must be considered an inherent difference between the two scales. On second thought this difference should not appear surprising, for only if the expansion of mercury within the glass capillary bears a linear relation to the change in resistance of the platinum wire should agreement be expected. Such a relationship does not exist, except approximately over short ranges of temperature.

If we extend the foregoing discussion to other thermometers, we are

Figure 2.3.   Two forms of three-lead resistance thermometers in bridge circuits. *A, B,* thermometer leads.

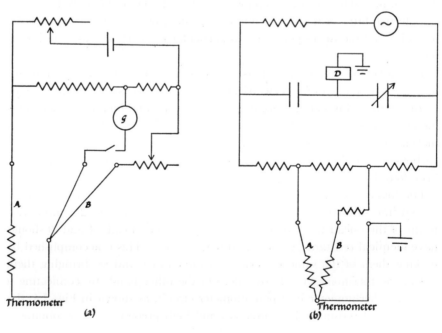

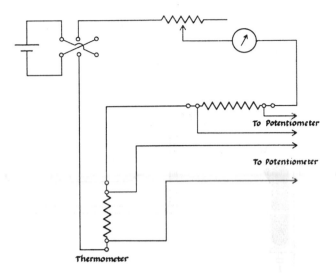

Figure 2.4. A four-lead resistance thermometer in a potentiometer circuit.

TABLE 2.2. *Comparison of the Mercury-in-glass and Platinum Thermometers.* *(Readings in Degrees Celsius.)*

Mercury-in-glass	0.00	20.00	40.00	60.00	80.00	100.00
Platinum resistance	0.00	20.15	40.25	60.27	80.20	100.00

tempted to conclude that no thermometer is a reliable device for measuring temperatures. After a little reflection, however, we decide that a scale of temperature ought to be defined independently of any thermometric substance. Fortunately, such a scale has been developed from thermodynamic considerations, but its description shall be postponed until Section 6.5. To be useful, the fundamental scale should be easily realizable in the laboratory so that scales on common thermometers may be calibrated against it. Such a standard scale has been devised which agrees almost exactly with the thermodynamic one.

2.6. Gas Thermometers and the Standard Scale of Temperature

In order to establish a standard scale, various temperature-sensitive devices are calibrated either against the primary fixed point or against the standard pair of fixed points, and then their scales are compared at many

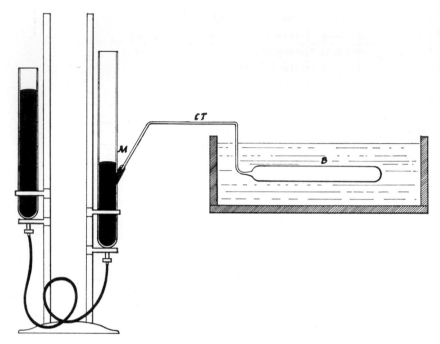

Figure 2.5.   A constant-volume gas thermometer. *B*, bulb in bath; *CT*, capillary tube; *M*, mercury manometer.

other points. Of all the thermometers that have been investigated, readings on those containing gases agree most closely with one another. For a gas thermometer, ordinarily either the pressure may be held constant and the volume allowed to vary or else the pressure may be adjusted to maintain the volume constant.[4] The constant-volume hydrogen thermometer and the constant-volume helium thermometer agree more closely than any others. However, since these gas thermometers are subject to numerous systematic errors they are rather impractical as everyday standards.

A schematic diagram of a simple constant-volume gas thermometer is shown in Fig. 2.5. The gas is contained in bulb *B*, which communicates with the mercury manometer *M* through capillary tube *CT*. The tip of the capillary tube extends into the closed end of the manometer a very short distance. In operation the mercury column in the closed arm is adjusted until its surface just touches the tip of the capillary. This is done by raising or lowering the open arm of the manometer. The pressure inside the bulb

---

[4] At high temperatures greater accuracy can be obtained if both the change in pressure and the change in volume are measured.

is obtained from the difference in height of the mercury levels and the barometric pressure. Several corrections must be made to this reading before it can be inserted in the equation for temperature. For the constant-volume gas thermometer, θ_0 in the thermometer equation is set equal to 273.16°K, X_0 equals the corrected pressure P_{tp} for the bulb at the temperature of the triple point of water, and X equals the corrected pressure P corresponding to the unknown temperature; thus

$$\theta = 273.16(P/P_{tp}). \tag{2.4}$$

Corrections to the pressure readings are made for the following sources of error. (1) The space above the mercury surface and around the tip of the capillary is called the "dead space." Gas entrapped in this space is at a temperature differing from that of the bulb. (2) The temperature of the gas in the capillary is not uniform and, furthermore, a pressure gradient may exist in it at low average pressures (Knudsen effect). (3) The volume of the bulb, capillary, and dead space actually is not constant as the temperature is changed because of the thermal expansion and pressure dilation of the wall materials. (4) Any gas absorption on the walls lowers the pressure reading; ordinarily this effect is greater at the lower temperatures. (5) Finally, the thermal expansion and compressibility of the mercury in the manometer and differences in the shapes of the two meniscuses may introduce errors. Errors from these sources are either eliminated or corrected for by careful design of the apparatus, by proper manipulation of it, and, in some instances, by rather elaborate computations. For details refer to discussions by Beattie[5] and by Saha and Srivastava.[6]

Experiments have shown beyond question that, regardless of the gas within, both constant-volume and constant-pressure thermometers yield temperature readings that agree more and more closely as the mass of gas in the thermometer is decreased. Here is a fact which may be utilized to establish a standard scale. As the mass is decreased and the gas becomes more rarefied the pressure corresponding to the triple point of water approaches zero; the gas behaves more nearly like an ideal gas. We can define an ideal gas here as any gas which satisfies Boyle's law exactly for all values of pressure and volume. That is, the pressure of the gas is inversely proportional to its volume, provided the temperature is uniform and does not change. Note that this definition of an ideal gas is applicable even though

[5] Beattie, J. A., "The thermodynamic temperature of the ice point," *Temperature, Its Measurement and Control in Science and Industry*, Vol. I, p. 75 (Reinhold, New York, 1941).

[6] Saha, M. N., and B. N. Srivastava, *A Text Book of Heat*, p. 11 (Indian Press, Allahabad, India, 1931).

the numerical value of temperature is unknown. Computed θ-values from the foregoing equation may be plotted against the corresponding triple-point pressures P_{tp} as the mass of gas in the thermometer is decreased. The resulting straight line is extrapolated to the temperature axis at zero pressure; its intercept is the ideal-gas temperature of the system. It is one point on the standard scale and is represented by the symbol T.

Suppose we wish to determine the ideal-gas temperature for the normal boiling point of sulfur. To do this a constant-volume real-gas thermometer (dry air, nitrogen, hydrogen) first is calibrated at the triple point of water; that is, a numerical value of P_{tp} is found for the mass of gas initially in the thermometer. The bulb of the thermometer is immersed in condensing sulfur vapor at standard atmospheric pressure, the mercury column of the manometer is adjusted to the fiducial point, a reading is obtained, all necessary corrections are made, and so pressure P is determined. A value of θ may then be computed. The next step is to reduce the mass of gas in the thermometer and then calibrate it once again at the triple point of water. A new value for P_{tp} is obtained. Also, a new value for the pressure P is found when the bulb is immersed in condensing sulfur vapor. Then a second value of θ is computed. This procedure is repeated several times for smaller and smaller amounts of gas in the thermometer. Finally, the computed values of θ are plotted against the measured values of P_{tp}, and the resulting straight line is extended until it intersects the θ axis at P_{tp} equal to zero. The intercept equals the ideal-gas temperature of the sulfur point. Figure 2.6 illustrates such curves for nitrogen, hydrogen, and oxygen. All of them intercept the θ axis at

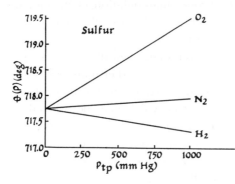

Figure 2.6. Curves for determining the boiling-point temperature of sulfur by means of different gas thermometers.

717.75°K, which is equivalent to 444.60°C.

Other fixed-point readings on the ideal-gas scale may be obtained by a similar procedure. In addition to the ice, steam, and sulfur points, the normal boiling point of oxygen and the normal melting points of antimony, silver, and gold are basic fixed points. Many other temperatures of phase transformations are secondary fixed points, some of which are shown in Table 2.3.

TABLE 2.3. *Ideal-gas Temperatures of Fixed Points. (International Temperature Scale, 1948.)*

Standard fixed point (*primary*)		
Triple point of water	273.160°K	0.0100°C
Basic fixed points		
Oxygen point (NBP of oxygen)	90.18*	−182.97
Ice point (defined in text)	273.15	0.000
Steam point (NBP of water)	373.15	100.000
Sulfur point (NBP of sulfur)	717.75	444.60
Antimony point (NMP of antimony)	903.65	630.5
Silver point (NMP of silver)	1233.95	960.8
Gold point (NMP of gold)	1336.15	1063.0
Secondary fixed points		
NBP of helium	4.22	−268.93
NBP of hydrogen	20.37	−252.78
NBP of nitrogen	77.34	−195.81
NFP of mercury	234.28	−38.87
Transition temperature of sodium sulfate		
decahydrate	305.53	32.38
Triple point of benzoic acid	395.51	122.36
NBP of naphthalene	491.11	217.96
NFP of tin	505.00	231.85
NBP of benzophenone	579.05	305.9
NFP of cadmium	594.05	320.9
NFP of lead	600.45	327.3
NBP of mercury	629.73	356.58
NFP of zinc	692.70	419.55
NFP of aluminum	933.25	660.1
NFP of copper in reducing atmosphere		1083
NFP of nickel		1453
NFP of cobalt		1492
NFP of palladium		1552
NFP of platinum		1769
NFP of rhodium		1960
NFP of iridium		2443
NMP of tungsten		3380

* In 1953 Aston and Moessen published a new value of 90.15°K ± 0.01° for the NBP of oxygen.

2.7. Thermocouples and Pyrometers

The thermocouple is a simple precision device which responds very rapidly to changes in temperature. Furthermore, its range extends well beyond the upper temperature limits of gas and resistance thermometers.

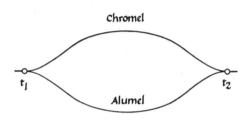

Figure 2.7. Chromel-alumel thermocouple.

For these reasons it is applied extensively in industry and in research laboratories. The thermocouple consists of two dissimilar metal wires or strips welded together at the two ends, as shown in Fig. 2.7. Familiar combinations are: iron and constantan, chromel and alumel, copper and constantan, and platinum and platinum-rhodium alloy (either 90% platinum–10% rhodium or 87% platinum –13% rhodium). If a temperature difference exists between the two junctions, a net electromotive force is developed, which may be detected by inserting a meter in the loop. This effect was discovered by Seebeck in 1821. Figure 2.8 shows the proper way to connect a thermo-

Figure 2.8. The proper way of connecting a thermocouple into a potentiometer circuit.

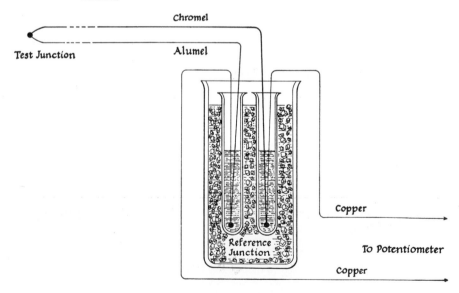

couple into a potentiometer circuit. As a rule the potentiometer should be placed at some distance from the system whose temperature is wanted, but the reference junction is placed near the test junction and for precision work may consist of a pair of thermojunctions connected to copper wire leads as shown in the diagram. The temperature of the reference junction is kept constant, at the ice point or at the triple point of water. Although the two copper leads to the brass terminals of the potentiometer form a pair of copper-brass thermojunctions, they give rise to no net thermal emf if they do not differ in temperature. In many applications where high precision is unnecessary, the potentiometer circuit is replaced by a suitable millivolt-meter.

The thermocouple is calibrated by maintaining the reference junction at 0°C and by allowing the test junction to come to equilibrium at several known temperatures. The measured thermal emf e over limited ranges usu-ally can be related to the Celsius temperature t by a quadratic equation of the form

$$e = a + bt + ct^2, \qquad (2.5)$$

in which the constants a, b, and c are different for each thermocouple and are evaluated by means of three fixed points. The range of a thermocouple depends upon the materials of which it is made. For platinum and platinum-rhodium alloy the range is $-200°C$ to approximately 1600°C.

At still higher temperatures optical methods are employed. The total-radiation pyrometer is a device in which all the radiation entering through a window is focused on an array of thermojunctions called a thermopile. It may be calibrated with radiation from a cavity which is heated to various temperatures over the useful range of the instrument, and for precision work it may be evacuated. This pyrometer is sensitive to all wavelengths.

When the radiation is in equilibrium with the walls of the inclosure, the energy density per unit wavelength interval at wavelength λ is given by the equation

$$u_\lambda = c_1\lambda^{-5}[e^{c_2/\lambda T} - 1]^{-1}, \qquad (2.6)$$

in which c_1 is a constant for each instrument and c_2 is a universal constant equal to 1.438 cm-deg Kelvin. This equation is a statement of Planck's law; it is discussed more fully in Chapter 16.

Another instrument which is rugged, simple, and often portable is the optical pyrometer. This is a device for comparing the brightness of the incandescent body whose temperature is wanted with the brightness of a calibrated source over a narrow range of wavelengths in the visible region of the spectrum. In the disappearing-filament type of instrument the cali-brated source is the filament of a small low-voltage lamp located in the focal plane of a low-power telescope through which the incandescent body is viewed. Ordinarily observations are made through a narrow-band filter centered at a wavelength of 0.665 μ. The current in the filament is adjusted until the image of the filament merges with the background. The brightness temperature of the body then is read off a calibration curve of temperature against filament current. Usually this temperature is less than the actual temperature because the body is not a blackbody; therefore a correction must be applied to the reading.

2.8. The International Temperature Scale

In 1948 the Ninth General Conference on Weights and Measures revised the International Temperature Scale, which had been adopted by the Seventh General Conference in 1927, in order to bring about better agreement between it and the standard scale of temperature. The International Scale does not replace the standard scale, but it does provide a much more convenient scale which can be easily and rapidly employed for calibrating scientific and industrial instruments. It is accurately reproducible and provides a means for uniquely specifying any temperature within the range of the scale.

The International Scale is made to agree with the standard scale at the fixed points listed in Table 2.3 under "basic fixed points." At temperatures between these points the difference between the scales is negligible. For convenience in interpolation between the fixed points the scale is divided into four parts as follows.

(1) From the ice point to the antimony point, temperature t is obtained from the resistance R_t of a standard platinum resistance thermometer by means of the formula

$$R_t = R_0(1 + At + Bt^2), \tag{2.7}$$

in which the constants R_0, A, and B are determined by calibrating the instrument at the ice, steam, and sulfur points. The platinum in the resistance thermometer must be annealed in the form of a wire with a diameter between 0.05 mm and 0.20 mm and of such purity that R_{100}/R_0 is not less than 1.391.

(2) From the oxygen point to the ice point, temperatures are read from the same platinum resistance thermometer by means of the formula

$$R_t = R_0[1 + At + Bt^2 + C(t - 100)t^3], \tag{2.8}$$

where R_0, A, and B have the foregoing values, and C is determined by calibrating the thermometer at the oxygen point.

(3) From the antimony point to the gold point, the interpolating instrument is a standard thermocouple consisting of a platinum wire and an alloy wire of 90% platinum and 10% rhodium by weight. The diameter of each wire must be between 0.35 mm and 0.65 mm. One junction of the thermocouple is maintained at the ice point. The constants a, b, and c in the thermocouple equation are evaluated by calibrating the instrument at the silver and gold points and by comparing it directly with a standard platinum resistance thermometer at a temperature within 0.2° of the antimony point.

(4) For all temperatures above the gold point, an optical pyrometer serves as a thermometer. Temperatures are given by Planck's law, in which the constant c_2 is assigned the value 1.438 cm-deg Kelvin, and the constant c_1 is determined by calibrating the instrument at the gold point for a wavelength equal to or near that at which the temperature measurements are made. The value for c_2 was derived in 1948 from a careful comparison of theoretical and experimental results; studies since then suggest that this value may be revised upward in the future to 1.4388 cm-deg Kelvin (see Section 16.8).

The International Temperature Scale has not been defined for temperatures below the oxygen point. The National Bureau of Standards has established a scale down to 20°K, but this is based solely on the calibration of a group of resistance thermometers against the gas thermometer, and no general resistance-temperature law has been obtained. Several other laboratories also are undertaking to extend the scale downward.

2.9. *Comparison of Temperature Scales*

In the preceding sections we have described how the ideal gas scale is established and how the International Scale is defined. We noted that the ideal gas scale is identical with the thermodynamic scale, and we have referred to both of them as standard scales. Sometimes the thermodynamic scale is called an "absolute scale." In order to indicate the relation between the International and the thermodynamic scales and to suggest a satisfactory notation, the Tenth International Conference on Weights and Measures accepted the formulation at the top of page 30.

In addition to the foregoing scales we have already mentioned the Fahrenheit scale, on which the ice point is at 32° and the steam point is at 212°. Corresponding to it there is an absolute scale which is named after Rankine. Because there is only one primary standard fixed point, presumably the Rankine and Fahrenheit scales may be related to it. The Rankine tempera-

International Scale	Thermodynamic Scale
1. International temperature t is identified by °C(Int., 1948) which reads degree Celsius (International, 1948).	1. Thermodynamic Celsius temperature $t_{th} = T - 273.15$ exactly is identified by °C(therm.) which reads degree Celsius (thermodynamic).
2. International Kelvin temperature $T_{int} = t + 273.15$ exactly is identified by °K(Int., 1948) which reads degree Kelvin (International, 1948).	2. Thermodynamic temperature T is identified by °K which reads degree Kelvin

ture may be defined as nine-fifths of the Kelvin temperature. The Rankine temperature of the triple point of water, therefore, would be $\frac{9}{5} \times 273.16°$K or 491.69°R. The ice point would be 491.67°R, and thus the zero of the Rankine scale would be 459.67°F below the zero of the Fahrenheit scale. The Celsius, Fahrenheit, Kelvin, and Rankine temperatures of the standard and basic fixed points are compared in Table 2.4.

TABLE 2.4. *Comparison of Temperature Scales at the Standard and Basic Fixed Points.*

Fixed Points	Celsius	Fahrenheit	Kelvin	Rankine
Absolute zero	−273.15	−459.67	0.00	0.00
Oxygen point	−182.97	−297.35	90.18	162.32
Ice point	0.00	32.00	273.15	491.67
Triple point of water	0.0100	32.02	273.16	491.69
Steam point	100.00	212.00	373.15	671.67
Sulfur point	444.60	832.28	717.75	1291.95
Antimony point	630.5	1166.9	903.65	1626.57
Silver point	960.8	1761.5	1234.0	2221.2
Gold point	1063.0	1945.4	1336.5	2405.1

Problems

1. Suppose the temperature function f(X, Y_0) is chosen to be a simple logarithmic relation,

$$\theta = f(X, Y_0) = \ln (kX),$$

in which k is a constant.

(a) If the thermometric property X is the pressure for an ideal gas, find a relation between this *logarithmic temperature* θ and the Kelvin temperature T. For this purpose assume readings on the two scales agree at the triple point of water.

(b) Find the values for the logarithmic temperatures of the ice and steam points.

(c) Is there an "absolute zero" on this scale?

2. Suppose the temperature function $f(X, Y_0)$ is chosen to be of the form

$$\theta = f(X, Y_0) = k/X,$$

where X represents the pressure of an ideal gas at constant volume.

(a) What value would you assign to k in order to have all values of θ equal simply the negative reciprocals of the Kelvin temperature?

(b) Is there an "absolute zero" on this scale?

(c) If bodies at low temperatures on this scale are "cold" and at high temperatures are "hot," at what Kelvin temperature would a body be "hottest"?

3. A reading of $50°$ is made on a liquid-in-glass thermometer for which the ice point is at $25°$ and the steam point is at $100°$.

(a) What does the reading $50°$ mean?

(b) Where is "absolute zero" on this scale of temperature?

4. If the ice point was set equal to $190.000°$ above absolute zero on a new scale of temperature, what value would be assigned to c_2 in Planck's radiation formula?

5. The suggestion has been made that the normal freezing point of very pure zinc $(419.505°C)$ replace the sulfur point in defining the International Temperature Scale. What advantages would the zinc point have over the sulfur point?

6. In applying Eq. (2.7) to obtain a value for temperature t, first R_0, A, and B are evaluated from ice, steam, and sulfur-point data, and then the desired temperature t is found by solving the quadratic equation. Callendar showed that the calculation could be simplified by rearranging Eq. (2.7) in the form

$$t = t_{Pt} + \delta[(t/100)^2 - (t/100)],$$

where

$$t_{Pt} = 100(R - R_0)/(R_s - R_0).$$

Here R_s is the resistance of the platinum resistance thermometer at the steam point and R is its resistance at temperature t. The value of t is obtained by successive approximations, since it differs from t_{Pt} only by the small correction term on the right. First a value for t_{Pt} is determined from the experimental data. This is substituted for t in the bracketed expression to compute a value for t on the left side of the equation. The new value for t may then be substituted on the right side. In this way the cycle is repeated until the computed value of t on the left side equals the value for t inserted on the right side.

(a) Evaluate δ in terms of A and B.

(b) In the laboratory δ is found simply by determining t_{Pt} for the sulfur point. The resistance of a certain platinum-resistance thermometer is 9.928

ohms, 13.764 ohms, and 26.086 ohms at the ice, steam, and sulfur points. Evaluate δ from these data.

(c) What is the temperature of a system in which this platinum-resistance thermometer reads 22.242 ohms?

2-7. The equation for the helium vapor-pressure thermometer over the range 4.2–5.2°K in terms of common logarithms is

$$\log p = 0.97864 - 2.77708/T + 2.5 \log T,$$

in which p is the vapor pressure in centimeters of mercury.

(a) Determine the ratio of the vapor pressure of helium at 5.2°K and 4.2°K.

(b) At what temperature in this range can the temperature be measured with greatest precision?

CHAPTER 3

Equations of State and Thermodynamic Processes

Classical thermodynamics is that part of thermophysics which deals with systems in equilibrium and with processes for changing from one equilibrium state to another. In order to apply its principles, equations relating equilibrium states are discovered by experimental methods, and suitable mathematical procedures are developed. These fundamental aspects of thermodynamics are introduced in this chapter.

A system occupies a thermodynamic equilibrium state if all its thermophysical variables remain constant and uniform over a period of time. In particular, a system is in mechanical equilibrium if no unbalanced generalized forces exist between parts of the system and between the system and its near-surround. It is in thermal equilibrium if its temperature is uniform throughout and if no heat is exchanged with the near-surround. Finally, it is in chemical equilibrium if no spontaneous chemical reactions take place and if there is no transfer of matter from one part of the system to another or between the system and its near-surround. As an illustration, a mixture of two parts of dry hydrogen to one part of dry oxygen in an enclosure at room temperature may be in mechanical and thermal equilibrium; but it is not in chemical equilibrium, for the gases can react chemically to form water. Only if a system satisfies the conditions of all three types of equilibrium can it be said to occupy a thermodynamic equilibrium state.

3.1. Equations of State for Fluid Systems

Any functional relation between two or more thermophysical variables of a system which is in thermodynamic equilibrium is an equation of state. Although the existence of such equations often may be demonstrated by suitable argument, as was done in Section 2.2, explicit forms of them must be discovered by experimentation and nonthermodynamic methods. In the absence of gravitational, electric, magnetic, surface, and other effects, the thermodynamic equilibrium states for a closed system may be described completely by an equation of state involving the three thermodynamic co-ordinates P, V, and T. One of the simplest such equations is that for an ideal gas.

From the experiments of Boyle, Charles, and Gay-Lussac a state equation of the form

$$Pv = RT \qquad (3.1)$$

was established for gases of low density at temperatures well above their condensation points. In this equation v represents the molar volume[1] of a gas at pressure P and temperature T, and R is the universal gas constant

$$R = 8.3144 \pm 0.0004 \text{ joules/gm} $$
$$\text{mole-deg.}$$

In thermodynamics an ideal gas is a gas which satisfies Eq. (3.1) exactly for all values of pressure, volume, and temperature, and in addition has a constant value for its specific heat capacity. Actually real gases fail to satisfy these conditions, especially at high densities and at temperatures near condensation regions, as illustrated in Fig. 3.1. There are plotted values of the compressibility factor Pv/RT against P for dry air, hydrogen, carbon dioxide, and water vapor.

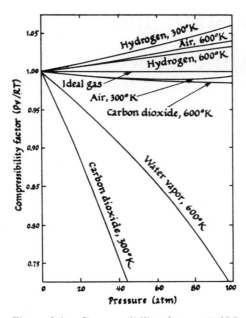

Figure 3.1. Compressibility factors Pv/RT for several gases at 300°K and 600°K.

---

[1] A molar volume is the volume occupied by one mole of gas; namely by a mass of one molecular weight (see also p. 51).

Of the many equations which have been suggested as better approximations for real gases, perhaps the most familiar is one developed by van der
Waals,

$$(P + a/v^2)(v - b) = RT, \qquad (3.2)$$

in which a and b are molar constants for the system. Values of a and b for
a few substances are listed in Table 3.1. Although the terms a/v^2 and b can

TABLE 3.1.   *van der Waals' Constants.* *

Substance	a $\left(\dfrac{\text{liter}^2\text{-atm}}{\text{mole}^2}\right)$	b $\left(\dfrac{\text{liter}}{\text{mole}}\right)$	Substance	a $\left(\dfrac{\text{liter}^2\text{-atm}}{\text{mole}^2}\right)$	b $\left(\dfrac{\text{liter}}{\text{mole}}\right)$
NH_3	4.170	0.03707	CH_4	2.253	0.04278
A	1.345	0.03219	Ne	0.2107	0.01709
CO_2	3.592	0.04267	N_2	1.390	0.03913
Cl_2	6.493	0.05622	O_2	1.360	0.03183
He	0.03412	0.02370	P	52.94	0.1566
H_2	0.2444	0.02661	SO_2	6.714	0.05636
Kr	2.318	0.03978	Xe	4.194	0.05105
Hg	8.093	0.01696	H_2O	5.464	0.03049

* From *Handbook of Chemistry and Physics*, 42nd ed., Chemical Rubber Publishing
Co., Cleveland, Ohio.

be related to intermolecular forces and molecular volumes, respectively, it is
sufficient here to treat the equation simply as an empirical one involving
macroscopic thermodynamic coordinates. A system which satisfies this equation exactly for all values of pressure, volume and temperature is a van der
Waals fluid.

Many other equations have been suggested as state equations for gas and
vapor systems. Among them are those of Dieterici, Berthelot, and Beattie
and Bridgman.

> Dieterici: $P(v - b) \exp(a/RTv) = RT$; (3.3)
> Berthelot: $(P + a/v^2T)(v - b) = RT$; (3.4)
> Beattie and Bridgman: $(P + A/v^2)v^2/(v + B)(1 - e) = RT$. (3.5)

Here $A = A_0(1 - a/v)$; $B = B_0(1 - b/v)$; $e = c/vT^3$; and A_0, B_0, a, b, and c
are constants. More than fifty other such equations are listed in the *Handbuch
der experimental physik* (Vol. viii, Part 2, pp. 224–225). The virial equation of
Kamerlingh Onnes in any of its variant forms has proven especially satisfactory. Two of its forms are:

$$Pv = RT(1 + B_v/v + C_v/v^2 + \ldots)$$

and

(3.6)

$$Pv = RT(1 + B_pP + C_pP^2 + \ldots),$$

in which B_v, C_v, ... and B_p, C_p, ... are virial coefficients and may be interrelated. Numerical values for them must be evaluated for each isotherm and are published in tables, such as those in the *American Institute of Physics Handbook*. Any one of the foregoing state equations may be written in virial form; for a van der Waals fluid we find that $B_v = b - a/RT$, $C_v = b^2$, and $D_v = b^3$. If the volume is sufficiently large and the pressure is small, all equations for gas and vapor systems reduce to the state equation for an ideal gas.

3.2. Equations of State for Other Systems

Radiative Systems. The total radiation within a uniformly heated enclosure may be considered a radiative system in equilibrium with the blackbody walls. The intensity of radiation J_b everywhere in this system is given by the fourth-power law

$$J_b = \sigma T^4,$$

(3.7)

in which σ is the universal radiation constant:

$$\sigma = 5.685 \times 10^{-8} \text{ watt/m}^2\text{-deg Kelvin}^4.$$

This law, discovered by Stefan in 1879, is discussed in greater detail in Chapter 16. Because J_b is the amount of radiant energy passing through a unit area in a unit time, radiant energy must occupy every unit volume within the enclosure; therefore the energy per unit volume also must be proportional to the fourth power of temperature on the absolute scale. The energy density u_b then is given by the equation

$$u_b = aT^4,$$

(3.8)

in which a is another universal constant which can be shown to equal $4\sigma/c$, where c represents the phase velocity of electromagnetic waves (see problem 3-4). This is an equation of state for the radiative system.

Elastic Systems. The isothermal extension of a wire over a limited range of values often is proportional to the applied force; in symbols,

$$F = k(L - L_0).$$

(3.9)

This is Hooke's law. Thermodynamically, it is an equation of state for the stretched wire. The constant k equals YA/L_0, in which A is the cross-sectional area of the wire, L_0 is its unstretched length, and Y is Young's modulus of the wire material.

Rubber and rubberlike systems do not satisfy Hooke's law. In 1941 James and Guth published a state equation which describes experimental data rather well. For limited extensions it reduces to the form

$$F = KA_0T[(L/L_0) - (L_0/L)^2]. \tag{3.10}$$

Here L_0 is the length and A_0 is the cross-sectional area of the unstretched sample, L is the length of the sample when stretched by force F, K is a constant of the material, and T is the absolute temperature. According to this equation a rubber strip under constant load should contract when it is heated. This characteristic of rubber was first observed by Gough in 1802.

Electrolytic Systems. An electrolytic cell is not in equilibrium when it is on open circuit. If the cell is connected to a source of emf which opposes that of the cell, so that no current flows, and if the temperature is uniform throughout, the cell is in thermodynamic equilibrium. When a saturated Weston standard cell is connected to a potentiometer and the circuit is balanced, the emf is given by the relation

$$E = E_0 + a(t - 20) + b(t - 20)^2 + c(t - 20)^3. \tag{3.11}$$

In this state equation t is the temperature in degrees Celsius, E_0 is the emf at 20°C, and a, b, and c are constants characterizing the constituents of the cell.

Paramagnetic Systems. For a paramagnetic gas or crystal in which the magnetic dipoles are well separated so there is no mutual interaction, the magnetic moment M is a function of the applied magnetic field intensity H divided by the temperature T of the system. Langevin found the state equation to have the form

$$M = N\mu_m[\coth(\mu_m\mu_o H/kT) - (kT/\mu_m\mu_o H)], \tag{3.12}$$

where μ_m is the magnetic moment of a single dipole, N is the number of dipoles in the gas or crystal, μ_o is the permeability of free space and k is the Boltzmann constant. In thermodynamics an ideal paramagnetic substance is a substance which satisfies Langevin's equation exactly for all values of dipole moment, magnetic field intensity, and temperature. In weak fields, where $\mu_m\mu_o H/kT \ll 1$, Langevin's equation reduces to

$$M = N\mu_m^2\mu_o H/3kT. \tag{3.13}$$

The proportionality between the dipole moment per unit volume (M/V)

and the ratio of magnetic field intensity to temperature (H/T) constitutes Curie's law. According to the Langevin equation the constant of proportionality, known as the Curie constant, equals $N\mu_m^2\mu_o/3kV$.

For many liquids and solids in which dipole interactions may be large, Weiss proposed the state equation

$$M = CVH/(T - \Theta_W). \qquad (3.14)$$

Here C is the Curie constant and Θ_W is the Weiss constant; Θ_W is characteristic of a substance and may be either positive or negative. This equation holds only for $T > \Theta_W$ and reduces to Curie's equation when Θ_W equals zero.

3.3. Reversible Quasistatic Process

A system of constant mass performs a quasistatic process when it traverses a series of states which are infinitesimally close to equilibrium. The thermodynamic coordinates for each of these states clearly must satisfy the equation of state for the system. The process is reversible if it can be performed in such a way that, at its conclusion, both the system and the near-surround can be restored to their initial states without producing any change in the far-surround. Such a process is an ideal abstraction; nonetheless, it is extremely useful in solving thermophysical problems. The reversible process may be classed with such other idealizations as frictionless mechanical processes, the flow of nonviscous fluids, and the interaction of point masses. In thermodynamics a process is reversible only if it is performed quasistatically and if no dissipative effects occur; it is irreversible if the conditions for thermodynamic equilibrium are not satisfied and if dissipative effects such as friction, viscosity, magnetic hysteresis, or eddy currents are present.

All processes occurring in nature appear to be irreversible, since either dissipative effects are present or else the conditions for thermodynamic equilibrium are not satisfied. Only occasionally does a natural process approach reversibility. In the laboratory and the engineering field the conditions for reversibility may be approximated rather closely. Dissipative effects in a device may be made negligible by lubrication, and acceleration effects are reduced by slow operation. The device then performs effectively a quasistatic process. The necessary experimental conditions are not always as easy to set up, but this should not prevent us from assuming them in *mental experiments*. A mental experiment may be impossible to perform in the laboratory, not because it violates scientific laws and principles, but because of physical limitations on real substances. Real substances, for instance, may satisfy Hooke's law over short ranges of elongation, yet we may imagine a substance that satisfies Hooke's law for all values of elongation. Many of the experiments studied in thermophysics are mental in this sense.

3.4. *Thermodynamic Processes*

An equation of state for a system often may be represented either as a continuous curve on a graph or, if three thermodynamic coordinates are involved, as a thermodynamic surface. Such a surface for an ideal gas is shown in Fig. 3.2. Sometimes an algebraic relation cannot be set down for a system, and a graph of the experimental data is the only way of represent-

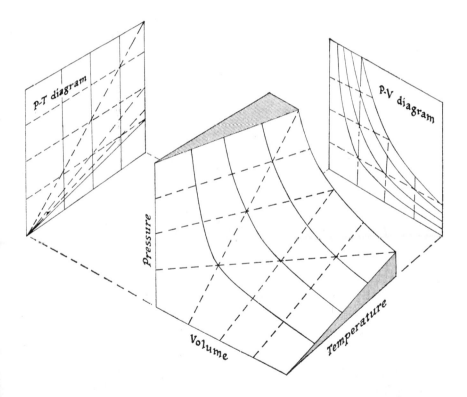

Figure 3.2.   *P-V-T* surface and projections showing *P-T* and *P-V* diagrams for an ideal gas.

ing its states. Any continuous curve on a thermodynamic surface, connecting a series of equilibrium states through which the system may pass, represents a thermodynamic reversible process. Of the large number of possible processes, those that occur with one or more of the thermodynamic variables held constant often are singled out for special study. We have seen that an isothermal process[2] may be represented by a curve of pressure as a function of volume at constant temperature on a P-V diagram. Likewise, an isobaric process takes place at constant pressure and an isochoric process at constant volume.

If a system is stretched linearly, its state may be described by sets of values of the applied force, length, and temperature. During an isometric process the length is held constant; during an isodynamic process the force is held constant. Isometrics and isodynamics are especially useful in the study of synthetic rubbers, silicones, tendon, muscle fibers, and other rubberlike substances. A wire experiences an isodynamic process during a thermal expansion experiment and an isothermal process during a Young's modulus experiment.

More than one thermodynamic coordinate may be constant during a process. Any normal change of phase of the first kind, such as melting and freezing, evaporation and condensation, sublimation, and transitions from one solid phase to another, occur under isothermal and isobaric conditions. The formation of weak solutions in the laboratory is nearly isochoric and isobaric. Creep in a wire is isothermal and isodynamic, and relaxation in rubber is isothermal and isometric.

3.5. Thermophysical Coefficients

Suppose the length L of a wire or rubber strand under constant load F is measured for several ambient temperatures t. A graph of $(L - L_0)/L_0$ against t represents the isodynamic process, and the slope of the resulting curve is a thermophysical coefficient. In this instance it is the coefficient of linear thermal expansion or simply the linear expansivity

$$\alpha = (1/L)(\partial L/\partial t)_F. \tag{3.15}$$

Because length L is a function of both the temperature and the load, it is necessary here to introduce the notation for a partial derivative. The symbol $(\partial L/\partial t)_F$ is read "the partial derivative of length L with respect to tempera-

---

[2] See Section 2.2. The prefix iso- (or is- before vowels) from the Greek word isos, meaning "equal," indicates that the thermophysical quantity which it modifies is constant or unchanging in the given process.

ture t at constant load F."[3] This mathematical operation is called partial differentiation to distinguish it from ordinary differentiation.

In general, if $f(x, y, \ldots)$ is a function of several variables, $\partial f/\partial x$ means that all these variables but x are held constant in finding the derivative. A quantity in thermophysics, however, may be a function of one set of independent variables or another, so those to be held constant in a given partial differentiation are not always clearly evident unless explicitly stated. It has become the universal practice therefore to indicate the variables held constant by subscript notation; thus $(\partial F/\partial L)_{VT}$ is the partial derivative of the force with respect to length of a system when both the volume and the temperature are held constant; and $(\partial P/\partial t)_{HV}$ is the partial derivative of the pressure with respect to temperature of a paramagnetic gas when both magnetic field and volume are held constant.

The coefficient of volume thermal expansion or volume expansivity is written

$$\beta = (1/V)(\partial V/\partial t)_p, \tag{3.16}$$

where $(\partial V/\partial t)_p$ is the slope of an isobar on a V-t diagram. Tabular values of β ordinarily are given for P equal to one atmosphere. The coefficient β, like α, may be a function of temperature as is suggested by the nonlinearity of the isobars.

The fact that the state equation for a linear medium involves only F, L, and t suggests that the temperature may be held constant as the system is stretched or compressed. It is this condition that applies in the usual experimental study of Hooke's law and the measurement of Young's modulus by static methods. The force constant in Hooke's law is simply the slope of an isotherm on an F-L diagram. In symbols it is $(\partial F/\partial L)_t$, and the isothermal Young's modulus Y_t is then defined by the equation

$$Y_t = (L/A)(\partial F/\partial L)_t. \tag{3.17}$$

The modifying adjective "isothermal" is included here to distinguish this Young's modulus from the adiabatic Young's modulus Y_s, in which the system does not exchange heat with its near-surround during the measurement.

Values of pressure plotted against volume of a system at constant temperature yield an isotherm whose slope is represented by $(\partial P/\partial V)_t$. Ordinarily it is convenient to define the isothermal compressibility of the system in terms of the reciprocal of this slope; thus

$$k_t = -(1/V)(\partial V/\partial P)_t. \tag{3.18}$$

---

[3] The symbol $(\partial f/\partial x)_y$ for the partial derivative usually implies that f is a function solely of the two independent variables x and y.

The minus sign is introduced to make the coefficient a positive number, because $(\partial V/\partial P)_t$ is intrinsically negative. If observations are made under adiabatic conditions, on the other hand, an adiabatic compressibility k_s is obtained.

Many other expressions involving partial derivatives may be defined for electric, magnetic, surface, and other systems. Only a small number of them are familiar enough, however, to have acquired special names.

3.6. Relations Among Partial Derivatives

Because of their fundamental role in thermodynamics, partial derivatives and the relations among them should be reviewed. The equation obtained by setting the function of any number of variables equal to zero may describe the states of a system. There is no loss in the generality of this discussion if we limit the number of variables to three; then

$$f(x, y, z) = 0 \qquad (3.19)$$

is such a function. This equation may now be solved for one of the variables in terms of the other two. For purposes of clarity in thermodynamics, the symbol of the dependent quantity also represents the function for it. Thus

$$z = z(x, y) \qquad (3.20)$$

is a symbolic solution of the state equation for z.

Suppose the total differential dz in terms of dx and dy is desired. For small finite changes in x and y of amounts Δx and Δy, the change in z is

$$\Delta z = z(x + \Delta x, y + \Delta y) - z(x, y),$$

which may be written

$$\Delta z = \left[\frac{z(x + \Delta x, y + \Delta y) - z(x, y + \Delta y)}{\Delta x} \right] \Delta x$$

$$+ \left[\frac{z(x, y + \Delta y) - z(x, y)}{\Delta y} \right] \Delta y.$$

Here we can apply the fundamental definition of a partial derivative: for a function $\varphi(u, v)$,

$$\left(\frac{\partial \varphi}{\partial u} \right)_v = \lim_{\Delta u \to 0} \left[\frac{\varphi(u + \Delta u, v) - \varphi(u, v)}{\Delta u} \right].$$

This is a simple extension of the definition for an ordinary first derivative. In the limit as both Δx and Δy approach zero, the coefficient of Δx becomes equal to $(\partial z/\partial x)_y$, and the coefficient of Δy becomes equal to $(\partial z/\partial y)_x$. Thus

$$dz = (\partial z/\partial x)_y dx + (\partial z/\partial y)_x dy. \qquad (3.21)$$

It should be noted here that the partial derivative of $(\partial z/\partial x)_y$ with respect to y equals the partial derivative of $(\partial z/\partial y)_x$ with respect to x. If any differential dz can be written in the form

$$dz = Mdx + Ndy, \qquad (3.22)$$

and if

$$(\partial M/\partial y)_x = (\partial N/\partial x)_y, \qquad (3.23)$$

it follows that dz is an exact differential.

If Eq. (3.21) is divided throughout by dz and y is held constant, the reciprocal relation $(\partial z/\partial x)_y(\partial x/\partial z)_y = 1$ is obtained. Here we note that dx/dz becomes the partial derivative $(\partial x/\partial z)_y$. On the other hand, Eq. (3.21) may be divided throughout by dx to obtain the equation

$$dz/dx = (\partial z/\partial x)_y + (\partial z/\partial y)_x(dy/dx). \qquad (3.24)$$

If z is held constant, then dy/dx becomes the partial derivative $(\partial y/\partial x)_z$. The quantities $(\partial z/\partial x)_y$ and $(\partial z/\partial y)_x$ are not variables but coefficients, and therefore they do not vanish when dz equals zero. By introducing the foregoing reciprocal relation we find the coefficients may be arranged in the symmetrical form

$$(\partial x/\partial z)_y(\partial y/\partial x)_z(\partial z/\partial y)_x = -1. \qquad (3.25)$$

Note that x, y, and z in the numerators, denominators, and subscripts are in cyclic order.

As an example in applying the foregoing equations consider a system in which the three thermophysical variables are P, V, and T. If we solve the general state equation for V in terms of P and T, then we can identify V with z, P with y, and T with x. Thus

$$dV = (\partial V/\partial P)_T dP + (\partial V/\partial T)_P dT \qquad (3.26)$$

and

$$(\partial P/\partial T)_V = -(\partial V/\partial T)_P(\partial P/\partial V)_T. \qquad (3.27)$$

If we now introduce the definitions of isothermal compressibility and volume expansivity from Section 3.5, these equations become

$$dV = -k_t V dP + \beta V dT \qquad (3.28)$$

and

$$(\partial P/\partial T)_V = \beta/k_t. \qquad (3.29)$$

Over limited ranges of pressure and temperature β and k_t may be practically constant, and we get

$$\ln V + k_t P - \beta T = \text{constant} \qquad (3.30)$$

as the state equation for the system whose isochorics have the constant slope β/k_t and therefore are linear.

Problems

1. Show that $(\partial F/\partial T)_L = -\alpha A Y_t$ and therefore that the compressional force required on the ends of a copper rod 1 cm² in cross-section to maintain its length constant is nearly 50 lb of force per degree rise in temperature.

2. How much pressure must be applied to a given mass of water to hold its volume constant as the room temperature is increased one degree Celsius?

3. The common definition of Young's Modulus is

$$Y = \text{stress/strain} = (F/A)/(e/L),$$

in which F is the applied force over cross-section A and e is the extension of the wire whose length is L. How do you justify then the equation for Y given in Section 3.5?

4. Prove that the universal constant a in the state equation for blackbody radiation equals $4\sigma/c$. To do this construct a parallelopiped of slant height $cd\tau$ on a base of area S (similar to Fig. 11.1), where c is the speed of electromagnetic radiation and $d\tau$ is an infinitesimal time interval. Let the angle of slant be θ and suppose the energy density is u_b. Now solve for the radiant energy within the parallelopiped and flowing in the direction of S, and then integrate the resulting expression over the hemisphere.

5. Show that the van der Waals equation can be written in virial form with

$$B_v = b - a/RT, \quad C_v = b^2, \text{ and } D_v = b^3.$$

6. The state equation for a monomolecular film on water has the form

$$(S - S_w)A = cT,$$

in which S and S_w are the surface tensions of the monomolecular film and of pure water, respectively; A is the area of the film; T is the absolute temperature; and c is a constant. Evaluate $(\partial A/\partial S)_T$, $(\partial S/\partial T)_A$, and $(\partial T/\partial A)_S$ and compute their product.

7. The state equation for a charged parallel-plate capacitor in rationalized MKS units has the form

$$Z = \epsilon A E/d,$$

where Z is the charge on a plate of area A, the plates are separated a distance d and have a difference of potential E, and ϵ is the specific inductive capacity of the medium between the plates (ϵ is a function of temperature). Show that

$$(\partial E/\partial T)_Z = -E[\partial(\ln \epsilon)/\partial T)]_Z.$$

8. For some paramagnetic solids at low temperatures the Weiss equation of state,

$$M = CVH/T - \Theta_W),$$

describes the experimental data somewhat better than the Curie equation. Show that Weiss' equation can be written in the form

$$M/V = C'H/T,$$

in which
$$C' = C[1 + (\Theta_W/T) + (\Theta_W/T)^2 + \ldots].$$

9. When a system undergoes an infinitesimal thermodynamic process the change in its specific internal energy du is related to the changes in specific entropy ds and volume dv by the equation

$$du = T\,ds - P\,dv.$$

The entropy function is discussed in Section 4.3. If the specific heat capacity at constant volume is given by the equation

$$c_v = T(\partial s/\partial T)_v,$$

show that $(\partial P/\partial s)_v = -(\partial T/\partial v)_s = \beta T/c_v k_t.$

CHAPTER 4

Work and Heat

ENERGY is exchanged between a system and its near-surround in three fundamental ways: by mechanical processes involving work, by thermal processes involving heat, and by chemical processes. Generally a chemical process takes place if an actual transfer of mass is associated with the energy exchange, and therefore it usually applies to open systems. Only work and heat are exchanged between a closed system and its near-surround.

4.1. Work

A system which is displaced or distorted by the application of forces has work done on it. If this work involves the system as a whole, the work is external. Work done by one part of a system on another part is internal. By and large we shall be concerned with external work, so unless otherwise indicated, the word "work" will mean external work.

The work done on a wire or strand by a force F to stretch it an infinitesimal amount dL is FdL. The work to stretch it from an initial length L_i to a final length L_f equals the integral of FdL from L_i to L_f. In the same manner the work required to increase the free surface of a liquid equals the integral of SdA from an initial area A_i to a final area A_f, where S is the work per unit area, commonly called surface tension. Perhaps the most common of the work integrals in thermophysics is that which expresses the work required to increase the volume of a system: the integral of $-PdV$. Many other such integrals exist; the amount of work required to charge an electrical condenser or a reversible cell or to change the dipole moment of a magnetized bar are examples. Note that the work integrals involve two quantities: a generalized force such as F, S, P, E, and H and a generalized displacement such as L, A, V, Z, and M. As a rule, the magnitude of a generalized force is independent of the dimensions of the system, whereas the magnitude of a generalized displacement is not. Because of this, generalized forces are intensive quantities, and generalized displacements are extensive quantities. The product of a generalized force and the corresponding generalized displacement has the dimensions of energy, and therefore we may say that the two quantities are conjugate with respect to energy.

Often it is convenient to divide an extensive quantity for a system by the mass of the system. The resulting parameter is said to be specific, as in specific volume (the reciprocal of the density), specific internal energy, specific heat capacity (or simply specific heat), specific charge, and so on. An extensive quantity per unit mass may be represented by the symbol for the extensive quantity in lower case; for example, v for specific volume and z for specific charge.

4.2. Graphical Representation of Work

Let Y represent a generalized force and X the corresponding generalized displacement for a given system. Values of Y may be plotted against X on a Y-X diagram, as shown by the solid curve in Fig. 4.1. The area under the curve between two ordinates, such as those at X_i and X_f (vertical lines), equals the integral of $Y dX$ between the limits X_i and X_f. We see from Table 4.1 that this represents work done on the system. That is, the curve connects a continuous series of points representing successive states of the system, and the area under it between two points A and B on the curve represents the work exchange with the near-surround as the system passes along the curve from A to B. The curve is called a path on the Y-X diagram, and evidently the work done will depend on the shape of this path (not the path on the work). In Fig. 4.1 a second path (dotted line) is shown connecting states A and B. Although the system goes from the same initial state to the same final state as before, the work exchange in this instance is *greater* by an amount represented by the area shaded with horizontal lines.

The very fact that the work done on a system in changing its state depends on the path means that work W cannot describe the state of a system, nor even the path by which the system changes its state, for many paths exist over which equal amounts of work can be exchanged between the system

TABLE 4.1. *Work Integrals for Several Systems.*

System	Intensive Quantity	Symbol	Extensive Quantity	Symbol	Work Integral	Eq. Number
Any system	generalized force	Y	generalized displacement	X	$\int_{X_i}^{X_f} Y\,dX$	(4.1)
Wire or strand	force	F	length	L	$\int_{L_i}^{L_f} F\,dL$	(4.2)
Free liquid surface	surface tension	S	area	A	$\int_{A_i}^{A_f} S\,dA$	(4.3)
System of constant mass	negative pressure	$-P$	volume	V	$\int_{V_i}^{V_f} P\,dV$	(4.4)
Electric condenser or reversible cell	emf	E	charge	Z	$\int_{Z_i}^{Z_f} E\,dZ$	(4.5)
Paramagnetic substance in magnetic field	magnetic field intensity	H	magnetic moment	M	$\int_{M_i}^{M_f} H\,dM$	(4.6)

and its near-surround. The infinitesimal amount of work $Y\,dX$ therefore is called an inexact differential and is represented by $d'W$, where the d' means inexact. Note that dX, on the other hand, is an exact differential, for it can be integrated between limits. This means that its integral is independent of the path and depends only on the initial and final states of the system. The mathematical criterion for the exactness of a differential was discussed in Section 3.6. Evidently $d'W$ can be converted to an exact differential by dividing it by Y. The reciprocal

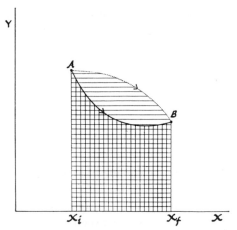

Figure 4.1. Graphical representation of work. The area under a Y-X diagram represents the work exchange between a system and its near-surround.

of Y is called an integrating factor. In general, when an integrating factor is multiplied into an inexact differential the product can be integrated between limits.

4.3. Heat

Frequently heat is confused with internal energy and sometimes with temperature. The term heat now has the precise meaning of energy as it is transferred by the thermal processes of conduction, convection, and radiation. (These processes are discussed in detail in later chapters.) The amount of heat supplied to a closed system and the work done on it by the near-surround together cause a change in internal energy given by the first law of thermodynamics in the form

$$U_f - U_i = Q + W. \tag{4.7}$$

Because work W depends on the path connecting the initial and final states of the system, it follows that heat Q also must depend on this path; otherwise $U_f - U_i$ would not come out independent of the selfsame path. That is, when a closed system is changed from an initial to a final state, the work and heat exchanges with the near-surround are observed to have different values depending on the path but always such as to add up to a constant amount of energy. It is for this reason that an internal energy state function can be introduced.

For an infinitesimal quasistatic change of state we now write

$$d'Q = dU - d'W \tag{4.8}$$
$$= dU - YdX.$$

Actually more than one work term may be necessary for a specific system, but for many applications not more than two are required and often one suffices. If an integrating factor for $d'Q$ can be found, then Eq. (4.8) can be transformed into an exact differential. In order to discover this factor it is necessary to introduce the second law of thermodynamics and to develop some of its implications. We shall anticipate the result by suggesting that the reciprocal of the absolute temperature T is the needed factor. This means that the integral of $d'Q/T$ must depend only on the initial and final states of the system and not on the path. We conclude therefore that a new state function S must exist which depends solely on the state of the system, so

$$dS = d'Q/T. \tag{4.9}$$

The function S is called entropy. It is an extensive quantity having the dimensions of energy per degree.

We see that no change in entropy of a system can occur during a quasi-static process if there are no heat exchanges with the near-surround. That is, a system which passes through a series of equilibrium states under adiabatic conditions undergoes an isentropic process. Its change in internal energy just equals the work done on the system, therefore this can be considered an operational definition of internal energy in terms of adiabatic work.

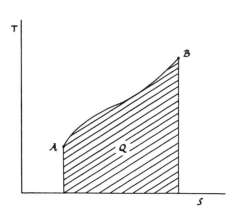

Figure 4.2.   Graphical representation of heat on a *T-S* diagram.

The foregoing equation may be solved for Q,

$$Q = \int_{S_i}^{S_f} T dS, \qquad (4.10)$$

but the integral generally is not very useful for computing heat exchanges because there is no direct way of measuring entropy. Instead, the equation often is integrated for the change in entropy. If the entropy of a system in each of a series of states relative to that of an arbitrary state can be computed, then a quasistatic process may be shown as a curve on a *T-S* diagram, as illustrated in Fig. 4.2. The heat Q exchanged with the near-surround, as the system passes from one state A to another state B, is represented by the area under the curve between these two states (hatched area in Fig. 4.2). Note that the heat exchanged depends on the shape of the path. In order to *measure* the heat exchanged between a system and its near-surround the concept of heat capacity is introduced.

4.4. Heat Capacity

As the science of thermophysics grew, often through an intuitive approach to the phenomena, new terms were invented and became fixed in the language. Unfortunately, many of these terms turned out to be poor choices. For instance, the heat capacity of a body suggests that the body is capable of holding a definite quantity of heat; but this erroneous notion arose through the confusion between internal energy and heat as discussed in Section 1.4. *By the heat or thermal capacity of a closed system of uniform temperature, pressure, and phase we shall mean the amount of energy transferred to the system by thermal processes to raise its temperature one degree.* The heat capacity thus depends on the scale of temperature chosen. The amount of heat entering a system therefore can be measured in terms of the heat capacity and temperature rise of the system.

The absolute magnitude for the heat capacity of a system may have almost any value between zero and infinity, but ordinarily it is convenient to specify only two special values. One of these is obtained by holding the generalized displacement constant during the thermal processes, the other by holding the generalized force constant. Heat capacities are represented by C with a suitable subscript to designate what is held constant. The heat capacity at constant length and at constant force for a stretched wire are represented by C_L and C_F; the heat capacity at constant volume and at constant pressure of a gas, liquid, or solid, by C_V and C_P; and the heat capacity at constant dipole moment and at constant magnetic field intensity, by C_M and C_H.

Heat capacity is an extensive quantity, similar to length, volume, charge, and dipole moment, for it is proportional to the mass of the system. The gram heat capacity applies to one gram, the molar heat capacity to one mole. One mole of a pure substance equals the chemical combining weight of that substance on a scale for which exactly 12 has been adopted as the combining weight of the most common isotope of carbon.[1] The heat capacity per unit mass commonly is called specific heat. For water at atmospheric pressure and 15°C the specific heat at constant pressure equals 4.1858 joules/gm-deg Celsius; and for dry air at atmospheric pressure and 0°C it is 1.004 joules/gm-deg Celsius.

In determining heat capacities such as C_F, C_P, and C_H, mechanical as well as thermal processes are involved, thus work is done while heat is added to the system. The work done is readily computed by means of the integrals in Table 4.1. As an illustration, consider the work exchange which takes place when 1 gm of dry air at 0°C is heated at a constant pressure of one standard atmosphere to a temperature of 1°C. The initial volume equals 773 cc and increases by 2.833 cc or 2.833×10^{-6} m^3. This increase occurs at a constant pressure of 101,325 newtons/m^2. The work exchange then equals $-101,325 \times 2.833 \times 10^{-6}$ or -0.287 joules; that is, 0.287 joules of work are done on the near-surround by the system. Because the dry air behaves very nearly like an ideal gas we find that the gram heat capacity at constant

----

[1] Oxygen 16 was the primary standard of combining weights until September 1961, when the Commission on Atomic Weights, International Union of Pure and Applied Chemistry, replaced it by carbon 12.

volume C_V equals $1.004 - 0.287$ or 0.717 joule/gm-deg Celsius. The ratio C_P/C_V, usually represented by γ, here equals $1.004/0.717$ or 1.400; the measured value equals 1.403.

The amount of heat supplied to a closed system of heat capacity C_q to raise its temperature through dt is $C_q dt$, where q represents the generalized force or displacement which is held constant during the heating. The total heat transferred, for a finite change in temperature from t_i to t_f, is therefore

$$Q = \int_{t_i}^{t_f} C_q dt. \tag{4.11}$$

Frequently C_q can be considered practically constant for a short range of temperature; then Q equals $C_q(t_f - t_i)$. By means of this equation we can now compute the amount of heat supplied to a system whose heat capacity is known.

4.5. C_v and C_p

The heat capacities at constant volume C_v and at constant pressure C_p will be introduced time and again in our discussions. Since C_p is the more easily measured, a table of specific heats ordinarily contains values of specific heat capacities at constant pressure. In theoretical studies of the structure and properties of substances, however, C_v usually is involved.

From the definition of heat capacity we see that

$$C_v = d'Q/dt \text{ (volume constant)}$$

and

$$C_p = d'Q/dt \text{ (pressure constant)}.$$

But from the first law of thermodynamics

$$d'Q = dU + PdV, \tag{4.12}$$

so that

$$C_v = (\partial U/\partial t)_V$$

and

$$C_p = (\partial U/\partial t)_p + P(\partial V/\partial t)_p.$$

However, if the pressure is constant, we may write

$$C_p = [\partial(U + PV)/\partial t]_p.$$

The quantity $U + PV$ appears so frequently in thermophysics that it is given a special symbol and name: it is represented by H and is called enthalpy. Thus we have

$$C_p = (\partial H/\partial t)_p. \tag{4.13}$$

Since U, P, and V are all thermophysical variables which describe the state of a system, H also is a state variable. The enthalpy is related to the heat capacity at constant pressure in the same way that the internal energy is related to the heat capacity at constant volume. For a quasistatic isochoric process, evidently

$$Q = \int_{t_i}^{t_f} C_v dt = U_f - U_i, \qquad (4.14)$$

and for a quasistatic isobaric process

$$Q = \int_{t_i}^{t_f} C_p dt = H_f - H_i. \qquad (4.15)$$

From these integrals, therefore, tables of values for specific internal energy and specific enthalpy may be constructed by assigning a zero value to the functions for a convenient but otherwise arbitrary state of the system. Tables of specific volumes, entropies, enthalpies, and other thermodynamic quantities for systems of special interest may be found in handbooks.

4.6. Measurement of C_p

The heat capacity of a system is sensitive not only to changes in temperature but also to changes in structure and impurity content. For this reason measurements of heat capacity as a function of temperature have become especially significant in investigations of the solid state. Great skill and excellent laboratory facilities are essential for these studies.

Perhaps the most common precision method of measuring the heat capacity of a specimen is electrical heating. A small coil is carefully mounted in a cavity within the specimen in such a manner that all the electrical energy which is converted to thermal energy heats the specimen. The electrical energy is supplied at a constant rate, and temperature measurements are made over a period of time. From these data a temperature-time graph is plotted. For greatest accuracy only a small temperature rise is allowed. In order to reduce heat losses the space around the specimen is evacuated, and throughout the experiment the wall of the enclosure is maintained, by suitable controls, at the same temperature as the specimen. When the apparatus is operated this way it is called an adiabatic calorimeter. A schematic diagram of an experimental adiabatic calorimeter is shown in Fig. 4.3.

Suppose the temperature of the specimen rises an infinitesimal amount dt during time $d\tau$. No work is done, even though the specimen expands, because the pressure on it is zero; therefore all the heat supplied increases the internal energy of the specimen by the amount $C_p dt$, where C_p is its heat

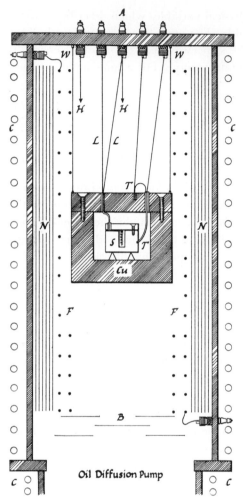

Figure 4.3. An experimental adiabatic calorimeter. A, electrodes in cover on a vacuum-tight chamber with seamless stainless steel cylindrical walls; B, baffles for condensing oil vapor from diffusion pump; C, coils of copper tubing for water cooling; N, several layers of thin nickel sheet to reduce radiation loss from interior; F, windings of furnace nichrome wire with auxiliary turns at either end to reduce axial temperature gradient; W, support wires for the calorimeter block; Cu, copper calorimeter block with heater wires around the outside (not shown); S, specimen metal cylinder with a small heating coil mounted inside; L, leads to specimen heating coil; H, leads to heating coils on the calorimeter; T, differential thermocouple. In addition, there are leads for measuring the difference of potential across the specimen coil and a thermocouple to the calorimeter block for measuring its temperature.

capacity at zero pressure. If the emf across the inner heating coil is E and the current in it is I, then the electrical energy $EId\tau$ equals $C_p dt$, or

$$C_p = \frac{EI}{(dt/d\tau)}. \tag{4.16}$$

A value of $dt/d\tau$ is obtained from the slope of the t-τ graph at the mean temperature, as shown in Fig. 4.4, and then C_p is computed.

In another method the system is heated in the adiabatic calorimeter to an elevated temperature. Heating then is stopped and the system is allowed to cool. The temperature of the system is measured as a function of time and a cooling curve is drawn, as in Fig. 4.5. From the curve, $dt/d\tau$ may be found at any one temperature. In a separate experiment heat is supplied to the system by the inner coil at such a rate that the system is maintained at the temperature for which $dt/d\tau$ is now known. The heat supplied then just equals that lost to the surrounding walls by radiation. The emf and the current required are measured and C_p is computed.

In either method the heating or cooling often takes place rather slowly over long periods of time. For this reason the apparatus usually involves automatic controls for supplying electrical energy, vacuum pumps, automatic recording equipment, and several protective devices to prevent damage if the electrical power fails or the water pressure drops below a critical value. A block diagram of such an automatically controlled experimental system is shown in Fig. 4.6.

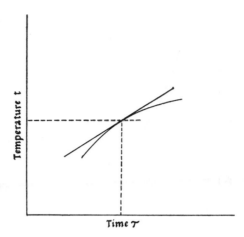

Figure 4.4.   Portion of a temperature-time heating curve to show how $dt/d\tau$ is determined.

4.7. *Latent Heat and Heat of Reaction*

Latent heat is another term which came into being as a result of the confusion between internal energy and heat. *The latent heat for the isothermal transformation of a single species of matter[2] from one phase to another is equal to the heat exchanged between a unit mass of this species and the near-surround during the transformation.* Note that, work as well as heat exchange takes place, just as it did in heating a system at constant pressure.

The most familiar phase transformations are the conversion of a solid to a liquid, a liquid to a vapor, and a solid to a vapor. These processes are termed melting, evaporation, and sublimation. The reverse processes are freezing and condensation. A less familiar transformation is that from one solid form to another, as from β-iron to γ-iron or from ice I to ice II. The passage of an electron gas from the interior of a hot metal to the region outside is called thermionic emission. Within the metal the gas is in a con-

---

[2] By a species of matter we shall mean a homogeneous isotropic substance of uniform chemical composition, such as water, nitrogen, iron oxide, or sulfur.

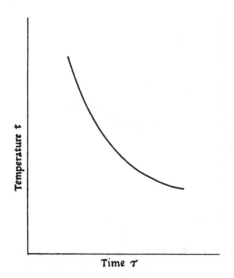

Figure 4.5. A temperature-time cooling
            curve from which $dt/d\tau$
            may be obtained.

densed phase, and outside the gas is in a rarefied phase; thus the emission process behaves like the sublimation of a solid at constant temperature.

Let us examine briefly the slow vaporization of 1 gm of water at a pressure of one standard atmosphere and at 100°C. The measured latent heat for these conditions equals 2255.7 joules/gm. During the transformation, however, the vapor expands until it occupies 0.001673 m³. The work done may be computed by means of Eq. (4.3). Here the pressure is maintained constant at 101,325 newtons/m², and the vapor expands into a volume of 0.001672 m³. The work done is

$$W = -P(v_f - v_i) = -101,325 \times 0.001672 = -169.4 \text{ joules.}$$

The minus sign indicates that the work is done by the system on the nearsurround. Therefore, of the heat supplied to evaporate 1 gm of water at 100°C and a standard atmosphere of pressure, 169.4 joules are converted to

Figure 4.6. Automatically controlled and recording apparatus for measuring specific heat capacities.

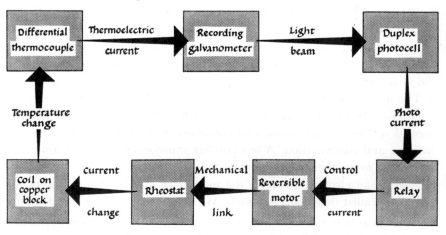

work on the near-surround. By the first law of thermodynamics we conclude that the remaining 2086.3 joules must enter the gram of water to become part of its internal energy.

When substances are mixed, go into solution, crystallize, or take part in a chemical reaction, generally heat is evolved or absorbed. A heat of reaction is associated with each of these processes; namely, a heat of mixture, a heat of solution, heat of crystallization, and a heat of formation. These heats of reaction are defined in the same way as is latent heat. Many other transformations are accompanied by a similar exchange of heat with the near-surround. The decrease in tension within a stretched strand of substance of constant length has a heat of relaxation; the decrease of charge in a battery at constant emf has a heat of discharge. Ordinarily, a distinction is made between the heats of reaction for a transformation where one or another thermophysical variable is held constant. There exists a heat of solution or a heat of formation at constant pressure and another at constant volume. The heat of relaxation is defined for a constant length of the specimen, and the heat of discharge for a constant emf of the battery.

4.8. Work and Heat Reservoirs

A work reservoir is any source of mechanical energy whose thermophysical variables remain unaltered as work exchanges take place between it and a system. Although a stretched spring or a mass in a gravitational field are sources of mechanical energy, they are not suitable as work reservoirs because large changes in their thermophysical variables ordinarily do occur whenever work is done. The work reservoir, as defined, is an ideal but useful construct, analogous to the point mass, the weightless string, the frictionless machine, and the incompressible fluid. For many purposes, however, a stiff spring with such a large force constant that minute changes in extension allow the exchange of work of any magnitude needed in a problem may serve as a practical work reservoir. Another is such a large body of water at an elevated level in the earth's gravitational field that only slight changes in its level are required to deliver any arbitrary amount of work.

Likewise, *a heat reservoir is any source of thermal energy whose thermophysical variables remain unaltered as heat exchanges take place between it and a system.* It, too, is an ideal construct. In practice, the unconfined atmosphere or large bodies of water may serve as heat reservoirs. The heat developed in an automobile engine, for instance, finally is delivered to the atmosphere by means of a radiator and fan system with no significant change in the temperature, pressure, or other thermophysical variables of the atmosphere.

Special symbols have been invented for the diagrammatic representation of many of the constructs and processes in thermophysics. For work and heat reservoirs the symbols shown in Fig. 4.7 often are employed. As a rule we will place reservoirs of high temperature above those of low temperature and work reservoirs at high potential to the left of those at low potential. The system which interacts with these reservoirs is represented by a circle between pairs of reservoirs. Any energy exchanges are indicated by arrows. Figure 4.8(a) is a diagram for the conduction of heat Q from one heat reservoir to another *through* a system. Figure 4.8(b) is a diagram for the conversion of work W into heat Q by means of a system such as an electrical heater.

Figure 4.7.   Diagrammatic symbols for heat and work reservoirs and for a general system.

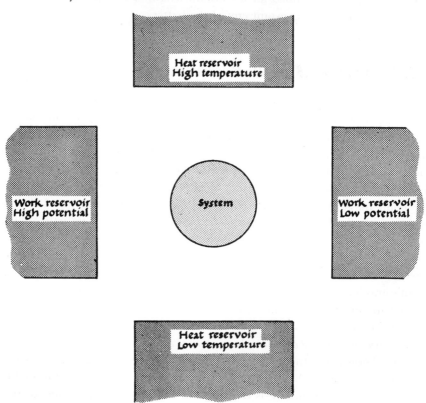

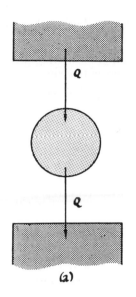

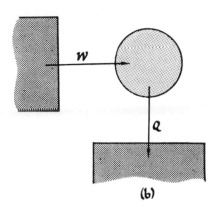

Figure 4.8. (a) Thermal conduction through a system. (b) Complete transformation of work into heat by a system.

Problems

1. During a slow adiabatic expansion of an ideal gas, the pressure at any moment is given by the expression

$$PV^\gamma = \text{constant},$$

in which γ is the ratio C_p/C_v. Show that the work done by the gas in expanding from the initial values of pressure and volume (P_i, V_i) to the final values (P_f, V_f) is given by the equation

$$W = (P_f V_f - P_i V_i)/(\gamma - 1).$$

2. For the slow increase in magnetization of a paramagnetic substance the field intensity is given by the expression

$$MT = CVH,$$

in which C is the Curie constant and T is the temperature. Show that the work done in the isothermal magnetization of the substance is

$$W = \tfrac{1}{2}(CV/T)(H_f^2 - H_i^2),$$

in which H_i and H_f are the initial and final values of the magnetic field intensities.

3. Compute the amount of work done on each of the following systems by the near-surround.

(a) A metal sphere is discharged from an initial charge Z_i to a final charge Z_f.

(b) A soap bubble is doubled in volume.

4. Show that the work $d'W$ to maintain a current i in a Rowland toroid of

length L and with N turns of wire equals $VHdB$, in which V is the volume of the core material, H is the magnetic field intensity, and B is the flux density.

5. A wire is stretched slowly from a length L_i to a length L_f. If the process is carried out adiabatically, solve for the change in internal energy of the wire.

6. How much work is done on 1 gm of ice to convert it to liquid water at 0°C, and what change takes place in its internal energy?

7. Define: (a) heat of solution; (b) heat of crystallization; (c) heat of formation.

8. Suppose we define a quantity which we shall call the *work capacity* of a system as follows: The work capacity of a closed system of uniform temperature, pressure, and phase equals the amount of energy transferred to the system by mechanical processes to increase its pressure a unit amount. Show that the work capacity at constant temperature is given by

$$C_T = (\partial A/\partial P)_T$$

in which A represents the Helmholtz function $U - TS$.

9. The bulb of a mercury-in-glass thermometer is heated at a rate which is proportional to the difference between its temperature and that of the near-surround. Show that the mercury level in the capillary rises at such a rate that at any time τ the reading t on it is given by the equation

$$t_f - t = (t_f - t_i) \exp(-k\tau/C_p),$$

in which t_i is the initial temperature of the bulb, t_f is the final temperature of the bulb (temperature of near-surround), C_p is the heat capacity of the bulb, and k is the proportionality constant for the rate of heating.

CHAPTER 5

Heat-Work Cyclic Processes

IT is fairly easy to set up a system which transforms work into heat with practically 100% efficiency; but the reverse process probably can never be realized. If a system is to continually convert work to heat or heat to work, either its state must never change or else it must return to its initial state periodically. If two bodies are rubbed together or if current is passed through a resistor, the work supplied from the near-surround may be converted completely to heat and removed as rapidly as it is produced by a flowing stream of water. The state of the bodies or of the resistor is assumed to remain constant throughout the conversion process; the system is in a steady state. On the other hand, no practical scheme is known for continually converting heat to work without altering the state of the system in a periodic manner. When this is done, the conversion is not complete.

5.1. A Simple Heat-to-work Converter

For a simple heat-to-work converter a quantity of gas may be confined in a cylinder with diathermic walls. At one end of the cylinder a tight-fitting frictionless piston conveys work to the near-surround. We suppose a continuous series of heat reservoirs are available with temperatures from a high value t_1 to a low value t_2. A finite number of processes now are performed to convert heat to work in such a way that the gas finally is returned

61

to its initial state. We shall construct a graph to illustrate the processes on a *P-V* diagram as we describe the operation of the device.

The piston-and-cylinder heat-to-work converter first is placed in contact with the heat reservoir at temperature t_1, and the gas in it is allowed to expand quasistatically and isothermally from the initial state *A* to an inter-

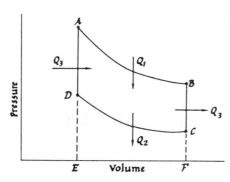

mediate state *B* (Fig. 5.1). Meanwhile heat Q_1 enters the system and work W_1 is done on the near-surround through the agency of the piston. The piston now is held firmly to prevent any work exchange while the converter is passed slowly over the continuous series of heat reservoirs in order to reduce the temperature from t_1 to t_2. The process is quasistatic and isochoric. Heat Q_3 flows out of the system, and the gas reaches an inter-

Figure 5.1.   *P-V* diagram for a simple heat-to-work converter.

mediate state *C*. Next the gas is compressed quasistatically and isothermally by the supply of mechanical energy from the near-surround to an intermediate state *D* where the volume equals the initial value. During this process heat Q_2 is delivered to the heat reservoir at temperature t_2 while work W_2 is done on the system by the near-surround. Finally, the system is brought back to state *A* by a quasistatic isochoric process. This is done by passing it over the series of heat reservoirs once again in reverse order. During the process, heat Q_3 flows into the system again. The inflow of heat during process *DA* equals the outflow during the process *BC*, provided the heat capacity at constant volume of the gas is a function of temperature only.

Works W_1 and W_2 are represented by areas *ABFE* and *DCFE*, and the net work $W_1 - W_2$ done by the system is represented by the area *ABCD*. The net heat which flows into the system equals $Q_1 - Q_2$. The gas in the cylinder has performed a heat-work cycle to convert heat $Q_1 - Q_2$ into work $W_1 - W_2$. Note that the processes in the cycle may be performed in reverse order to deliver heat Q_2 from the cold reservoir at temperature t_2 to the hot reservoir at temperature t_1 by the near-surround doing work $W_1 - W_2$ on the system. The device then performs a reversible refrigeration cycle.

5.2. The Carnot Cycle

The foregoing reversible cycle is one of many that may be performed by the gas system. Similar cycles may be devised for any other system we may choose. Ordinarily, the cycles easiest to analyze consist of isothermal, isochoric, isobaric, adiabatic, and other processes where at least one thermodynamic variable is held constant. Perhaps the most notable of them is the Carnot cycle. It is made up of two reversible isotherms and two reversible adiabats. The cycle was first analyzed by the young French engineer Sadi Carnot in 1824. (He contributed little else to science during his short life span of 36 years.) Although he employed the then current caloric theory in his analysis, the results turned out to be independent of the theory of heat adopted. This single achievement made Carnot immortal among men.

Any system whatever may be carried through a Carnot cycle. Because all the processes in this cycle are reversible, and therefore ideal, the operations are performed mentally. Many real systems, however, perform actual processes sufficiently close to the ideal to make the study of Carnot cycles of practical significance. A few such cycles are illustrated in Fig. 5.2.

Figure 5.2(a) illustrates a gas confined in the cylinder of a heat-to-work converter and carried through a Carnot cycle. From a to b the gas is allowed to expand quasistatically and isothermally while the cylinder is in contact with a heat reservoir at temperature t_1. Work is done on the near-surround. From b to c the cylinder is enclosed in an adiabatic wall, and the gas continues to expand quasistatically and do work as its temperature falls to t_2. From c to d the gas is compressed quasistatically and isothermally while the cylinder is in contact with a heat reservoir at temperature t_2. Work is done on the system. Finally, the cycle is completed from d to a by enclosing the cylinder in an adiabatic wall once again and by performing a quasistatic adiabatic compression until the gas returns to its initial state at temperature t_1. Some additional work is done on the system during this process. We find that the net work output equals the net heat input and is represented by the area enclosed within the four paths.

Figure 5.2(b) illustrates the Carnot cycle of a stretched wire. Here the isotherms are described by Hooke's law and therefore are straight lines with positive slopes. The adiabats over limited ranges of extensions also are straight lines, but with smaller slopes. From a to b the wire undergoes a quasistatic adiabatic extension by the slow application of a load. Its temperature increases from t_1 to t_2. Then from b to c the wire is further extended

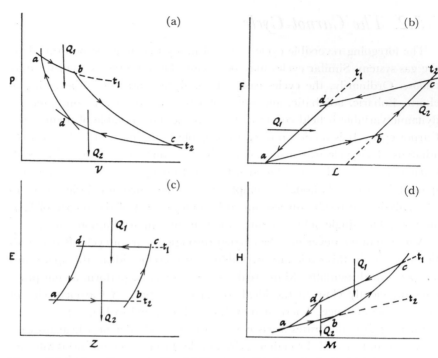

Figure 5.2.   Four Carnot cycles: (a) Real gas, (b) Stretched wire, (c) Ideal electric
cell, (d) Ideal paramagnetic substance.

quasistatically but now isothermally at the temperature t_2. From c to d it
undergoes a quasistatic adiabatic contraction until the temperature again
equals t_1. Finally, from d to a the wire is allowed to return to its initial state
by quasistatic isothermal contraction. The work output during the contraction processes exceeds the work input during the extension processes by
the net heat input during the isothermal processes.

Figure 5.2(c) illustrates the Carnot cycle for an ideal electric cell. The
isotherms for such a cell are parallel to the Z axis on an E-Z (emf-charge)
diagram, as suggested by the state equation. The adiabats cut across them
as shown. Process ab represents quasistatic isothermal charging in which
positive charges are slowly transferred from the negative to the positive
electrode through an external circuit. Heat Q_2 flows out of the cell into a
heat reservoir at temperature t_2. The cell is now encased in an adiabatic
wall while further charging goes on (process bc) until its temperature rises
to t_1. Process cd represents isothermal discharging and process da adiabatic
discharging until the cell returns to its initial state. During these discharge
processes positive charge is transferred from the positive to the negative

electrode through the external circuit, where work is done on the near-surround. Heat Q_1 must flow into the ideal electric cell during the isothermal process. Here again the net work output equals the net heat input. The charge-discharge processes in a real cell are not as simple because an irreversible transformation of electrical energy takes place in the internal resistance of the cell.

The Carnot cycle for an ideal paramagnetic substance is shown in Fig. 5.2(d). From Curie's law we find that the isothermals are represented by straight lines which pass through the origin of an H-M diagram. The adiabatic curves cut across them, but also intersect at the origin. From a to b slow isothermal magnetization is brought about by raising the magnetic field intensity while the paramagnetic specimen is in contact with a heat reservoir at temperature t_2. From b to c the specimen is surrounded by an adiabatic wall, and magnetization is continued until the temperature rises to t_1. From c to d the specimen is allowed to demagnetize quasistatically and isothermally at temperature t_1. Finally the specimen is again surrounded by the adiabatic wall and allowed to further demagnetize until it regains its initial state at a. The net heat input during the isothermal processes is converted to work, which is represented by the area within the cycle on the H-M diagram.

5.3. Heat Engines and Refrigerators

Any system that is carried through a cycle in such a way as to convert some heat into work is a heat engine. In general, the processes of the cycle need not be reversible. The substance of the system is the working substance. The gas within the cylinder described in Section 5.1 is the working substance of the simple heat engine. A system operating through a Carnot cycle to derive work from heat is a Carnot engine.

The thermal efficiency of a heat engine equals the absolute ratio of the net work output to the *total* heat input. Here the outflow of heat is considered an energy loss so far as work output is concerned. Ordinarily the work output and heat input are expressed in the same units, so the ratio has no units.

Let the net work output of a heat engine for one complete cycle be W, and suppose that heat Q_1 flows into the system from the reservoir of higher temperature and that heat Q_2 flows out of it into the reservoir of lower temperature during the cycle. The efficiency of the engine then equals W/Q_1. Because the system returns to its initial state at the end of a cycle, the change of internal energy equals zero. Therefore, by the first law of thermodynamics,

$$Q_1 - Q_2 - W = 0,$$

and the efficiency may be written

$$\eta = W/Q_1 = (Q_1 - Q_2)/Q_1. \tag{5.1}$$

The efficiency can be 100%, that is, η can equal unity, only if Q_2 equals zero. To have no outflow of heat from the working substance of an operating heat engine, so that Q_2 is zero, cannot be realized in practice. We shall find that only if a Carnot engine were to reject heat into a cold reservoir at 0°K would it have an efficiency of 100%; but, as discussed in Chapter 6, a temperature of 0°K cannot be attained.

If a system is operated cyclically in such a way that heat is removed from one thermal reservoir and is delivered to another at a higher temperature, the system performs a refrigeration cycle. The processes in this cycle need not be reversible. If all the processes are reversible, however, the heat inflow from the hot reservoir, the heat outflow to the cold reservoir, and the work done by the system when operating as an engine are equal to the heat outflow to the hot reservoir, the heat inflow from the cold reservoir, and the work done on the system, respectively, when operating as a refrigerator. Processes of special interest are those for which at least one thermodynamic variable is held constant. The ideal refrigerator of this nature is a Carnot engine operated backward; it is called a Carnot refrigerator. The common household and industrial vapor-compression refrigerators involve at least one definitely irreversible process; they are not heat engines operated in reverse.

A refrigerator is rated by its coefficient of performance rather than by its efficiency. The coefficient of performance is equal to the ratio of the heat from the reservoir of lower temperature, or cold box, during a cycle to the net work done on the refrigerant. If Q_2 represents the heat removed from the cold reservoir, Q_1 the heat delivered to the hot reservoir, W the work done on the system by the near-surround, the coefficient of performance is

$$K = Q_2/W = Q_2(Q_1 - Q_2), \tag{5.2}$$

where W equals $Q_1 - Q_2$ by the first law of thermodynamics. Note that K may have a value greater than unity.

5.4. The Four-stroke Gasoline Engine

Generally, the processes of actual heat engines are irreversible and the processes of their idealizations are assumed reversible. Furthermore, it is convenient to replace the working substance of the actual heat engine by an ideal gas, a van der Waals fluid, or some other ideal fluid for computational purposes. Let us now examine briefly the four-stroke gasoline and diesel engines, the gas turbine, and jet-propulsion devices.

In Fig. 5.3 is shown the empirical pressure-volume curve, or indicator diagram, for a four-stroke gasoline engine with a schematic diagram of a cylinder below it. When the piston reaches its farthest position on the left it is said to be at the head-end dead center (HDC), and when it reaches the farthest position on the right it is at the crank-end dead center (CDC). The space between HDC and the head of the cylinder is the clearance or unswept volume. The ratio of the cylinder volume (the volume in the cylinder when the piston is at

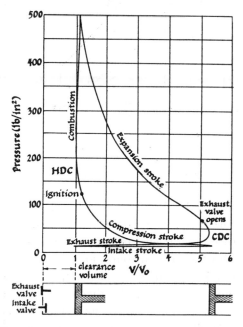

Figure 5.3. Indicator diagram for a four-stroke gasoline engine. [Adapted from A. G. Worthing and D. Halliday, *Heat*, Wiley, New York, 1948.]

CDC) to the clearance volume is called the compression ratio of the engine.

With the intake valve open and a cam holding the exhaust valve closed, a mixture of gasoline vapor and air enters the cylinder at subatmospheric pressure during the intake stroke. The intake valve then closes, and the mixture is compressed during the compression stroke. Just before HDC this mixture is ignited, usually by means of an electric spark, and a rapid rise in pressure and temperature with little change in volume occurs. This is followed by the expansion or power stroke. Before the power stroke comes to an end at CDC the exhaust valve opens, the pressure in the cylinder is reduced to atmospheric, and the exhaust stroke takes place.

The ideal cycle used by the engineer for studying the four-stroke gasoline engine is named for Nikolaus August Otto, a German engineer who, with Eugen Langen, in 1876 made the first engine to operate successfully in accord with the principles laid down by the French engineer A. Beau de Rochas, in 1862. A *P-V* diagram for the Otto cycle is shown in Fig. 5.4. Ordinarily the engineer conceives the gasoline and air mixture to be replaced

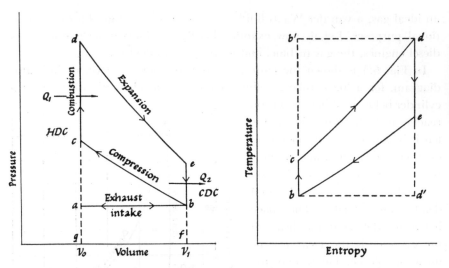

Figure 5.4. *P-V* and *T-S* diagrams for an Otto cycle.

entirely by dry air, and he refers to the cycle as an air-standard Otto cycle. The intake and exhaust strokes take place at the same constant pressure (one atmosphere) over the same range of volumes, so the work exchanges with the near-surround for these processes cancel one another. The compression and power strokes are assumed to take place by reversible adiabatic processes and, finally, the combustion and depressurizing reversible processes are assumed to occur at the constant volumes V_0 and V_1, respectively.

During the combustion process very little heat is exchanged with the near-surround; actually an irreversible chemical process occurs to increase the temperature of the gases. In the ideal Otto cycle this combustion process is replaced by a reversible isochoric process in which heat is assumed to flow into the system from the near-surround.

Let T_b, T_c, T_d, and T_e represent the absolute temperatures of the ideal gas system in states b, c, d, and e, respectively. In order for the isochoric processes to be reversible the system exchanges heat with a continuous series of reservoirs at temperatures ranging from T_b to T_c and from T_e to T_d. During these processes, then,

$$Q_1 = C_v(T_d - T_c)$$

and

$$Q_2 = C_v(T_e - T_b),$$

where C_v is the heat capacity of the ideal gas at constant volume. The efficiency of the Otto engine then can be written

$$\eta = 1 - (T_e - T_b)/(T_d - T_c). \qquad (5.3)$$

For the reversible adiabatic processes,

$$T_b V_b^{\gamma-1} = T_c V_c^{\gamma-1}$$

and

$$T_d V_d^{\gamma-1} = T_e V_e^{\gamma-1}.$$

But V_b and V_e equal V_1; V_c and V_d equal V_0. Thus we find

$$T_c/T_b = T_d/T_e = (V_1/V_0)^{\gamma-1}.$$

The ratio V_1/V_0 has been defined as the compression ratio and usually is represented by r. We now eliminate T_d and T_c from the equation for η and obtain

$$\eta = 1 - r^{1-\gamma}. \tag{5.4}$$

Because γ is greater than unity, high efficiencies are associated with high compression ratios. In practice, however, high compression ratios lead to excessive heating of the mixture of gasoline and air on compression, and pre-ignition takes place with a consequent loss of power and other undesirable results. For an engine operating on an Otto cycle with γ equal to 1.4 and r equal to 5.3, the efficiency is 49%. The real engine of the indicator diagram in Fig. 5.3 has an efficiency of 29%. In spite of this discrepancy between the ideal and the actual efficiencies of the four-stroke gasoline engine, the simplified analysis illustrated here has proven very useful as a guide to the engineer. Closer agreement may be obtained by means of the idealized fuel-air engine in which the working substance is a mixture of fuel, air, and exhaust gases rather than all air.

The output of the Otto engine, as represented by area *bcde* in Fig. 5.4, is much less than the output of a Carnot engine operating between the temperatures T_d and T_b, as represented by area *bb'dd'*.

5.5. *The Diesel Engine*

The patent for this engine was obtained by Rudolf Diesel in 1893. Its principal advantages over other internal combustion engines are that it can use cheap fuel oil, that it requires no special ignition system, and that its compression ratio may be very high. However, only about a third of the energy supplied by the fuel during combustion is used to perform external work. The rest of it is lost to the water jacket and to the exhaust. In the Diesel engine air is drawn into the cylinder and compressed during the intake and compression strokes. Near the end of the compression stroke the fuel is injected as a fine spray and ignites in the hot air. This process continues over a short part of the cycle at approximately constant pressure.

Meanwhile expansion begins. The fuel supply then is cut off, and the hot gases continue to expand during the principal part of the power stroke. When the piston is nearly at the end of its path, the exhaust valve opens and the pressure drops rapidly to approximately atmospheric. Finally, the spent gases are forced out during the exhaust stroke. As we did for the gasoline engine, we again imagine the working substance to be replaced by an ideal gas and the actual processes to be approximated by a series of reversible processes. The cycle of events is like that for the Otto cycle save for the combustion process, which takes place at constant pressure rather than at constant volume. A diagram of the Diesel cycle is shown in Fig. 5.5; V_0 is the clearance volume, V_2/V_0 is the compression ratio r_c, and V_2/V_1 is the expansion ratio r_e. By means of the equation of state and the adiabatic law for an ideal gas it may be shown that the efficiency of the ideal Diesel engine is

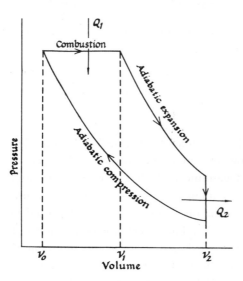

Figure 5.5. P-V diagram for a Diesel cycle.

$$\eta = 1 - (r_e^{-\gamma} - r_c^{-\gamma})/\gamma(r_e^{-1} - r_c^{-1}). \qquad (5.5)$$

For the air-standard Diesel cycle γ equals 1.40, but for an ideal gas cycle which approaches the real one more closely γ may have a slightly different value.

In either the gasoline or the Diesel engine the exhaust gases may be blown out and fresh fuel may be blown in by means of auxiliary equipment. In this way the engine becomes a two-stroke rather than a four-stroke engine, and the power output occurs during one cycle rather than two.

The Diesel engine we have considered is of the liquid-fuel type. For the solid-fuel type the initial stage of the combustion process is explosive in character and, therefore, it is assumed to take place at constant volume in the ideal cycle. This stage is followed by a slower burning one which occurs at nearly constant pressure. The idealization for the solid-fuel Diesel engine is called a Dual cycle, and its thermal efficiency may be computed in a manner similar to that for the Otto and Diesel cycles.

5.6. *The Gas Turbine and Jet Engine*

These devices operate in a similar manner and therefore can be considered together. Simple schematic diagrams for them are shown in Fig. 5.6. In the gas turbine the air is compressed in an axial flow compressor from an initial pressure p_0 to a final pressure p_1. The injected fuel burns in the combustion chamber, and the products expand at nearly constant pressure. Then they enter the gas turbine, where they continue to expand, until the pressure again becomes equal approximately to p_0. Finally, the exhaust gases must be cooled to the initial temperature in order to complete the cycle. The work in excess of that required to operate the compressor may be utilized externally, for example, to operate an electrical generator. In the diagram the mechanical connections between compressor, gas turbine, and generator are indicated by double lines. The essential difference between the simple gas turbine and the related jet engine is that in the latter the hot combustion products expand to an intermediate pressure p' in the gas turbine part of the device, and then they pass through a discharge nozzle where the pressure falls toward p_0 as external work is done by the jet. The pressure p' is chosen such that the work output of the turbine is equal to that required to operate the compressor.

The ideal cycle for these devices is called the Joule or Brayton cycle. It consists of two isobaric and two adiabatic reversible processes, as shown in Fig. 5.7. For this cycle the efficiency is given in terms of the working pressures p_0 and p' by the equation

$$\eta = 1 - (p_0/p')^{(\gamma-1)/\gamma}. \tag{5.6}$$

The work of compression is represented by area *fabh*; that of isobaric expan-

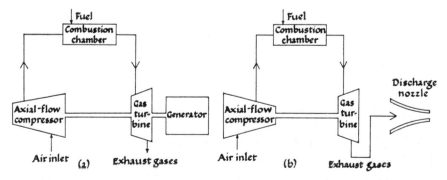

Figure 5.6.   (a) A gas turbine. (b) A jet engine.

sion by *hbcg*; that of adiabatic expansion by *gcde*; and that of isobaric compression to complete the cycle by *fade*. The net work output is represented by area *abcd*.

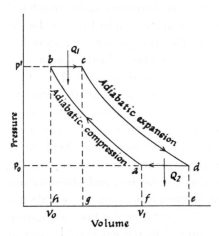

Figure 5.7. *P-V* diagram for the Joule or Brayton cycle.

In the jet engine only enough of the excess heat is converted to work by the gas turbine to operate the compressor, and the rest of it is converted to external work at the discharge nozzle. Nevertheless, the ideal Joule cycle applies to it, and the results of the analysis are like those for the simple gas turbine.

Jet-propulsion devices may be classified as either the self-contained rocket type or the air-stream type. In the self-contained device, liquid or dry fuel and the oxygen needed to burn it are carried by the rocket. In the air-stream device, oxygen of the air is used to burn the fuel; the jet engine and the ram-jet are of this type. When the ram-jet attains sufficiently high speeds in the atmosphere, air entering the intake scoop at the front is compressed, and by the time it reaches the rear fuel can be injected and burned. The combustion products then fly out the discharge nozzle at the rear.

The simple gas turbine is superior to gasoline and Diesel engines in two important respects: it has only one moving member, and for a given power output it occupies a very much smaller space. On the other hand, its efficiency may be less. However, the efficiency can be increased by preheating the compressed air in a heat exchanger, before it enters the combustion chamber, with the hot external gases from the turbine. A further increase is possible if the compressing takes place in stages with intercooling; but the study of these systems is beyond the scope of this book.

5.7. The Vapor-compression Refrigerator

Although common refrigerators are not heat engines operated in reverse, they do perform heat-work cycles. Ordinarily at least one process is definitely irreversible. The conventional vapor-compression refrigerator consists of a compressor, a condenser, a storage tank, a throttling valve, and an evaporator connected by suitable tubes with intake and outlet valves. The working substance is a liquid which vaporizes readily through the throttling valve near room temperature, dropping to a lower temperature in the proc-

ess. Among the most common refrigerants are ammonia, sulfur dioxide, and certain halide compounds of methane and ethane. Perhaps the most widely used of these in industry is ammonia; in the household it is dichlorodifluoromethane (Freon-12). A schematic diagram for a conventional refrigeration system is shown in Fig. 5.8.

The refrigerant partially vaporizes and cools as it passes through the throttling valve where the irreversible throttling process takes place. Nearly constant pressures are maintained on either side of this valve by means of the compressor. The mixed liquid

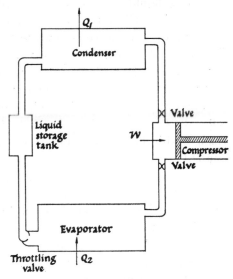

Figure 5.8.   A   conventional   vapor-compression refrigeration system.

and vapor, which is colder than the near-surround, absorbs heat from the interior of the refrigerator box or cold room and completely vaporizes. The vapor then is compressed to a smaller volume by the compressor. At the same time its temperature and pressure increase. Finally, the refrigerant pours through the outlet valve into the condenser, where it cools down and condenses to the liquid phase. Here heat is transferred to

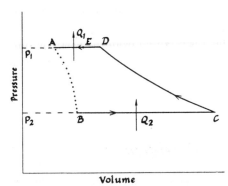

Figure 5.9.   *P-V* diagram for a conventional refrigeration system. The dotted line from *A* to *B* represents the irreversible throttling process.

the cooler near-surround, either to air blown across the cooling coils or to water flowing by the cooling chamber of the condenser. This series of processes may be idealized to some extent and a *P-V* diagram of them may be drawn, as in Fig. 5.9.

Because the throttling process is irreversible it is indicated by a dotted line from the starting point A to B. Only part of the liquid refrigerant vaporizes. From B to C we suppose a reversible isobaric process takes place where the remaining liquid is vaporized. The refrigerant now is compressed adiabatically along CD to pressure P_1 at an elevated temperature. From D to E the compressed vapor cools down isobarically to approximately room temperature; and from E to A it is liquefied in the condenser under isobaric isothermal conditions. From C to D work is done on the system by the near-surround through the compressor piston, and from D to A further work is done on the system during the cooling and condensation processes. Processes AB and CD are approximately adiabatic. Therefore nearly all the heat exchanges with the near-surround take place during the isobaric processes BG and DA.

Comparative tests have shown that the coefficient of performance of vapor-compression refrigerators depends very little on the nature of the refrigerant. Because of mechanical inefficiency of the cooling system and other factors its actual value for a household installation may be 40–75% of the ideal value. Ordinarily the actual value lies between 2 and 3. If a household refrigerator in which Freon-12 is the refrigerant is operated between $-15°C$ and $30°C$, its ideal coefficient of performance equals 4.8, but its actual value may be only 2.8. On the other hand, the coefficient of performance for a Carnot refrigerator operating between these same temperatures equals 5.7.

A refrigerator is, so to speak, a heat pump, for it extracts heat from a low-temperature region and delivers it to a high-temperature region, resembling a mechanical pump which lifts water from a low-pressure region and delivers it to a high pressure region. One interesting application of such a device has been made to household heating and air conditioning. The system is so designed that during the winter months heat is pumped from the earth or outside air into the building, and during the summer months heat is pumped in the reverse direction. This system is practical only where power is relatively inexpensive.

5.8. The Vapor-absorption Refrigerator

Another practical refrigerating system (such as that used in the Servel Electrolux refrigerator) involves vapor absorption. This system was invented by two Swedish engineering students, Munters and von Platen, while they were undergraduates at the Royal Institute of Technology in Stockholm. In this system there are no moving parts; the added energy comes from a gas

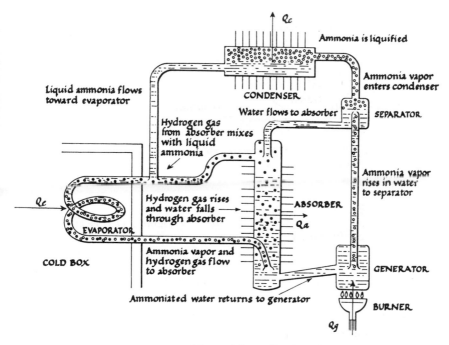

Figure 5.10.   The Servel Electrolux refrigerator.

or kerosene burner or an electrical heater as heat rather than from a compressor as work. A simplified diagram of a vapor-absorption refrigerator is given in Fig. 5.10. The refrigerant is ammonia gas, which is liberated from a water solution and transported from one region to another by the aid of hydrogen. The total pressure throughout the system is constant, and therefore no valves are needed.

In this system heat from the external source is supplied to the generator. A mixture of ammonia and water vapor with drops of ammoniated water is raised to the separator in the same manner as water is raised to the coffee in a percolator. Ammonia vapor escapes from the liquid in the separator and rises to the condenser, where it cools and liquefies. Before the liquefied ammonia enters the evaporator in the cold box, hydrogen, rising from the absorber, mixes with it and aids in the evaporation of the ammonia. Finally, the mixture of hydrogen and ammonia vapor enters the absorber, where water from the separator dissolves the ammonia. The ammonia water then returns to the generator to complete the cycle. In this cycle heat enters the system not only at the generator but also at the evaporator, and heat leaves the system at both the condenser and the absorber to enter the atmosphere by means of radiating fins.

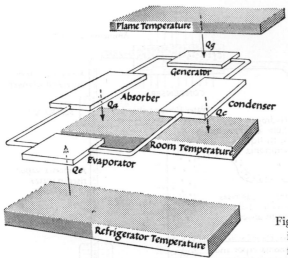

Figure 5.11. Heat exchanges in the vapor-absorption refrigeration system.

A schematic diagram of the system is shown in Fig. 5.11. No external work is done, and the change in internal energy during a complete cycle is zero. The total heat $(Q_a + Q_c)$ released to the atmosphere equals the total heat $(Q_g + Q_e)$ absorbed from the heater at the generator and from the cold box at the evaporator:

$$Q_g + Q_e = Q_a + Q_c.$$

The coefficient of performance then may be defined as

$$K = Q_e/Q_g = [(Q_a + Q_c)/Q_g] - 1, \tag{5.7}$$

which is greater than unity.

The vapor-absorption refrigerator has no motor or mechanical pump, and accordingly it is free from the intermittent noises of common vapor-compression systems. On the other hand, it requires a continuous supply of heat, as from bottled gas or electrical generators, which may be expensive. Refrigerators of this type have found application in camps and farmhouses not supplied with commercial electric power and in apartment houses where unnecessary noise is forbidden.

Problems

1. (a) What characteri.tics are common to all Carnot cycles?
   (b) From the state equation and other elevant information for a mono-

molecular film on a clean water surface construct an *S-A* diagram to illustrate a Carnot cycle (see Problem 6 in Chapte 3).

2. One liter of an ideal gas at atmospheric pressure goes through a reversible cycle consisting of three processes. First it is compressed adiabatically until its pressure is doubled; then it expands at the new pressure to it original volume; finally it returns to its initial state by an isochoric decrease in pressure.

    (a) Construct a *P-V* diagram for the cycle.

    (b) If $\gamma = 1.5$, how much work is done by the system during each process and during the cycle?

    (c) Compute the thermal efficiency of the system.

3. Derive the equation of thermal efficiency for an ideal Diesel engine and for an ideal gas turbine.

4. The Dual cycle represents the operation of an ideal solid-fuel Diesel engine. It differs from the ordinary Diesel cycle only by having the combustion stroke start explosively to produce an isochoric increase in pressure before the isobaric expansion takes place as the fuel burns more slowly.

    (a) Construct a *P-V* diagram for the cycle.

    (b) Obtain an equation for the efficiency of this Diesel engine in terms of the compression and expansion ratios and the ratio of the pressure over the isobaric part of the cycle to that at the start of the compression stroke.

5. Compute the coefficient of performance of a Carnot refrigerator which operates between $-15°C$ and $30°C$.

CHAPTER **6**

The Second Law of Thermodynamics

THE fundamental principles of physics summarize the physicist's experiences with reality both inside and outside his laboratory. They stand out as broad generalizations. The zeroth and first laws of thermodynamics are such generalizations, but they are not sufficient to describe all that takes place in thermophysics. When a hot body is placed in contact with a cold body we know *from experience* that heat is transferred from the hot to the cold body until thermal equilibrium is established; it is never observed to transfer by itself from the cold to the hot body to continually increase the temperature of the hot body while the cold body grows colder. Likewise, a body rolls downhill from a high level to a low level, and water flows from a high-pressure region to a low-pressure region. The reverse processes do not occur without the aid of external agents. This "onewayness" appears to be a very fundamental characteristic of natural processes. The second law of thermodynamics epitomizes our experiences with respect to the direction taken by thermophysical processes.

6.1. Two Equivalent Statements of the Second Law of Thermodynamics

Of the many statements of the second law of thermodynamics two have been widely published:

78

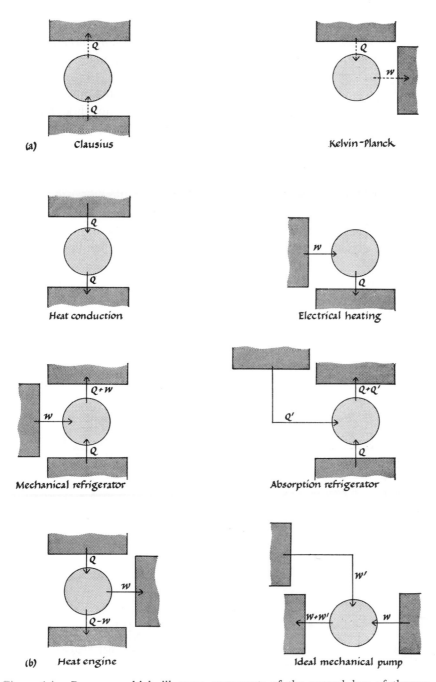

Figure 6.1.   Processes which illustrate statements of the second law of thermodynamics. (a) Impossible processes. (b) Possible processes.

A. *Clausius' Statement:* No process exists whereby the only effect is to transfer heat from a cold to a hot thermal reservoir. Specifically, no refrigerator which operates in a cycle can convey heat from a cold to a hot region without some other effect on its near-surround.

B. *Kelvin-Planck Statement:* No process exists whereby the only effect is to convert heat from a single thermal reservoir completely to work. This may be applied to a heat-to-work converter. No engine which operates in a cycle can transform heat from a thermal reservoir to an equivalent amount of work without some other effect on its near-surround.

In Fig. 6.1 are diagrams of several processes which illustrate statements A and B. In order to demonstrate the equivalence of these statements, consider the process for a mechanical refrigerating system as shown in Fig. 6.2(a). Let heat $Q' - Q$ be converted completely to work W and returned to the work reservoir, in violation of statement B (indicated by the dotted arrow). If the system were to operate in this way, the only result would be a transfer of heat Q from the cold to the hot reservoir with no other effect on the near-surround, in violation of statement A. We may equally well begin with the process for a heat engine, as shown in Fig. 6.2(b). Here we violate statement A by allowing heat Q to be transferred from the cold to the hot reservoir, and then observe that statement B has been violated as well. We conclude therefore that one statement of the second law of thermodynamics implies the other.

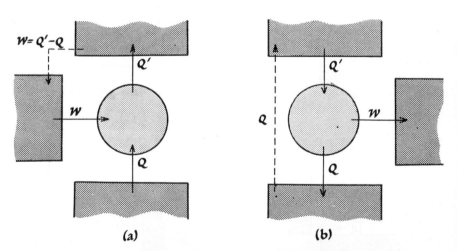

(a)   (b)

Figure 6.2.   The equivalence of the Clausius and Kelvin-Planck statements of the second law of thermodynamics.

6.2. Carnot's Theorem

By means of the second law of thermodynamics we are able to prove Carnot's theorem: *A Carnot engine operating between two heat reservoirs is more efficient than any other heat engine operating between the same two reservoirs.* To prove this theorem a Carnot engine is operated in reverse as a refrigerator by means of an arbitrary heat engine, in such a way that the combination forms a closed self-acting device. The work output of the arbitrary heat engine is assumed to equal the work required for operating

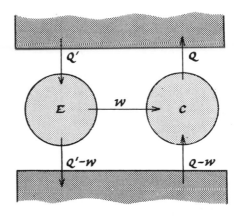

Figure 6.3.   A self-acting device to illustrate the proof of Carnot's theorem: ℰ, an arbitrary heat engine; ℭ, a Carnot engine operated as a refrigerator.

the Carnot refrigerator. This self-acting device is illustrated in Fig. 6.3.

Let the arbitrary engine extract heat Q' from the hot reservoir and convert part of it to work W. Then the remaining energy $Q' - W$ is delivered to the cold reservoir. Work W operates the Carnot refrigerator to extract heat $Q - W$ from the cold reservoir and deliver heat Q to the hot reservoir. The net amount of heat extracted from the cold reservoir and delivered to the hot reservoir by the self-acting device then equals $Q - Q'$. By the second law of thermodynamics this process is impossible unless Q' is greater than or equal to Q; thus heat actually is transferred from the hot to the cold reservoir or is not transferred at all. But the efficiencies of the arbitrary and the Carnot engines are W/Q' and W/Q, respectively, so the efficiency of the Carnot engine cannot be less than that of the arbitrary engine.

Carnot's theorem may be generalized to any reversible heat engine. The reversible heat engine is operated as a refrigerator by an arbitrary heat engine between a continuous series of hot reservoirs and a continuous series of cold reservoirs. Figure 6.3 now is interpreted to apply to infinitesimal processes, and the second law of thermodynamics is applied to them. By summing over the infinitesimal processes during a cycle we find that the heat extracted from all the hot reservoirs must equal or exceed the heat delivered to all the cold reservoirs. But this result implies that the efficiency of the reversible heat engine cannot be less than that of the arbitrary engine and therefore not less than that of any other heat engine operating between the same two series of reservoirs.

6.3. A Corollary to Carnot's Theorem

The arbitrary engine in Fig. 6.3 may be replaced by a second Carnot engine with a different working substance. Because either Carnot engine can operate the other as a refrigerator in the self-acting device, it follows that Carnot's theorem is satisfied only if the efficiencies of the two Carnot engines are equal. *The efficiency of a Carnot engine, therefore, is independent of its working substance.* This result may be generalized to a reversible heat engine operating between two series of thermal reservoirs.

6.4. The Kelvin Temperature

The thermal efficiency of a reversible heat engine can depend only on the thermodynamic properties of the working substance and on the temperatures of the reservoirs between which it operates, since there is no dissipation of energy by mechanical processes. But the efficiency of any reversible engine is independent of the working substance, as discussed in Section 6.3, and therefore it is a function of temperature only. In general, the efficiency of any heat engine is equal to $1 - Q_2/Q_1$, where Q_1 represents the heat from the hot reservoirs and Q_2 represents the heat delivered to the cold reservoirs. A Carnot engine, however, operates between a single hot reservoir at temperature t_1 and a single cold reservoir at temperature t_2. Because t_1 and t_2 may be entirely arbitrary and independent of one another, it follows that Q_1 is a function of t_1 only and Q_2 is a function of t_2 only. These functions presumably are of the same form and are represented by T_1 and T_2. They are called the Kelvin temperatures of the reservoirs. We can write

$$Q_2/Q_1 = f(t_2)/f(t_1) = T_2/T_1, \qquad (6.1)$$

as a direct application of the second law of thermodynamics. The efficiency of a Carnot engine now can be written in the form

$$\eta_c = (T_1 - T_2)/T_1. \qquad (6.2)$$

Although the arguments presented here are plausible in terms of physical models and methods, they are considered unsatisfactory from a mathematical point of view.

Several attempts have been made to develop the second law of thermodynamics and the existence of temperature and entropy functions without recourse to heat engines, thermal reservoirs, and cyclic processes. In 1909 Carathéodory[1] published the first of two famous papers in which he showed that this development can be done in a systematic way from two mathematical axioms with suitable definitions of terms. A somewhat simpler treatment of this problem has been given by Buchdahl[2] and, more recently, by Turner[3] and by Thomson.[4] These methods are formally axiomatic. Their study should be expecially rewarding to students with a mathematical turn of mind.

6.5. The Kelvin Temperature Scale and the Third Law of Thermodynamics

This scale of temperature is established by treating the heats Q_1 and Q_2 as thermometric properties. Suppose a Carnot engine is operated between a reservoir at an arbitrary Kelvin temperature T and a reservoir at the Kelvin temperature of the triple point of water, namely, 273.16°K: then

$$T = 273.16(Q/Q_{tp}). \qquad (6.3)$$

This Kelvin or thermodynamic scale of temperature is independent of the working substance. The zero of this scale occurs at the point where Q equals zero. That is to say, if a system undergoes a reversible isothermal process without a transfer of heat, the temperature at which the process takes place is 0°K. This is not a temperature at which all motions cease, nor is it necessarily a temperature at which a substance has no internal energy. It is simply the temperature of a body or reservoir which absorbs no thermal energy.

Although every attempt has been made to reach 0°K, no one as yet has done so. There is a general belief that this limiting temperature is unattainable. We can state it this way: *The temperature of a system cannot be reduced to 0°K in a finite number of operations no matter how idealized they may be.* This is one

---

[1] Carathéodory, C., *Math. Ann.*, **67**, 35 (1909); Sitzber. preuss. Akad. Wiss. Physik. math. Kl., 39 (1925).

[2] Buchdahl, H. A., *Am. J. Phys.*, **17**, 44, 212 (1949); **22**, 182 (1954); **23**, 65 (1955).

[3] Turner, L. A., *Am. J. Phys.*, **28**, 781 (1960); **29**, 40 (1961).

[4] Thomson, J. S., *Am. J. Phys.*, **29**, 300 (1961).

version of the third law of thermodynamics. It was first recognized by Nernst in another form, and later it was named the third law by Fowler and Guggenheim. A further discussion of this topic is given in Section 7.3.

6.6. Equality of the Kelvin and the Ideal Gas Temperature

To demonstrate the equivalence of the Kelvin temperature and the ideal gas temperature consider the Carnot cycle for an ideal gas of constant mass

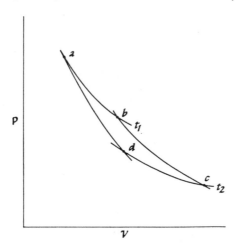

Figure 6.4. *P-V* diagram of a Carnot cycle for an ideal gas.

(Fig. 6.4). Processes *ab* and *dc* are isothermal at the ideal gas temperatures t_1 and t_2, and processes *ad* and *bc* are adiabatic. The ratio of the work exchanges W_1/W_2 for the isothermal processes is computed from Eq. (4.4) and is

$$\frac{W_1}{W_2} = \frac{t_1 \ln (V_b/V_a)}{t_2 \ln (V_c/V_d)}. \quad (6.4)$$

For the adiabatic processes, however, $tV^{\gamma-1}$ is constant. Thus

$$(t_1/t_2) = (V_a/V_d)^{\gamma-1} = (V_b/V_c)^{\gamma-1},$$

and, therefore,

$$V_b/V_a = V_c/V_d.$$

The ratio W_1/W_2 now reduces to

$$W_1/W_2 = t_1/t_2. \quad (6.5)$$

From the first law of thermodynamics we can write

$$W_1 = \Delta U_1 - Q_1$$

and

$$W_2 = \Delta U_2 - Q_2$$

for the isothermal processes. But the internal energy of an ideal gas is a function of temperature only,[5] and, therefore, ΔU_1 and ΔU_2 both equal zero. We now find that

$$W_1/W_2 = Q_1/Q_2 = t_1/t_2. \quad (6.6)$$

---

[5] This fact is more conveniently discussed later, in Sections 8.3 and 9.2, quite independently of our conclusions here.

The Kelvin temperature scale was defined by a similar equation, and, therefore,

$$T_1/T_2 = t_1/t_2. \tag{6.7}$$

Now we identify T_1, t_1 with any temperature T, t and T_2, t_2 with the temperature of the triple point of water T_{tp}, t_{tp}. Since $T_{tp} = t_{tp} = 273.16°K$, it follows that

$$T = t. \tag{6.8}$$

The Kelvin temperature thus can be set equal to the ideal gas temperature which is measured by means of a gas thermometer.

6.7. General Form of the Clapeyron Equation

The result of applying the second law of thermodynamics to a Carnot engine, regardless of the engine's working substance, allows us to derive a fundamental equation of thermophysics. Imagine two isotherms close to one another on a Y-X diagram where Y is the generalized force and X is the generalized displacement, as illustrated in Fig. 6.5. These curves are represented by the functions $Y(X,T)$ and $Y(X,T')$, for the upper and lower isotherms, as determined from the state equation of the working substance. Let the isotherms be cut by two adiabats ai and bf, to form a Carnot cycle. The work *output* for this cycle is represented by the inclosed area, namely

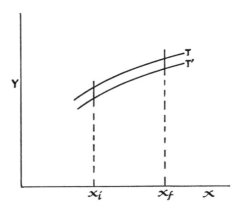

Figure 6.5. Y-X diagram for derivation of a general form of the Clapeyron equation. X_a and X_b are very close to X_i and X_f.

$$W = - \int_{X_i}^{X_f} Y(X,T)dX - \int_{X_f}^{X_b} Y(X,t)dX$$

$$+ \int_{X_i}^{X_a} Y(X,t)dX + \int_{X_a}^{X_b} Y(X,T')dX, \tag{6.9}$$

where t is the variable temperature along the adiabatic curves which are nearly vertical. The last integral can be split into three parts, thus,

$$\int_{X_a}^{X_b} Y(X,T')dX = \int_{X_i}^{X_f} Y(X,T')dX + \int_{X_f}^{X_b} Y(X,T')dX - \int_{X_i}^{X_a} Y(X,T')dX.$$

Make the substitution in Eq. (6.9) and combine terms:

$$W = -\int_{X_i}^{X_f} [Y(X,T) - Y(X,T')]dX - \int_{X_f}^{X_b} [Y(X,t) - Y(X,T')]dX$$
$$+ \int_{X_i}^{X_a} [Y(X,t) - Y(X,T')]dX.$$

Now multiply and divide the first of these integrals by $T - T'$, and then allow the two isotherms to approach infinitesimally close to one another. We see that $T' \rightarrow T$, $X_a \rightarrow X_i$, and $X_b \rightarrow X_f$. In the limit,

$$d'W = -dT \int_{X_i}^{X_f} (dY/dT)dX, \qquad (6.10)$$

and therefore the thermal efficiency of the Carnot engine is

$$\eta = d'W/Q = -(dT/Q) \int_{X_i}^{X_f} (dY/dT)dX, \qquad (6.11)$$

where Q is the heat input. But we know from the discussion in Section 6.4 that this efficiency equals dT/T; therefore,

$$\int_{X_i}^{X_f} (dY/dT)dX = -Q/T, \qquad (6.12)$$

which may be considered a generalized form of the Clapeyron equation.

Many systems can undergo processes in which dY/dT is independent of X. Equation (6.12) then reduces to an especially simple form, namely

$$(dY/dT) = -Q/T(X_f - X_i). \qquad (6.13)$$

It is this equation which we apply in the following sections. If we replace $-Y$ by pressure P, X_f and X_i by specific volumes v_f and v_i, and Q by the heat of transformation per mole l, we obtain the equation first derived by Clapeyron in 1834. In 1850 it was derived again by both Clausius and William Thomson. Often it is called the Clausius-Clapeyron equation.

6.8. The Common Phase Transformation

When a pure substance changes reversibly from a liquid to a vapor, from a solid to a liquid, or from a solid to a vapor, a definite amount of heat must be supplied to each unit mass during the transformation. Also, the specific volume of the substance always changes a finite amount. Such processes are isothermal and isobaric; thus the Clapeyron equation for the slope of the phase transition curve is

$$dP/dT = l/T(v_f - v_i). \qquad (6.14)$$

$l = 291.6 \quad 0.871T \qquad joules/gm$
$l = 0.2916 - 0.871 \times 10^{-3}\,T \quad kJ/gm$
$1\ mol = 32\,gm$

The heat of transformation l and the temperature T are both positive. Therefore the sign of the slope depends on the relative magnitudes of specific volumes v_f and v_i. For the liquid-vapor and solid-vapor transformations v_f is always greater than v_i. For the solid-liquid transformation, however, v_f is less than v_i for a substance that expands on freezing (for example, water or bismuth) and greater than v_i for a substance that contracts on freezing.

Over a limited range of temperatures, l for a pure substance may be nearly a linear function of temperature, as is illustrated by the heats of vaporization of several substances shown in Table 6.1. For transformations to the vapor

TABLE 6.1.   *Empirical Equations for Heats of Vaporization.**

Substance	Equation (l in joules/gm)	Temperature range (°K)
Carbon dioxide	$l^2 = 2075(304 - T) - 8.247(304 - T)^2$	248–304
Nitrogen	$l = 288.2 - 1.145T$	64–77
Oxygen	$l = 291.6 - 0.871T$	55–90
Platinum	$l = 2750 - 0.054T$	
Sulfur dioxide	$l = 717.6 - 0.831T - 0.00142T^2$	273–293
Tungsten	$l = 4957 - 0.041T$	
Water	$l = 394.35(638 - T)^{5/16}$	273–373

$Pt\ 515\ kJ/mol$
$515 \times 10^{3}\ J/mol$

* Adapted from Table 162, *Smithsonian Physical Tables*, 9th rev. ed. (1951).

phase, often the specific volume in the liquid or solid phase is so much smaller than it is in the vapor phase that it may be neglected, and, with little error, the vapor may be assumed to satisfy the state equation for an ideal gas. Thus we obtain

$$\frac{dP}{dT} = \frac{(A + BT)P}{RT^2},$$

$l = 9.33 - 2.79 \times 10^{-2}\,T \quad kJ\,mol^{-1}$
$l = 9330 - 27.9\,T$ for Oxy.

which is rearranged and integrated between temperatures T_0 and T and between vapor pressures p_0 and p to yield

$$\ln (p/p_0) = (A/R)(T_0^{-1} - T^{-1}) + (B/R) \ln (T/T_0). \qquad (6.15)$$

Sometimes the heat of transformation changes so slowly with temperature that B may be set equal to zero and, therefore, Eq. (6.15) reduces to a linear function between $\ln p$ and T^{-1}. This form is especially useful in evaluating heats of vaporization and sublimation from experimental values of vapor pressure. In Fig. 6.6 are such plots for several metals with values of the heats of transformation in kilojoules per mole, as determined from their slopes, beside them.

Even for ice the heat of sublimation changes very slowly with temperature; it increases from 2835 joules/gm at 0°C to 2840 joules/gm at -28°C and

Atomic wt   Mo
            W   183.85
            Pt   195.09 gm

$O = 16$

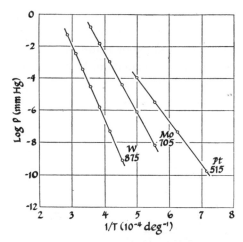

Figure 6.6. Logarithmic plots of vapor pressure for several metals as a function of temperature. The slopes of these linear curves are proportional to the heats of vaporization; numerical values in kilojoules per mole are given under the symbols of the metals.

then remains practically constant down to −40°C. On the other hand, the heat of vaporization of liquid water at first is nearly a linear function of temperature, but then decreases more and more rapidly until it vanishes near 374°C, as shown in Fig. 6.7. This phenomenon is discussed in greater detail in Chapter 10.

By means of Eq. (6.14) we can compute the effect of a small change in pressure on boiling and freezing points. For sufficiently small changes in P and T we can replace dP/dT by $\Delta P/\Delta T$, and, because Δt on the Celsius scale is equivalent to ΔT on the Kelvin scale, we find

$$\Delta t = T(v_f - v_i)\Delta P/l. \quad (6.15)$$

An increase occurs if v_f is greater than v_i, as for *all* boiling points, and a decrease occurs if v_f is less than v_i, as for the freezing points of water and bismuth. From direct measurement the normal boiling point of pure water is found to increase by 0.037°C/mm Hg and

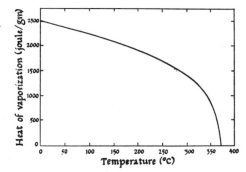

Figure 6.7. Heat of vaporization of pure liquid water.

its normal freezing point to be depressed by 0.0072°C per atmosphere.

6.9. Liquid Surfaces

If the free surface of a liquid is to be enlarged, work must be done to move subsurface liquid into the surface, and if the temperature is to remain constant, heat must flow into the system as well. The process is not one of stretching a film of constant mass, but rather one of creating additional film from bulk material. The surface film and bulk liquid together constitute a two-phase system. For this system a quantity λ, analogous to heat of transformation l, may be defined as the amount of heat per unit area required for an isothermal increase in area. Then Q in Eq. (6.13) equals $\lambda(A_f - A_i)$, where A_i and A_f are the initial and final areas of the free surface. Next, Y is replaced by S, the "surface work," known commonly by its misnomer surface tension, and X_i and X_f are replaced by A_i and A_f. Here we assume that S is a function of temperature only, and therefore Clapeyron's equation for a pure liquid surface reduces to the form

$$dS/dT = -\lambda/T. \tag{6.16}$$

In Fig. 6.8 we see that S decreases rather rapidly as the temperature is raised, until a characteristic temperature of the liquid T' is reached when the surface appears to vanish. For many pure liquids S satisfies an equation of the form

$$S = \mu(T' - T)^{\nu}, \tag{6.17}$$

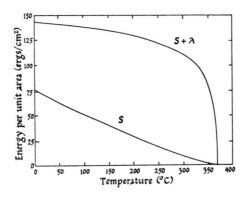

Figure 6.8. Surface tension and surface energy of pure water. Both vanish near the critical point.

in which the exponent ν is a constant, having a value between 1 and 2. For water it equals 1.28, where T' has the value of 641°K. The coefficient μ for one set of data on water was found to be very nearly 0.04, for S measured in ergs per square centimeter and T in degrees Kelvin.

Suppose a system consists of a liquid and its free surface of initial area A_0. Let the area be enlarged isothermally to A. We suppose that the change in internal energy of the system from U_0 to U arises solely from the increase in area. The heat input would be $\lambda(A - A_0)$ and the work done on the system simply $S(A - A_0)$. Thus

$$U - U_0 = (S + \lambda)(A - A_0). \tag{6.18}$$

Because both S and λ are independent of the size of the area, we may let the initial area approach zero, whence U_0 is the internal energy of the surfaceless liquid. We now eliminate λ between Eq. (6.16) and Eq. (6.18). Then we find the equation for the internal energy per unit area of free liquid surface is

$$\text{Surface energy} = S - T(dS/dT). \tag{6.19}$$

Values of surface energy may be computed by means of this equation from experimental data of surface tension as a function of temperature. Because dS/dT is intrinsically negative, the surface energy is greater than S, as is illustrated in Fig. 6.8 for water.

Problems

1. A company advertises a new highly efficient generator that is said to produce 24 kilowatt-hours of electrical energy while it admits 200,000 BTU at 410°F and rejects 120,000 BTU at 110°F. Would you advise a prospective customer to purchase one of these generators?

2. Does a living system violate the second law of thermodynamics? Does a nuclear-energy power plant? Explain.

3. Prove that it is impossible for two quasistatic adiabatics to intersect. To do this assume they do intersect, complete a cycle with an isotherm, and show that a system which performs this cycle would violate the second law of thermodynamics.

4. Suppose a sequence of Carnot engines with equal work outputs are operated such that each engine admits the heat rejected by the preceding one at the temperature at which it is rejected. Show that all the engines operate between equal temperature intervals.

5. From the specific volumes of ice and pure water and the heat of fusion compute a value for the change in the freezing point of water per atmosphere increase in pressure, and compare it with a measured value. Carry out a similar computation and comparison for the boiling point of water.

6. The empirical equation for the heat of vaporization of pure water given in Table 6.1 is approximated by the linear form

$$3166 - 2.44T \text{ joules/gm}$$

to within a few tenths of one percent. Compute a value for the vapor pressure of water at 20°C, and compare it with a measured value as found in a handbook of physical data.

CHAPTER 7

Thermodynamic Entropy

ENTROPY has been introduced *a priori* as a state function whose differential is exact and equals $d'Q/T$ for reversible processes. It cannot be a fundamental quantity if energy and temperature are fundamental, for it has the dimensions of energy divided by temperature. Thermodynamic entropy is no more difficult to define than kinetic energy, nor is it more abstract. Because it is less familiar, however, it has acquired a reputation of abstruseness. Here we shall discuss how the concept of entropy comes about naturally from the application of the second law of thermodynamics to reversible processes, and thereby we shall show that dS equals $d'Q/T$. Later we shall relate entropy to statistical probability and molecular disorder.

7.1. The Clausius Theorem

First we need to prove the auxiliary theorem: *An arbitrary reversible process, in which the temperature may change in any manner, can be replaced by two reversible adiabatic processes connected by a reversible isothermal process in such a way that the heat exchanged over the isothermal process equals that exchanged over the original arbitrary process.*

Consider an arbitrary reversible process AB, represented by the smooth solid curve on the Y-X diagram in Fig. 7.1. Curves for the adiabatic processes which pass through states A and B are shown as dashed lines. A curve CD for an isothermal process now is drawn such that the area under the curves for the adiabatic and isothermal processes from A to B equals the area under

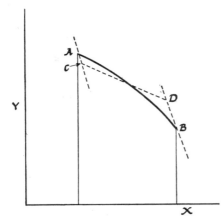

the solid curve for the arbitrary process between the same two states. The isotherm must cut the solid curve in at least one point. Because of the equality of the two areas, the work done in traversing either path from A to B is the same, and, furthermore, because the two paths connect

Figure 7.1. An isothermal and two adiabatic processes equivalent to an arbitrary reversible process AB.

the same states, the changes in internal energy are identical. Therefore the heat exchanges also must be equal in order to satisfy the first law of thermodynamics. For the dashed path, however, heat exchanges take place only over the isothermal part. This completes the proof of the auxiliary theorem.

Consider now the arbitrary reversible cycle $ABCD$ in Fig. 7.2. It may be cut by many closely spaced adiabatic paths. These can be made parts of infinitesimal Carnot cycles by adding appropriate isothermal paths. The pair of isotherms for each cycle is selected such that the area within the Carnot cycle just equals the area within the arbitrary cycle between the two adiabats, and also such that each isothermal path crosses the given arbitrary path at least at one point. Such an infinitesimal Carnot cycle is illustrated at $abcd$ in Fig. 7.2.

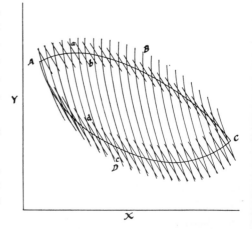

Figure 7.2. Arbitrary reversible cycle replaced by Carnot cycles in proof of the Clausius theorem.

For cycle $abcd$, heat $\Delta'Q_1$ at temperature T_1 enters the system and heat $\Delta'Q_2$ at temperature T_2 leaves it. If a positive sign represents inflow of heat and a negative sign outflow, by the second law of thermodynamics

$$(\Delta'Q_1/T_1) + (\Delta'Q_2/T_2) = 0. \tag{7.1}$$

A similar relation may be set down for each of the infinitesimal Carnot cycles, where T_1 and T_2 change in value from cycle to cycle. The sum of these relations for all the Carnot cycles covering the entire arbitrary reversible cycle in the limit then may be written in integral form,

$$\oint d'Q/T = 0, \tag{7.2}$$

where the symbol $\oint$ means integration around a *closed* path. In words: *The integral of d'Q/T around an arbitrary reversible cycle equals zero*. This is the Clausius theorem.

7.2. *Thermodynamic Entropy*

The integral of $d'Q/T$ around the closed path $ABCDA$ in Fig. 7.2 may be split into two parts, the integral from A to C along the upper path and the integral from C to A along the lower path of the cycle. These are but two of many reversible paths connecting states A and C of the system. By the Clausius theorem,

$$\oint d'Q/T = \underset{\substack{\text{upper}\\\text{path}}}{\int_A^C d'Q/T} + \underset{\substack{\text{lower}\\\text{path}}}{\int_C^A d'Q/T}$$

$$= \underset{\substack{\text{upper}\\\text{path}}}{\int_A^C d'Q/T} - \underset{\substack{\text{lower}\\\text{path}}}{\int_A^C d'Q/T} = 0;$$

and, therefore,

$$\underset{\substack{\text{upper}\\\text{path}}}{\int_A^C d'Q/T} = \underset{\substack{\text{lower}\\\text{path}}}{\int_A^C d'Q/T}. \tag{7.3}$$

Because the paths ABC and ADC are arbitrary it follows that *the integral of d'Q/T from one equilibrium state of the system to another is independent of the reversible path connecting the two states.*

The foregoing result suggests that there exists a thermodynamic function which characterizes the state of a system, such that the difference between its values for two states is equal to the integral of $d'Q/T$ along an arbitrary reversible path connecting these two states. This function is the thermodynamic entropy S of the system. We now write

$$S_C - S_A = \int_A^C d'Q/T. \tag{7.4}$$

The quantity $1/T$ thus proves to be an integrating factor for the inexact differential $d'Q$.

It must be emphasized that this equation for $S_C - S_A$ applies only to reversible paths. Even so, systems which proceed from one equilibrium state to another by irreversible processes can be studied by means of it, for the entropy of a system in an equilibrium state does not depend on how the system arrived at that state. If a system has undergone an irreversible process from one equilibrium state to another, its change in entropy may be found by joining the initial and final states by any series of reversible paths and by applying Eq. (7.4) to each path.

An "absolute" zero of entropy cannot be specified in thermodynamics; only differences or changes in entropy may be found. This situation is similar to that for mechanical and electrical potential energy. For convenience, therefore, any single arbitrary state of a system may be chosen to have zero entropy for a given computation. In the study of water systems, for instance, frequently liquid water at 0°C and one standard atmosphere of pressure is taken to have zero entropy. Entropy tables for engineering applications are computed in terms of conventional zero values and may be found in handbooks.

7.3. The Third Law of Thermodynamics

In order to study the change in entropy of a system it is convenient to construct a T-S diagram. Suppose the thermodynamic state of the system is described by its temperature T and another parameter P (such as volume or magnetic field intensity). We plot T against S for two different values of P denoted by P_1 and P_2 (Fig. 7.3). Consider now a reversible isothermal process

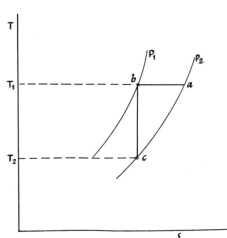

ab followed by a reversible adiabatic process bc. This pair of processes carries the system through half a Carnot cycle and lowers its temperature from T_1 to T_2, with no change in P. A similar pair of processes may be performed again and again to reduce the temperature toward 0°K in a sequence of

Figure 7.3. T-S diagram to show drop in temperature from a sequence of reversible isothermal and adiabatic processes.

steps. But we know from experience that it becomes more and more difficult to lower the temperature of a system as 0°K is approached; the third
law of thermodynamics is an explicit statement of the unattainability of this
null temperature.[1] We conclude therefore that the two curves in Fig. 7.3
must converge in such a way that the temperature difference along an
isentropic becomes less and less as the temperature is reduced.

In the end the two curves meet
on the entropy axis as shown in
Fig. 7.4. They cannot meet below
the axis since this would allow
0°K to be reached during one of
the isentropic processes in violation of the third law; and they
do not meet above the axis for
this would imply the existence
of an unattainable temperature

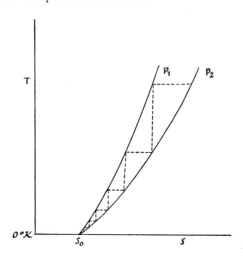

Figure 7.4.   The unattainability of
            zero-point entropy and
            the vanishing of entropy
            difference.

greater than 0°K in contradiction to our experience and our definition
of the thermodynamic scale of temperature. We conclude that the *entropy
change associated with a reversible isothermal process decreases toward zero as the temperature of the system approaches 0°K.* This is another way of stating the third
law of thermodynamics.

We observe that all the T-S curves for the system of Fig. 7.4 intersect in
one point, the zero-point entropy, at 0°K. The third law therefore is stated
in still another way: *It is impossible to reduce the entropy of a system to its zero-
point value by a finite number of operations, no matter how idealized they may be.* This
and the foregoing statements of the third law of thermodynamics are especially useful in the fields of physical chemistry and statistical mechanics.

As an illustration, for any first-order phase transition the latent heat is
equal to $T(s_f - s_i)$, and therefore the Clapeyron equation, Eq. (6.14), may
be written in the form

$$dP/dT = (s_f - s_i)/(v_f - v_i).$$

But according to the third law, as the temperature is lowered toward 0°K
the entropy difference approaches zero. Since $v_f - v_i$ is not zero we find

[1] See Section 6.5.

$$\lim_{T \to 0} (dP/dT) = 0,$$

a result which is substantiated by experimental observations on melting, sublimation, and vaporization of substances at very low temperatures.

7.4. Total Entropy Change of the Local Universe During Reversible Processes

The thermodynamic entropy of a *system* has been found to change by an amount equal to the integral of $d'Q/T$ over the limits of a process, provided the process is reversible. At the same time the entropy of the near-surround is altered. As usual, the far-surround is assumed to be unaffected by the process. We now ask: By how much does the entropy of the near-surround change, and what is the total entropy change of the local universe?

Consider a system as it undergoes a reversible process. At every point it is in quasistatic thermodynamic equilibrium with the near-surround, and, therefore, it is in thermal equilibrium with a continuous series of reservoirs whose temperatures equal those of the system throughout the process. For each infinitesimal transfer of heat $d'Q$ the thermodynamic entropy of the system changes by the amount $d'Q/T$ and the corresponding reservoir by the amount $-d'Q/T$, so the change experienced by the system and the reservoir together is zero. This result applies at all points of the process. The series of reservoirs, however, constitute the thermal part of the near-surround for the system, and therefore we conclude that *for a reversible process the change in thermodynamic entropy of the system and its near-surround, namely the local universe, is zero.*

7.5. Total Entropy Change of the Local Universe During Irreversible Processes

Suppose a system undergoes an irreversible process between two equilibrium states A and B, as shown by the dotted line in Fig. 7.5. The entropy values for the system in states A and B are characteristic of the system and do not depend in any way on the process by which the system changes from A to B. In order to determine the difference in entropy $S_B - S_A$ all that needs to be done is to perform a series of arbitrary reversible processes from state A to state B, such as AC and CB in Fig. 7.5. Then the sum of the en-

tropy changes *for the system* during
these reversible processes must
equal the entropy change of the
system during the irreversible proc-

Figure 7.5. An arbitrary irreversible
        process *AB* (dotted line)
        may be replaced by two
        reversible processes *AC*
        and *CB* in order to evalu-
        ate the change in entropy
        of the system in passing
        from state *A* to state *B*.

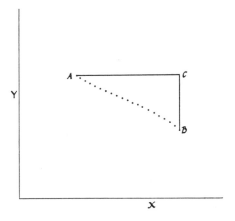

ess. This does not mean that the entropy change of the local universe has
the same value for the two paths from *A* to *B*.

On the other hand, if tables and graphs of thermodynamic properties
have been prepared for a substance, entropy values may be read from them
for the two end states and their difference found. Sometimes the equation
for the entropy as a function of other thermodynamic variables is known,
and therefore the change in entropy may be computed from it. But these
methods are rather special and of course apply equally well to the computation of entropy changes for reversible processes.

It is believed that *the change in entropy of the local universe is greater than zero
for all irreversible processes*. This entropy principle is difficult to prove in a
completely rigorous manner, but the fact that no process is known to violate
it lends support to its validity.

During any arbitrary irreversible change of state of a system energy is
exchanged by thermal, mechanical, and chemical processes, between parts
of the system and between the system and its near-surround in such a way
that the system is not always in equilibrium and dissipative effects occur. If
the system is enclosed in an adiabatic wall, it is isolated from the surroundings
and any change of state is completely "internal." On the other hand, a system undergoes an "external" process when it exchanges energy with work
and heat reservoirs. However, we can imagine an enlarged system to include
these reservoirs and thereby become effectively isolated from its surroundings.
Processes in this enlarged system then are adiabatic.

Let a closed system undergo an adiabatic irreversible process from an
equilibrium state *A* to another equilibrium state *B*, as depicted by the dotted
line in Fig. 7.6. If states *A* and *B* have the same value of entropy, they may
be connected by a return reversible adiabatic path, because a reversible

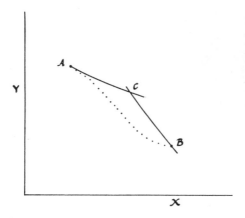

adiabatic process is isentropic. The system then has performed a completely adiabatic cycle. No heat exchange takes place with the near-surround; the internal energy of the system returns to its

Figure 7.6. An irreversible adiabatic process AB is replaced by a reversible isothermal process AC and a reversible adiabatic process CB.

initial value; and, for energy to be conserved, no work exchange occurs between the system and the near-surround. If a system and its near-surround are returned to their initial states without altering the far-surround, then they must have undergone a completely reversible process. But the initial process from A to B was irreversible. Therefore the assumption that states A and B have the same entropy is wrong. A system cannot reach a final state whose entropy equals that of the initial state solely by an irreversible adiabatic process. But the system may be returned to its initial state by a reversible adiabatic process plus a reversible isothermal process, as shown in Fig. 7.6. We wish now to prove that the change in entropy $S_B - S_A$ is greater than zero. For the reversible adiabatic process S_C equals S_B, and for the reversible isothermal process the heat exchange Q equals $T(S_A - S_C)$ or, by substitution, $T(S_A - S_B)$. For the cycle, the first law of thermodynamics must be satisfied, and therefore Q is equal to the work performed. By the second law of thermodynamics heat must leave the system if any work is done; that is, $T(S_A - S_B)$ is equal to or less than zero, and therefore $S_B - S_A$ is equal to or greater than zero. But S_B was shown to differ from S_A. We conclude that the entropy of the system must increase during an irreversible adiabatic process. The entropy of the near-surround is unchanged meanwhile, and thus that of the local universe is increased.

This analysis applies to any other irreversible process, provided we conceive the heat and work reservoirs and the system under study to constitute an enlarged system. Perhaps the simplest irreversible process is one in which a system conveys heat from a hot to a cold reservoir without altering its state. Let the temperature of the hot and cold reservoirs be represented by T_h and

T_c. As much heat Q leaves the cold end of the conducting system as enters the hot end in a finite interval of time. The change in entropy of the reservoirs and the system together is

$$\Delta S = (Q/T_c) - (Q/T_h), \tag{7.5}$$

which is greater than zero and actually represents the change in entropy of the local universe.

Suppose a system of constant mass and composition transforms work W completely to heat Q and delivers it to a reservoir at temperature T without altering its state. This situation is represented by an electric heater in running water and a generator actuated by a falling weight. Here the entropy of the enlarged system, consisting of the initial system and the heat and work reservoirs, changes by the amount W/T, which is positive and equals the change in entropy of the local universe.

Other nonadiabatic irreversible processes are more complex than the foregoing. Even so, by forming enlarged systems we may isolate them and thereby find that our general analysis for any adiabatic irreversible process applies.

7.6. The Second Law of Thermodynamics Restated

In Sections 7.4 and 7.5 we have demonstrated that the entropy of the local universe remains unchanged for reversible processes and increases for irreversible processes. Both these results stemmed from an application of the second law of thermodynamics. The second law may be restated thus: *The total thermodynamic entropy of a system and its near-surround never decreases during a thermophysical process.* This statement implies that the entropy of an isolated system should increase until it reaches a maximum value for the physical conditions of the system. Both the system and the near-surround are included in this statement of the second law, and only an inequality can be obtained from it for irreversible processes. Nevertheless it can be modified such that reference is made solely to the system.

If a system undergoes a change of state as a result of mechanical, thermal, and chemical processes, its thermodynamic entropy is increased by the entropy carried in with any added matter, by the entropy of heat inflow, and by the entropy created through irreversible processes within the system. Let S_j represent the entropy of the jth species of matter entering the system and ΔS_{irr} represent the entropy from internal irreversible processes. The change in entropy of the system is given by the equation

$$S_f - S_i = \Sigma_j S_j + \int d'Q/T + \Delta S_{irr}, \qquad (7.6)$$

where $\int d'Q/T$ is the net entropy carried into the system by heat exchanges with thermal reservoirs. For cyclical and steady-state processes in closed systems S_f equals S_i, $\Sigma_j S_j$ equals zero, and the expression reduces to a simple form.

Many common processes involve a dissipation of mechanical energy to the near-surround and within the system. Such processes are the irregular stirring of a viscous fluid, the coming to rest of a fluid which is initially in motion, the inelastic deformation of solids, the transfer of electrical charge through a resistor, magnetic hysteresis, and the damping of a vibrating rod or wire.

Once again consider the system of constant mass and composition which transforms work W completely to heat Q and delivers it to a reservoir at temperature T without altering its state. Here $\int d'Q/T$ equals $-Q/T$, so we can write the reduced form of Eq. (7.6) as

$$\Delta S_{irr} - Q/T = 0. \qquad (7.7)$$

The production of entropy associated with the irreversible transformation of work to heat is Q/T, or simply W/T. On the other hand, if this system is thermally insulated from the surroundings, any work done on it changes its temperature from T_i to T_f. In order to compute its change in entropy we replace the irreversible process by a reversible process which carries the system from the initial to the final equilibrium state. If these states are at the same pressure, it is convenient to replace the irreversible process by a reversible isobaric one. Then the infinitesimal heat exchange for this process equals $C_p dT$. For many systems over limited temperature ranges the heat capacity at constant pressure C_p is nearly constant, so

$$S_f - S_i = \Delta S_{irr} = C_p \ln (T_f/T_i). \qquad (7.8)$$

The first two terms on the right side of Eq. 7.6 equal zero.

Other irreversible processes are those of diffusion (such as mixing two fluids at different temperatures), of conduction or radiation, and of metabolism in living systems. Only the last process sometimes has been said to violate the second law of thermodynamics, but there is no sound evidence for this point of view.

7.7. *The Degradation of Energy*

At this point we may begin to wonder where all this discussion regarding reversibility and irreversibility and the production of entropy is leading us. Suppose entropy is continually created by irreversible processes. Of what significance is it? After all, energy is conserved, and the second law of thermo-dynamics in its original form did tell us the direction in which a process would go. What more have we gained by introducing the concept of entropy and the fact that it is continually created and never destroyed?

In the first place, we observe that by means of the entropy function we can express the second law in quantitative terms. It gives us a measure for deter-mining whether a process is physically possible. A chemist wishes to know whether two substances will react chemically at certain temperatures, pres-sures, and concentrations. Or, an engineer asks whether a proposed power plant will operate. They can find out by computing changes in entropy. If the chemical reaction or the operation of the plant would result in a decrease of entropy of the local universe, it is impossible.

Over and beyond these applications, however, the entropy concept has given us a greater insight into the workings of nature. It is this aspect of it which we shall want to investigate more fully. We find, for instance, that something about the energy has become irretrievably lost during an irre-versible process, even though the energy itself is conserved. Sears has called this *something* "opportunity—the opportunity to convert internal energy to mechanical energy"; others call it "availability"—availability of energy to do external work. Let us examine a very simple situation. Consider the flow of heat Q through a conductor from a hot reservoir at temperature T_h to a cold reservoir at temperature T_c. The very fact that heat Q has been de-graded, that is, passed from a high-temperature reservoir to a low-tempera-ture reservoir, has reduced its capacity for conversion to external work. Let us evaluate this loss.

We suppose there exists a reservoir whose temperature T_0 is lower than T_c. Let a Carnot engine operate between the reservoirs of temperatures T_h and T_0. The work output W of this engine for heat input Q is

$$W = Q(1 - T_0/T_h).$$

Similarly, the same Carnot engine operating between the reservoirs of tem-peratures T_c and T_0 has a work output W' for heat input Q

$$W' = Q(1 - T_0/T_c).$$

The difference $W - W'$ then represents the "work loss" from heat Q as a result of the flow process:

$$W - W' = Q\left(\frac{T_0}{T_c} - \frac{T_0}{T_h}\right) = T_0\Delta S, \qquad (7.9)$$

where ΔS is the increase in entropy resulting from the irreversible flow of heat Q through the conductor between the reservoirs at temperatures T_h and T_c. This unavailable work decreases with T_0. That is, the smallest loss would result by utilizing a reservoir of lowest possible temperature. The loss could be made to vanish by choosing a reservoir at $0°K$, but such a reservoir does not exist. Practical reservoirs have temperatures far above $0°K$. Although Eq. (7.9) has been developed from a consideration of the irreversible conduction of heat from a hot to a cold reservoir, it may be shown to apply to any irreversible process by more general methods of analysis.[2]

Actually, $W - W'$ in Eq. (7.9) is not a satisfactory measure of energy unavailability because its value depends on an arbitrary low temperature T_0. Even so, the concept which it embodies does suggest a very fundamental philosophical question which we introduce by a syllogism.

All natural processes are irreversible.

Every irreversible process continually makes energy unavailable for external work.

All natural processes, therefore, continually make energy unavailable for external work.

No energy is "lost" during a natural process, but some of it is transformed into a less available form. In other words, energy appears to be "running down" or degraded. Somehow much or all of the energy around us occurred at some time in the past in a highly available form, and ever since it has been changing to less available forms. This principle of the degradation of energy was first enunciated by Kelvin. It presents the question: How did the energy arrive in the highly available form in the first place? This question cannot be answered by present thermophysical methods.

7.8. Irreversibility in Thermodynamics

The entropy principle appears to be closely tied up with irreversibility. If all processes were reversible, there would be no second law of thermodynamics and the entropy concept would not have been invented. To put it

---

[2] Zemansky, M., *Heat and Thermodynamics*, 4th ed., p. 186 (McGraw-Hill, New York, 1957).

another way, problems involving strictly reversible processes generally can be solved without introducing the entropy function. Of course, natural processes as we know them would be excluded from our study. Here is the paradox. Classical thermodynamics deals with systems in equilibrium and therefore with quasistatic processes which are reversible. Natural processes are irreversible.

To circumvent this difficulty we introduce artifices. First, we do not try to follow an irreversible process, but rather we consider the system at the start and end to be in equilibrium and consequently to be subject to the principles and methods of thermodynamics in these extreme states. Or, second, we may neglect the irreversible processes and thereby idealize the natural process. Third, we may restrict the application of thermodynamics to one aspect of equilibrium in a system, even though the system is not in complete thermodynamic equilibrium. None of these procedures is entirely satisfactory. They do not give us as deep an insight into irreversible processes as we should like.

For this reason new principles are being discovered and new methods evolved for handling irreversible processes. At the core of them lie the concepts of entropy and its rate of change. These we shall discuss in Chapter 20 under thermophysics of the steady state.

7.9. Entropy and Disorder

We now see that entropy is an extensive property which attains a maximum value for a system in thermodynamic equilibrium. As a system approaches equilibrium, however, it proceeds in the direction of less order. By this we mean that it changes its state toward one in which physical properties of the system are as uniform throughout as possible under the prevailing conditions. If we place a salt crystal in a beaker of pure water, it dissolves, and the ions diffuse throughout the water to form a uniform solution. If we mix a liter of hot water with a liter of cold water, the final equilibrium mixture comes to a uniform temperature equal to the average of the initial temperatures, provided no thermal losses occur. If we inclose a hot body and a cold body within an evacuated thermally insulated space, radiation exchanges take place until the two bodies come to the same temperature. All these systems initially are not in equilibrium but proceed naturally to states of equilibrium by irreversible processes.

If we examine each of these systems we note that a greater degree of order prevails at the start than at the end. The crystal clearly is a highly ordered structure, and also salt and water as separate entities represent a modicum of order. The solution, however, is less ordered; both the salt and the water have been dispersed and intermingled. Similarly, the mixture of water in its final equilibrium state is conceived to have less order than did the original beakers of hot and cold water. Likewise the hot and cold bodies change from a more ordered state to a less ordered state. An increase in entropy is associated with a decrease in order.

Problems

1. A liter of water in a well-lagged container is at a temperature of 20°C and at atmospheric pressure. It is stirred vigorously until the temperature rises to 21°C. Find the change in entropy of the water in joules per degree Kelvin.

2. For many crystalline solids of pure substances at very low temperatures the molar heat capacity at constant volume satisfies the T-cube law

$$c_v = 12\pi^4 RT^3/5\Theta^3,$$

in which R is the gas constant and Θ is the Debye temperature. Show that the specific entropy is given by the equation

$$s = s_0 + \tfrac{1}{3}c_v.$$

Here s_0, the value of s at 0°K, usually is equated to zero.

3. One-half kilogram of water at 0°C is mixed adiabatically with one-half kilogram of water at 100°C.
   (a) Compute the change in entropy of the water.
   (b) How much change in entropy takes place in the local universe?
   (c) If the water at 0°C had been warmed slowly to 50°C and the water at 100°C had been cooled slowly to 50°C, what would have been the change in entropy of the water and of the local universe?
   (d) The mixed water is returned to its initial state by heating half of it slowly to 100°C and by cooling the other half slowly to 0°C through the agency of appropriate reservoirs. Compute values for the overall changes in entropy of the water and of the local universe.

4. Two equal masses of water at temperatures T_1 and T_2 are mixed adiabatically at constant pressure. Show that the entropy of the local universe changes by the amount

$$C_p \ln \left[(T_1 + T_2)/2(T_1T_2)^{1/2} \right],$$

where C_p is the heat capacity of the water. Demonstrate that this change is greater than zero.

5. Show that the molar specific entropy of an ideal gas with constant heat capacities is given by the equations

$$s = c_v \ln T + R \ln v + \text{constant}$$

and

$$s = c_p \ln T - R \ln P + \text{constant}.$$

6. By running water a 40-ohm resistor is maintained in a steady state at a temperature of 10°C while a current of 5 amp exists in it. During one minute how much change takes place in the entropy of the resistor and of the local universe?

7. The specific heat capacities of liquid water and ice at atmospheric pressure for several degrees Celsius below the ice point are given by the equations

$$c_{p(\text{water})} = 4222 - 22.6t$$

and

$$c_{p(\text{ice})} = 2112 + 7.5t$$

in joules per kilogram-degree. The heat of fusion of water at atmospheric pressure equals 3.337×10^5 joules/kgm. What is the specific entropy in joules per degree of supercooled water and of ice at $-10°C$? Which of these systems may be considered in the more ordered state?

8. A quantity of water may be heated to increase its temperature from 0°C to 100°C in either of two ways: it may be placed in contact with a large thermal reservoir at 100°C, or it may be placed first in contact with a thermal reservoir at 50°C until its temperature rises to this value and then in contact with a second reservoir at 100°C.
   (a) What is the total change in entropy of the water, the thermal reservoirs, and the local universe by each method?
   (b) Explain how the water might be heated from 0°C to 100°C with practically no change in entropy of the local universe.

9. A reversible heat engine operates between two identical large bodies initially at temperatures T_1 and T_2. If the pressure of the working substance remains constant and no phase changes occur, show that the final equilibrium temperature of the system is $(T_1 T_2)^{1/2}$ and that the total work output of the engine is

$$W = C_p[T_1 + T_2 - 2(T_1 T_2)^{1/2}],$$

where C_p is the heat capacity of the system at constant pressure. What are the changes in entropy of the complete system and of the local universe?

CHAPTER 8

Gas Systems

THERMODYNAMICS, unlike kinetic theory and statistical thermophysics, does not require a knowledge of the microstructure of a system. With comparatively few fundamental assumptions we can deduce rather far-reaching consequences. Imagine any system whatever confined in a chamber in such a way as to be completely isolated from its surroundings; then neither work nor heat can be exchanged with the near-surround. No matter what process the system may undergo, reversible or irreversible, we know that its total energy cannot change. We need not know the structure of the system or what kinds of interactions take place between its parts. Furthermore, if the first law of thermodynamics is not to be violated, the internal energy in the final equilibrium state must equal that of the initial equilibrium state.

Generally, however, we wish to carry out our investigations beyond the deduction of very general results. We would like to discover relationships between quantities for specific systems. For this purpose we must know, at least, what kind of system we are talking about—whether it is gaseous, liquid, solid, electrical, magnetic, radiative, living, or some other. It is helpful to have determined its equation of state and to have measured several of its macroscopic physical properties. Then, often enough, we can compute values for other physical properties and can derive other important equations for the system by means of the thermodynamic principles and methods we have developed. It is this aspect of our subject which we shall pursue in this and the following chapter.

Perhaps the least complex system to investigate is a pure crystal or a pure gas, the first because it is highly ordered and the other because it is highly disordered. In one the entropy has a relatively small value; in the other it is relatively large. That is, the pure crystal and the pure gas lie near the extremes of an entropy scale. Largely because it is the conventional practice we shall examine gas systems first, even to the extent of studying mixtures of nonreacting gases. In later chapters we shall investigate pure crystal systems.

8.1. Free Expansion of a Gas Under Adiabatic Conditions

Suppose the chamber of our introductory paragraph is partitioned into two compartments. One compartment contains a gas (not necessarily ideal) and the other is empty (Fig. 8.1). Suddenly the partition is removed so that a free expansion occurs. We know that the internal energy of the gas at the end of the expansion equals its initial value. No change in the internal energy of a gas occurs as a result of a free expansion between two equilibrium states.

To discover the effect of the free expansion on the entropy of the gas is another problem. Because the process is irreversible we surmise that the entropy should increase. We replace the irreversible process by a controlled reversible one. The partition is

Figure 8.1. Irreversible free expansion of a gas under adiabatic conditions.

assumed to be a piston which is allowed to move slowly through the evacuated compartment until the gas fills the entire volume (Fig. 8.2). Work is done on the near-surround (the piston) by the expanding gas, and, therefore, in order to have no change in internal energy, heat is allowed to flow into the system from suitable reservoirs through a diathermic window. The system ends up with the same values of pressure, temperature, volume, and internal energy it had after the irreversible process.

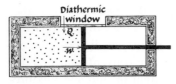

Figure 8.2. Reversible expansion of a gas under isothermal conditions.

For an infinitesimal reversible process in one mole of the gas we write the first law of thermodynamics in the form

$$du = Tds - Pdv. \quad (8.1)$$

For the foregoing quasistatic expansion, however, du equals zero. We solve for ds and integrate between the initial and final values of specific volume:

$$s_f - s_i = \int_{v_i}^{v_f} (P/T)dv. \quad (8.2)$$

This is a perfectly general result for the change in specific entropy of the gas and depends only on the initial and final states, not on the process by which the change was brought about. That is, Eq. (8.2) gives the change in entropy of one mole of the gas for the original irreversible process.

The change in specific entropy for an ideal gas may be found by replacing P/T in Eq. (8.2) by R/v, from its state equation, and by carrying out the integration. The result is

$$s_f - s_i = R \ln (v_f/v_i), \quad (8.3)$$

which is greater than zero, as we had anticipated.

The effect of the free expansion on the temperature of the gas is not as easy to find. The direct procedure would be to measure the temperature of the gas immediately before and immediately after the free expansion. This was attempted by Gay-Lussac (1807) and, later, by Joule (1845). Joule allowed air at an elevated pressure in one vessel to rush into another evacuated vessel, both vessels being immersed in a calorimeter containing water (Fig. 8.3). No change in temperature of the water was observed. Because the heat capacity of the air is so much less than that of the container, calorimeter, and water, this result was not

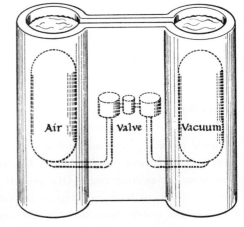

Figure 8.3. Joule's apparatus for observing the free expansion of a gas.

unexpected. The experiment was designed to obtain an experimental value for either $(\partial T/\partial v)_u$ or $(\partial T/\partial P)_u$, which are called Joule coefficients. Results of the direct experiment suggest that values of these coefficients cannot be very large.

8.2. The Experiments of Rossini and Frandsen

The most accurate work on the problem of determining the effect of a free expansion on the temperature of a gas has been done by indirect methods. Instead of isolating the system it is allowed to exchange both work and heat with the near-surround in such a way that the temperature of the system remains constant. The internal energy changes, and therefore the experiment is designed to measure the coefficients $(\partial u/\partial v)_T$ and $(\partial u/\partial P)_T$. The Joule coefficients can be obtained from these by applications of Eq. (3.25); thus

$$(\partial T/\partial v)_u = -(\partial T/\partial u)_v(\partial u/\partial v)_T \qquad (8.4)$$

and

$$(\partial T/\partial P)_u = -(\partial T/\partial u)_P(\partial u/\partial P)_T. \qquad (8.5)$$

Rossini and Frandsen of the National Bureau of Standards reported such indirect experiments in 1932. In their apparatus a vessel, B in Fig. 8.4,

Figure 8.4. The apparatus of Rossini and Frandsen for measuring changes in internal energy of a gas during isothermal expansion.

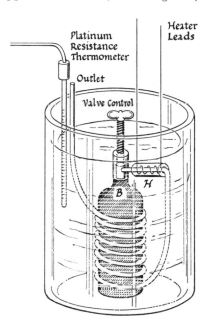

contains n moles of a real gas at elevated pressure P. The gas is allowed to flow slowly and continuously to the atmosphere through a long tube coiled around the vessel. The entire apparatus is immersed in a water bath which is maintained at the ambient temperature. While the gas flows out of the vessel both heat and work are exchanged with the near-surround. The gas in expanding does work

$$W = -P_0(nv_0 - V_B), \qquad (8.6)$$

where P_0 is atmospheric pressure, v_0 is

the specific molar volume of the gas at atmospheric pressure and temperature, and V_B is the volume of the vessel. As the gas expands it absorbs heat
from the water bath. An equal amount of heat is supplied to the water by
electric heater H to maintain constant temperature. Thus heat Q absorbed
by the gas is equal to the electrical energy supplied to the heating coil, and
this energy is readily measured.

Let the internal energy per mole of gas at the given temperature before
and after an expansion be $u(P)$ and $u(P_0)$, respectively. By the first law of
thermodynamics,

$$u(P) - u(P_0) = -(W + Q)/n. \tag{8.7}$$

Since W, Q, and n are measured quantities, experimental values of
$u(P) - u(P_0)$ may be determined for several values of initial pressure P.
Rossini and Frandsen found the values of the difference in specific internal
energy for air, oxygen, and mixtures of oxygen and carbon dioxide to be
linear functions of P with slopes which depend only on the ambient temperature. We can write this result in the form

$$(\partial u/\partial P)_T = f(T). \tag{8.8}$$

This may be integrated by holding $f(T)$ constant for the integration and then
adding a function of temperature, $g(T)$, for the integration constant,

$$u = f(T) \cdot P + g(T). \tag{8.9}$$

For an isothermal expansion the internal energy of a real gas is a linear
function of pressure.

As pressure P is reduced to zero the real gas behaves more and more like
an ideal gas, and the specific internal energy in the limit equals $g(T)$. We
conclude that *the internal energy of an ideal gas is solely a function of temperature.*
The temperature of an ideal gas is not changed by a free expansion.

We now recall that $(\partial u/\partial T)_v$ equals c_v, and furthermore we note that

$$(\partial u/\partial v)_T = (\partial P/\partial v)_T(\partial u/\partial P)_T = -(k_t v)^{-1}f(T), \tag{8.10}$$

where k_t is the isothermal compressibility of the gas. By substituting these
values of $(\partial u/\partial T)_v$ and $(\partial u/\partial v)_T$ into Eq. (8.4) we get

$$(\partial T/\partial v)_u = (c_v k_t v)^{-1}f(T). \tag{8.11}$$

This Joule coefficient does not vanish unless $f(T)$ equals zero. In general,
the temperature of a real gas is changed by a free expansion.

8.3. *The Joule-Thomson Porous-plug Experiment*

The inconclusiveness of Joule's free-expansion results led Thomson and Joule to devise a substantially different experiment which they first performed in 1852. In it the gas is allowed to pass through a porous wall at a steady rate. Whereas these men used a plug of silk or cotton wool between two pieces of wire gauze for the porous wall, researchers today often employ unglazed ceramic tubes. The pressures on either side of the wall are maintained at different constant values, and the temperature difference in the gas across the wall faces is measured with a differential thermocouple or a pair of platinum resistance

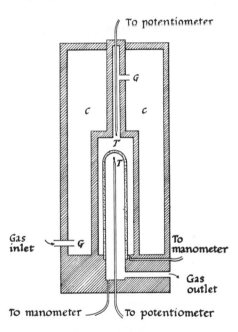

Figure 8.5.   Flow apparatus for studying the Joule-Thomson effect in gases. Gas passes through a long coiled tube between *G* and *G* which is immersed in a constant temperature bath in chamber *CC*.

thermometers. As seen in Fig. 8.5 the junctions of the thermocouple *TT* are placed a short distance away from the faces to avoid the turbulent region where temperature fluctuations are apt to occur. The entire assembly is thermally insulated. Once a steady state is reached the temperature difference, as indicated by the thermocouple, can be ascribed to the irreversible flow of gas through the porous wall.

Table 8.1 contains some of Roebuck and Osterberg's experimental values (in degree Celsius per atmosphere) of $\Delta t/\Delta P$ for nitrogen. A positive value means that the temperature drops when nitrogen expands through a porous wall. Thus, if the overall temperature equals $-75°C$ and expansion occurs from 145 atm to 135 atm of pressure, the temperature *decreases* 1.74°C. On the other hand, if the expansion between the same pressure values occurs

TABLE 8.1. *Experimental Values for the Joule-Thomson Effect for Nitrogen.* *

P (atm)	$-160°C$	$-150°C$	$-75°C$	$0°C$	$75°C$	$150°C$	$300°C$
1	1.633	1.266	0.5033	0.2656	0.1555	0.0868	0.0140
20	0.724	1.125	0.4671	0.2494	0.1421	0.0776	0.0096
33.5	0.311	0.1704	0.4318	0.2377	0.1336	0.0734	0.0050
60	0.0068	0.1601	0.3712	0.2088	0.1191	0.0628	−0.0013
100	−0.0088	0.0202	0.2682	0.1679	0.0941	0.0482	−0.0075
140	−0.0175	−0.0056	0.1735	0.1316	0.0740	0.0348	−0.0129
180	−0.0263	−0.0211	0.1026	0.1015	0.0583	0.0248	−0.0160
200	−0.0315	−0.0284	0.0800	0.0891	0.0543	0.0228	−0.0171

* Roebuck, J. R., and H. Osterberg, *Phys. Rev.*, **48**, 450, 1935 (corrected).

at $-150°C$, the temperature *increases* by 0.056°C. Apparently nitrogen may be cooled by successive expansions from 20 atm to 1 atm until it liquefies, even if initially it is at room temperature. This effect is applied in modern gas liquefiers (see Chapter 18).

Although values of $\Delta t/\Delta P$ are measured in the Joule-Thomson experiment, it must be clear that these are not values of the Joule coefficient, for here the internal energy of the gas is changed by expansion through the porous wall. How then should we characterize $\Delta t/\Delta P$?

Imagine a chamber inclosed in adiabatic walls and divided into two compartments by a porous wall. Gas of specific volume v_f at pressure P_f on

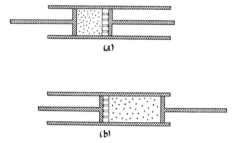

(a)

(b)

Figure 8.6.   The throttling process: (a) at the start; (b) at the end.

the upstream side of the wall is forced slowly into the region on the downstream side of the wall at pressure P_f less than P_i. This may be accomplished by means of a pair of pistons, as illustrated in Fig. 8.6, which permit the pressures to be maintained constant throughout the process. In the end the initial quantity of gas has specific volume v_f at pressure P_f. No heat is exchanged between the system and its near-surround, and the work exchange per unit mass is simply $P_i v_i - P_f v_f$. By the first law of thermodynamics, therefore, this work must equal the change in specific internal energy $u_f - u_i$. We now obtain the equality

$$u_f + P_f v_f = u_i + P_i v_i. \qquad (8.12)$$

The specific enthalpy at the end of the process equals that at the beginning. This result does not mean that the enthalpy is constant *during* the process. Thermodynamic principles and equations apply only to equilibrium states, and the gas system is not in equilibrium during the process. We say it has performed an irreversible throttling process.

Suppose now the foregoing throttling process is repeated several times on the same mass of gas, always by starting with the same values of P_i and v_i but by ending with different values of P_f and therefore v_f. The initial temperatures and enthalpys have the same values, and by Eq. (8.12) all the final values of enthalpy also are identical. The final temperatures, however, may differ. We plot these final temperatures against the corresponding final pressures, as shown in Fig. 8.7, and so obtain a series of points which lie on an isenthalpic curve. This curve does *not* represent a thermodynamic process or even a throttling process, but rather it represents the locus of end-equilibrium isenthalpic states for a series of irreversible throttling processes. We now see that the

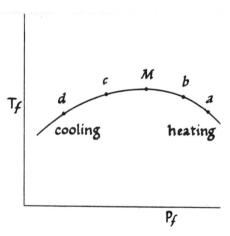

Figure 8.7.   An isenthalpic curve showing an inversion point at M.

data in Table 8.1 really are limiting values of $\Delta t/\Delta P$ as ΔP approaches zero for the throttling process. That is,

$$\lim_{\Delta P \to 0} (\Delta t/\Delta P)_h = \lim_{\Delta P \to 0} (\Delta T/\Delta P)_h = (\partial T/\partial P)_h, \qquad (8.13)$$

where the subscript h indicates that specific enthalpy is held constant. Here, $(\partial T/\partial P)_h$ represents the slope of an isenthalpic curve and is called the Joule-Thomson coefficient.

Often the isenthalpic curve has a maximum, as at M in Fig. 8.7, which implies that the temperature of the system rises if a pressure decrease occurs to the right or negative-slope side of M and that the temperature falls if a pressure decrease occurs to the left or the positive-slope side of M. Point M is called an inversion point. A series of isenthalpic curves may be obtained for a given gas system by adjusting the initial pressure and specific volume over a range of values. In Fig. 8.8 is reproduced a series of isenthalpic

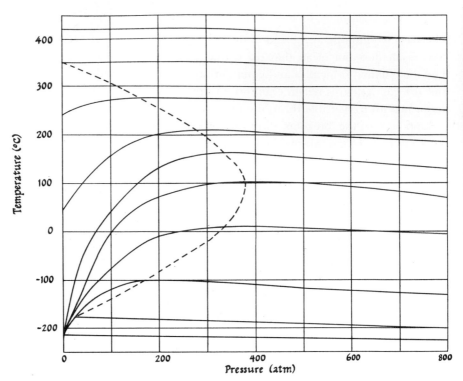

Figure 8.8.   Isenthalpic curves for nitrogen from Roebuck and coworkers. [After
M. W. Zemansky, *Heat and Thermodynamics*, McGraw-Hill, New York,
1957.]

curves for nitrogen as constructed by Roebuck and his co-workers. The
dotted line through their maxima, the inversion curve, separates regions
where a fall in temperature occurs from regions where a rise in temperature
occurs.

8.4. Thermodynamic Equation for the Joule-Thomson Coefficient

Since the Joule-Thomson coefficient often is difficult to measure directly,
a suitable relation for it in terms of other measurable quantities is useful.
Applying Eq. (3.25) we find

$$(\partial T/\partial P)_h = -(\partial h/\partial P)_T/(\partial h/\partial T)_p, \qquad (8.14)$$

in which $(\partial h/\partial T)_p$ equals specific heat c_p, as we recall from Eq. (4.13), and

$(\partial h/\partial P)_T$ may be evaluated by means of the Planck function. Planck made extensive use of this function in his excellent *Treatise on Thermodynamics*[1]; it is

$$\psi = s - h/T, \qquad (8.15)$$

which has the dimensions of entropy. For an infinitesimal reversible process,

$$d\psi = ds - T^{-1}dh + hT^{-2}dT$$
$$= -vT^{-1}dP + hT^{-2}dT, \qquad (8.16)$$

where dh has been replaced by its equivalent $Tds + vdP$. Because $d\psi$ is an exact differential we apply Eq. (3.23) and find after reduction that

$$(\partial h/\partial P)_T = v - T(\partial v/\partial T)_p. \qquad (8.17)$$

This equation is now combined with Eq. (8.14) to obtain the relation for the Joule-Thomson coefficient which we set out to find; namely

$$(\partial T/\partial P)_h = c_p^{-1}[T(\partial v/\partial T)_p - v]. \qquad (8.18)$$

For an ideal gas the term $T(\partial v/\partial T)_p$ equals v, and therefore $(\partial T/\partial P)_h$ vanishes, as it should. For real gases and other systems, however, this coefficient generally differs from zero (except at inversion points), as can be demonstrated by inserting the appropriate equation of state into Eq. (8.18).

In order to compute values of $(\partial T/\partial P)_h$ from experimental data, Eq. (8.18) may be rewritten in the form

$$(\partial T/\partial P)_h = (v/c_p)(\beta T - 1), \qquad (8.19)$$

where β is the volume expansivity of the system. Measured values of β, v,

TABLE 8.2.   *Joule-Thomson Coefficients for Several Substances.*

Fluid	t (°C)	β (deg $^{-1}$)	v (cm^3-gm^{-1})	c_p (joule gm^{-1}-deg^{-1})	$(\partial T/\partial P)_h$ (deg-atm^{-1}) Computed	Observed
Air	0	0.0036706	773.5	1.0037	0.205	0.208
Carbon dioxide	0	0.003724	505.8	0.822	1.07	1.005
Hydrogen	0	0.003660	11,126	14.19	-0.022	-0.039
Nitrogen	0	0.003673	800.1	1.037	0.255	0.266
Liquid water	20	0.000207	1.00177	4.1819	-0.023	-0.02

and c_p for several gases and the computed and directly observed values of $(\partial T/\partial P)_h$ are gathered in Table 8.2. The computed values are seen to have

---

[1] Planck, M., *Treatise on Thermodynamics*, Trans. A. Ogg (Longmans, Green, New York, 1903).

116   GAS SYSTEMS [CHAP. 8]

the right order of magnitude and proper sign. Unfortunately, the error in the computed value can be large if βT is nearly unity.

Nothing in Eq. (8.18) and Eq. (8.19) restricts them to the gaseous phase, and consequently we should expect a Joule-Thomson effect in liquids. In fact, in Table 8.1 the boxed-in data for nitrogen at $-160°C$ apply to the liquid phase. Furthermore, the computed and observed values of $(\partial T/\partial P)_h$ for liquid water in Table 8.2 are in rather good agreement.

8.5. Thermal Effusion

In experiments for observing the Joule-Thomson effect a gas or liquid is forced through a porous wall by a constant pressure gradient under adiabatic conditions, and any temperature difference across the wall arising from this irreversible flow process is measured. Does the contrary process exist? Will a gas or liquid pass through a porous wall because of a temperature gradient and thereby produce a pressure difference? It is not surprising that such an effect exists, but to have it appear in three different aspects does present a problem.

Reynolds, in 1879, investigated the flow of gas, resulting from a temperature gradient, through a porous disk consisting of many minute channels and called the phenomenon thermal transpiration. The gas tended to flow from the cool to the warm side. Lippmann, in 1907, and later Aubert, in 1912, described a similar effect in which water passed through membranes of gelatine and other materials under the influence of a temperature gradient, but the effect was complicated by the presence of dissolved electrolytes in the membrane. Denbigh, in 1949, and Denbigh and Raumann, in 1950, reported observations on the passage of carbon dioxide and hydrogen through a rubber membrane arising from a temperature difference between its surfaces. The carbon dioxide passed from the cool to the warm side, whereas hydrogen passed in the reverse direction. This is the phenomenon of thermo-osmosis. Finally, Allen and Jones, in 1938, discovered the fountain effect, in which liquid helium II flows spontaneously through a capillary between two vessels at different temperatures. The flow takes place from the cool to the warm region. This phenomenon is described in greater detail in Chapter 19.

Although from a microscopic point of view the mechanisms for these effects may differ from one another, macroscopically they are equivalent in that as a result of a temperature gradient the fluid simply redistributes itself between two chambers separated by a permeable wall. We group these effects together under the name of thermal effusion.

Because a thermal effusion process is irreversible, like the throttling process, it cannot be described by thermodynamic variables. Only end equilibrium states can be related. We may set out to develop appropriate equations, much as we did for the Joule-Thomson effect, but difficulties arise immediately because the process is not adiabatic and the entropy changes must be accounted for explicitly. Consequently, we are forced to abandon this approach and, instead, to examine the problem as a steady-state flow process. This we shall do in Chapter 20; here we simply quote the result. For thermal effusion processes,

$$dP/dT = -q^*/vT, \tag{8.20}$$

where q^* is the heat absorbed from one chamber and liberated in the other when one mole of fluid is transferred between them through a permeable wall because of a temperature gradient.

8.6. The Difference $c_p - c_v$

Let us return to another problem to which reference was made in Section 4.5. Ordinarily, the specific heat at constant volume is not as easy to measure as the specific heat at constant pressure. Fortunately, the difference between them can be related to other measurable quantities.

From the first law of thermodynamics we have already found that c_v equals $(\partial u/\partial T)_v$ and c_p equals $(\partial u/\partial T)_p + P(\partial v/\partial T)_p$; hence

$$c_p - c_v = P(\partial v/\partial T)_p + (\partial u/\partial T)_p - (\partial u/\partial T)_v. \tag{8.21}$$

For an ideal gas the internal energy is independent of both P and v, so the last two terms cancel and $(\partial v/\partial T)_p$ equals R/P; hence

$$c_p - c_v = R = 8.31 \text{ joules/gm-deg.} \tag{8.22}$$

For real gases and other systems we utilize Eq. (8.21), but we put it in a more compact form.

Suppose u is a function of v and T. Then

$$du = (\partial u/\partial v)_T dv + (\partial u/\partial T)_v dT.$$

When this equation is divided through by dT and the pressure is held constant we get

$$(\partial u/\partial T)_p - (\partial u/\partial T)_v = (\partial u/\partial v)_T(\partial v/\partial T)_p. \tag{8.23}$$

This equation is now combined with Eq. (8.21) to yield

$$c_p - c_v = [(\partial u/\partial v)_T + P](\partial v/\partial T)_p. \tag{8.24}$$

To evaluate the expression in brackets we apply still another state function which was introduced originally by Massieu[2]:

$$\mu = s - u/T. \tag{8.25}$$

For an infinitesimal reversible process,

$$d\mu = ds - T^{-1}du + uT^{-2}dT$$
$$= PT^{-1}dv + uT^{-2}dT. \tag{8.26}$$

Because $d\mu$ is an exact differential Eq. (3.23) can be applied. The result after reduction is

$$(\partial u/\partial v)_T + P = T(\partial P/\partial T)_v. \tag{8.27}$$

The coefficient $(\partial P/\partial T)_v$ ordinarily is difficult to measure, and therefore we replace it by $-(\partial v/\partial T)_p(\partial P/\partial v)_T$ from Eq. (3.27). Finally, we combine Eq. (8.27) with Eq. (8.24) to obtain the relation we seek:

$$c_p - c_v = -T(\partial v/\partial T)_p^2(\partial P/\partial v)_T. \tag{8.28}$$

This equation reduces to Eq. (8.22) if the right side is evaluated for an ideal gas. Values of $c_p - c_v$ for real gases and other systems may be found in the same way by introducing the appropriate state function.

From Eq. (8.28) we note three important conditions on the heat capacities:

(1) at $0°K$ c_p equals c_v;

(2) because $(\partial P/\partial v)_T$ is intrinsically negative and both T and the square of $(\partial v/\partial T)_p$ are positive, c_p is always greater than c_v;

(3) c_p equals c_v if $(\partial v/\partial T)_p$ vanishes.

The third condition applies for any substance with a maximum density and, therefore, a minimum value of specific volume on a v-T diagram. A good illustration is liquid water at 3.98°C. For gases and vapors, however, $(\partial v/\partial T)_p$ always is greater than zero.

For the experimentalist, Eq. (8.28) can be written in the form

$$c_p - c_v = \beta^2 T v/k_t, \tag{8.29}$$

where β is the volume expansivity, v is the specific volume, and k_t is the isothermal compressibility of the system. For liquid water at 20°C k_t equals 4.91×10^{-5} atm^{-1}. If this quantity and the data in Table 8.2 are inserted into Eq. (8.29), the difference $c_p - c_v$ is computed to equal 0.0259 joule/gm-deg. Hence c_v for liquid water equals $4.1819 - 0.0259$ or 4.1560 joules/gm-deg. For gases at 0°C the isothermal compressibility is very

[2] Massieu, F., *Comptes Rendus Acad. Sciences, Paris*, **69**, 858 (1869).

nearly equal to the reciprocal of the gas pressure. Therefore we can compute $c_p - c_v$ for standard conditions and compare the result with the value of R to see how closely the real gas approaches an ideal gas in this respect. If the data in Table 8.2 for air and hydrogen are inserted into Eq. (8.29) and if we suppose P equals one standard atmosphere, $c_p - c_v$ equals 8.05 joules/mole-deg for air and 8.29 joules/mole-deg for hydrogen. Comparing these values with 8.31 joules/mole-degree for the ideal gas, we see that hydrogen is more nearly "ideal" than is air, which agrees with previous conclusions.

8.7. *Second Equation of State for an Ideal Gas*

In Section 4.5 we showed that c_v equals $(\partial u/\partial T)_v$ and c_p equals $(\partial h/\partial T)_p$. But the specific internal energy and enthalpy for an ideal gas depend only on temperature; therefore

$$du = c_v dT = T ds - P dv \tag{8.30}$$

and

$$dh = c_p dT = T ds + v dP. \tag{8.31}$$

For a quasistatic adiabatic process ds equals zero; consequently, on dividing one equation by the other,

$$(\partial P/\partial v)_s = -(c_p/c_v)(P/v). \tag{8.32}$$

The ratio of specific heats c_p/c_v commonly is represented by γ. For an ideal gas γ is constant, and therefore Eq. (8.32) may be integrated to yield

$$Pv^\gamma = f(s), \tag{8.33}$$

which is a general form of the second equation of state for an ideal gas.

In order to obtain an explicit expression for $f(s)$ we divide Eq. (8.30) and Eq. (8.31) throughout by T and then integrate them between limits. For the ideal gas,

$$s - s_0 = c_v \ln (T/T_0) + R \ln (v/v_0) \tag{8.34}$$

and

$$s - s_0 = c_p \ln (T/T_0) - R \ln (P/P_0), \tag{8.35}$$

where P_0, v_0, and T_0 are the pressure, volume, and temperature of the gas when the entropy equals s_0. We now eliminate T/T_0 from these equations to find

$$f(s) = K e^{s/c_v}, \tag{8.36}$$

where K is another universal constant for one mole of an ideal gas.

8.8. Direct Measurement of γ for Gases

In Section 4.6 we described the general methods commonly employed today for measuring c_p, and in Section 8.6 we developed an equation for computing c_v from c_p. If an independent method can be devised for measuring γ, then we have another way of computing values of c_v from c_p. Fortunately, this can be done, especially for gases. Although there exist three essentially different methods for measuring γ, all of them involve adiabatic processes.

Adiabatic Expansion. The earliest determination of γ was made by the French physicists Clément and Desormes in 1819. The gas is contained in a large metal vessel which is provided with a manometer and a large poppet valve or stopcock for allowing the vessel to be opened and closed rapidly to the outside atmosphere. Initially the gas is in equilibrium at room temperature and at a pressure P_1 somewhat in excess of atmospheric pressure P_0. When the valve is opened momentarily gas rushes out, the pressure within the vessel is reduced to P_0, and the temperature falls as a result of the adiabatic expansion. After a few minutes the gas returns to thermal equilibrium at a new pressure P_2. From these values of pressure γ may be computed by the equation

$$\gamma = \frac{\log P_1 - \log P_0}{\log P_1 - \log P_2}, \tag{8.37}$$

which is derived by application of the equations for an ideal gas. Although the method is very simple, significant errors are introduced because of unavoidable oscillations of the gas on opening and closing the poppet valve.

Lummer and Pringsheim modified this method in 1894. The vessel is thermally insulated, and the temperature of the gas before and after opening the poppet valve is measured. Then γ is given by

$$\gamma = \frac{\log (P_1/P_0)}{\log (P_1/P_0) - \log (T_1/T_2)}, \tag{8.38}$$

in which T_1 and T_2 are the initial and final temperatures, P_1 is the initial pressure of the gas, and P_0 is atmospheric pressure. A somewhat more elaborate procedure was devised by Maneuvier, in which pressure changes are determined by a null method.

Mechanical Oscillation. This method was first described by Rüchardt in 1929. The apparatus is illustrated in Fig. 8.9. The gas is contained in a large vessel of volume V which is closed with a tight-fitting one-hole stopper. The stopper supports a vertical glass tube with uniform and accurate bore of cross-sectional area A. Into the tube there is dropped a metal sphere of mass m. Although the sphere fits sufficiently snugly to behave like a piston, it must be somewhat loose to reduce friction. Because of the snugness of fit the sphere at first compresses the gas, momentarily comes to rest, and thereafter executes oscillatory motion with decreasing amplitude. If the amplitudes and period are sufficiently small, we may assume that the gas undergoes an approximately quasistatic adiabatic process for which $(\partial P/\partial V)_s$ equals $-\gamma P/V$. Let Δy represent the displacement of the sphere from its equilibrium position and let ΔF equal the force exerted on the sphere as a result of the decrease in pressure ΔP over the equilibrium value as the volume is increased by ΔV. Now ΔF equals $A\Delta P$ and ΔV equals $A\Delta y$, so $\Delta P/\Delta V$ equals $\Delta F/A^2\Delta y$. For this adiabatic process in the limit therefore, $(\partial P/\partial V)_s$ equals $A^{-2}(\partial F/\partial y)_s$, and finally

$$(\partial F/\partial y)_s = -\gamma A^2 P/V.$$

Because all the quantities on the right can be treated as constants, the oscillatory motion of the sphere is simple harmonic of period

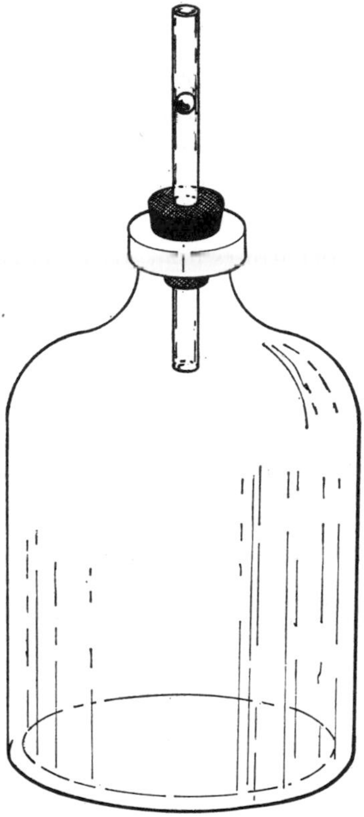

Figure 8.9.   Rüchardt's apparatus for measuring γ.

$$\tau = 2\pi\sqrt{-m/(\partial F/\partial y)_s}.$$

Combining these equations we find

$$\gamma = (4\pi^2 mV)/(A^2 P\tau^2). \tag{8.39}$$

By this method Rüchardt obtained values of γ for air and for carbon dioxide in good agreement with those obtained by calorimetric measurements. Even so, the errors are likely to be large because of slight off-roundness of the sphere and tube and the unavoidable friction between them.

A modification of Rüchardt's method was described in 1956 by Christy and Rieser who introduced the gas to be measured into the large vessel through a side tube at a constant rate. With proper adjustment of the gas inflow, the sphere can be made to oscillate at constant amplitude and period. The foregoing equations apply. Another modification was suggested by Rinkel, in 1929. The sphere is dropped into the tube from a point where the pressure is exactly atmospheric, and the initial total distance of fall is measured. Now the work done in compressing the gas must just equal the decrease in potential energy of the sphere. From this equality we find

$$\gamma = 2mgV/A^2P_0L, \qquad (8.40)$$

where P_0 is atmospheric pressure and L is the distance of fall.

Figure 8.10 is a diagram of a precision apparatus, devised by Clark and Katz in 1940 and improved by Katz, Woods, and Leverton in 1949, for measuring γ of a real gas as a function of pressure. In this method accurate account is taken of the real equation of state for the gas, of the friction, and of departures from strictly adiabatic conditions. A steel piston at the center of a horizontal cylindrical tube, which is closed at both ends, divides the gas into two equal volumes. The piston may be driven at any desired frequency by means of an alternating current in a set of external coils. Friction between the piston and cylinder is reduced by supporting the piston in an electromagnetic field. Vibration amplitudes are measured, with a microscope and micrometer eyepiece, as a function of applied frequency, and a resonance curve is drawn. From the resonance frequency and other measurable parameters of the apparatus and gas, γ can be computed. The equations and calculations are rather elaborate and are omitted in this account. Instead we quote in Table 8.3 the results obtained by this method.

Figure 8.10. Schematic diagram of Clark and Katz's apparatus for measuring γ.

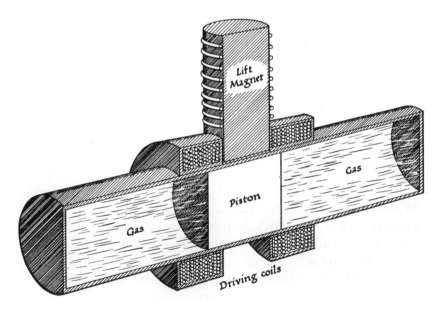

TABLE 8.3.   *Pressure Variation of γ for Real Gases from 1 to 25 Atmospheres.*
$(\gamma = a + bP + cP^2.)$

Gas	Temperature (°C)	a	b (atm^{-1})	c (atm^{-2})
He	23.1	1.6669	−0.0002	0
A	24.2	1.6667	+0.00353	0
H_2	24.4	1.4045	0.00025	0
N_2	23.0	1.4006	0.00221	0
CO_2	29.9	1.2857	0.00629	0
CO_2	23.8	1.2948	0.00500	0.00017/9
N_2O	25.3	1.2744	0.00225	0.000973
CH_4	25.1	1.3029	−0.00105	0.000484

Wave Velocity. The fundamental equation for the speed of a compressional wave in a three-dimensional homogeneous isotropic medium is

$$\mathcal{S} = 1/\sqrt{k_s\rho} \qquad (8.41)$$

in which k_s is the adiabatic compressibility and ρ is the density of the medium. This equation was first derived by Newton, who assumed the compressibility to be isothermal. A century later Laplace pointed out that pressure variations due to the wave occur so rapidly that the medium really experiences adiabatic changes and, therefore, that the compressibility should be the adiabatic one. We already know from our discussion in Section 3.6 that the adiabatic compressibility equals $-V^{-1}(\partial V/\partial P)_s$. For an ideal gas this reduces to $(\gamma P)^{-1}$, so on solving for γ we get

$$\gamma = \rho\mathcal{S}^2/P = \rho V\mathcal{S}^2/RT$$
$$= m\mathcal{S}^2/RT, \qquad (8.42)$$

where m is the molecular weight of the gas. The speed of a sonic wave may be measured by a resonance tube or by another method, and then γ is computed by means of this equation. On the other hand, if γ is known, a value for the temperature of the medium may be computed instead.

8.9. *Mixtures of Ideal Gases*

Consider a homogeneous mixture of inert ideal gases at pressure P and temperature T in a chamber of volume V. Let there be n_1 moles of gas 1, n_2 moles of gas 2. and so on up to n_k moles of gas k. The mole fraction x_i of the

ith gas equals the ratio of n_i to the total number of moles of all the gases n, namely

$$x_i = \frac{n_i}{n} = \frac{n_i}{n_1 + n_2 + \cdots + n_k}. \tag{8.43}$$

Because the sum of the x_i equals unity, one of the mole fractions is dependent and can be computed in terms of the others.

The partial pressure P_i of the ith gas is now defined to be the pressure this gas would exert if it alone occupied volume V, so

$$P_i = n_i RT/V. \tag{8.44}$$

Because the gases are ideal and inert, therefore, the total pressure is given by the equation

$$P = nRT/V = (n_1 + n_2 + \cdots + n_k)RT/V \tag{8.45}$$
$$= P_1 + P_2 + \cdots + P_k,$$

which is Dalton's law of partial pressures.

The partial entropy S_i of the ith gas is defined similarly to the entropy of this gas if it alone occupied volume V, so from Eq. (8.34),

$$S_i = S_{0i} + n_i c_{vi} \ln (T/T_0) + n_i R \ln (V/V_0), \tag{8.46}$$

in which c_{vi} is the molar heat capacity at constant volume for the ith gas and n_i is the number of moles of this gas in volume V at temperature T. The total entropy of the mixture is given by the equation

$$S = S_0 + C_v \ln (T/T_0) + nR \ln (V/V_0), \tag{8.47}$$

in which C_v is the heat capacity at constant volume and n is the total number of moles of all the gases in the mixture. But C_v equals the sum of $n_i c_{vi}$ for these gases; thus

$$S - S_0 = \Sigma_1^k n_1 c_{vi} \ln (T/T_0) + \Sigma_1^k n_i R \ln (V/V_0)$$
$$= \Sigma_1^k [n_i c_{vi} \ln (T/T_0) + n_i R \ln (V/V_0)]$$
$$= \Sigma_1^k (S_i - S_{0i}). \tag{8.48}$$

We identify S with $\Sigma_1^k S_i$ and S_0 with $\Sigma_1^k S_{0i}$ and thus obtain the result that the entropy of a mixture of ideal gases equals the sum of the partial entropies of the gases. This is Gibbs' law of partial entropies.

8.10. Isothermal Interdiffusion
of Two Ideal Gases

Imagine a chamber partitioned into two compartments of different sizes. Each compartment contains an ideal gas. Let one compartment contain n_1

moles of gas 1 and the other compartment contain n_2 moles of gas 2. Initially the temperature and pressure in the two compartments are the same, and the total entropy equals

$$S_i = (n_1 c_{p1} + n_2 c_{p2}) \ln (T/T_0) - (n_1 + n_2) R \ln P + n_1 s_{01} + n_2 s_{02}$$
$$= C_p \ln (T/T_0) - nR \ln P + S_0. \tag{8.49}$$

The partition is now broken and interdiffusion occurs under isothermal conditions. When equilibrium is reestablished the total entropy is given by the equation

$$S_f = C_p \ln (T/T_0) - R(n_1 \ln P_1 + n_2 \ln P_2) + S_0, \tag{8.50}$$

in which P_1 and P_2 are the partial pressures of the two gases in the mixture. The change of entropy then equals

$$S_f - S_i = nR \ln P - R(n_1 \ln P_1 + n_2 \ln P_2). \tag{8.51}$$

In terms of mole fractions this equation reduces to

$$S_f - S_i = -nR(x_1 \ln x_1 + x_2 \ln x_2). \tag{8.52}$$

Because both x_1 and x_2 are less than unity, the logarithms are negative, and therefore $S_f - S_i$ actually is a positive quantity, as it should be for an irreversible process.

Notice that Eq. (8.52) contains no quantities, such as specific heats, entropies, or internal energies, which would distinguish one gas from the other. The change in specific entropy of the mixture depends only on the mole fractions of the two gases and the universal gas constant. The result is the same no matter how similar or dissimilar the physical properties of the gases may be. But if the two gases are identical, the concept of diffusion is meaningless and there is no change in entropy. This is a curious conclusion, for generally we expect quantities to change in a continuous fashion. Here as the two gases in the mixture are made more nearly alike in their physical properties the change in entropy on mixing them has a definite constant value which suddenly changes when the gases are identical. This is known as Gibbs' paradox. The paradox was resolved by Bridgman, who called upon the operational point of view. To distinguish between the two gases requires a set of experimental operations. As the physical properties of the gases become more nearly alike, these operations become more difficult and involved. In the limit when the gases are identical a discontinuity in the experimental operations occurs, for there are none by which the gases can be distinguished. For this reason we should expect a discontinuity in the entropy change. The Gibbs paradox may be further elucidated in terms of the quantum statistical treatment of an ideal gas.[3]

---

[3] E. Schroedinger, *Statistical Thermodynamics*, p. 58 (The University Press, Cambridge, 1952). See also M. J. Klein, *Am. J. Phys.*, **26**, 80 (1958).

Problems

1. Prove that the adiabatic curve is steeper than the isothermal curve through a point on a P-V diagram by the factor γ.

2. An arbitrary quasistatic process for an ideal gas is said to be polytropic which may be represented by the equation

$$PV^k = \text{constant.}$$

    (a) What is the value of exponent k: (1) for an isobaric process; (2) for an isothermal process; (3) for an adiabatic process; and (4) for an isochoric process?

    (b) Show that the heat capacity of an ideal gas for a polytropic process is given by

$$C = C_v(\gamma - k)/(1 - k).$$

3. The Curie law for an ideal paramagnetic substance undergoing isochoric magnetization is

$$MT = CHV,$$

where M is the magnetic dipole moment and V is the volume of the specimen, H is the applied magnetic field intensity, C is the Curie constant, and T is the thermodynamic temperature. It may be shown that the internal energy of an ideal paramagnetic substance which satisfies the Curie law is a function of temperature only (see Section 9.4).

    (a) From the definitions of heat capacity at constant dipole moment C_M and at constant magnetic field intensity C_H derive the equation

$$C_H = C_M + M^2/CV$$

    for an ideal paramagnetic substance satisfying the Curie law.

    (b) If γ_M equals C_H/C_M, show that the state equation for a quasistatic adiabatic and isochoric magnetization process is

$$HM^{-\gamma_M} = \text{constant.}$$

    [Adiabatic curves for an ideal paramagnetic substance are illustrated in the Carnot cycle of Fig. 5.2(d).]

4. Show that

$$(\partial P/\partial T)_S = \gamma P/(\gamma - 1)T$$

for a quasistatic process in an ideal gas.

5. (a) Atmospheric pressure changes with altitude at the rate

$$dP/dh = -\rho g,$$

in which ρ is the density of air at height h, and g is the gravitational acceleration. Air is assumed to behave like an ideal gas. Show that ρ is equal to mP/RT, in which m is the average molecular weight of air, R is the universal gas constant, and P and T are the pressure and thermodynamic temperature at height h.

(b) Suppose a mass of warm air rises and expands. Relatively little heat exchange takes place with the surrounding atmosphere, and therefore the expansion is nearly adiabatic. Combine the equations in part (a) with the value of $(\partial P/\partial T)_S$ in problem 4, and find a numerical value for the dry-air lapse rate $(\partial T/\partial y)_S$ in degrees per kilometer. (For meteorological purposes the lapse rate is more nearly -6 deg/km because of nonideal conditions.)

6. Prove that the specific enthalpy of an ideal gas depends only on temperature.

7. Evaluate $c_p - c_v$ for a van der Waals fluid.

8. An empirical equation for the specific volume of water in the temperature range 0–33°C is

$$v = v_0(1 + at + bt^2 + ct^3),$$

in which $a = -6.43 \times 10^{-5}$ deg^{-1}, $b = 8.505 \times 10^{-6}$ deg^{-2}, and $c = 6.79 \times 10^{-8}$ deg^{-3}.
 (a) Show that

$$(\partial T/\partial P)_h$$
$$= (1/\rho_0 c_p)[-1.0175 + 0.00466t + 6.40 \times 10^{-5}t^2 + 1.36 \times 10^{-7}t^3].$$

 (b) Evaluate $(\partial T/\partial P)_h$ at 20°C.

9. Derive the thermodynamic equations

$$(\partial T/\partial V)_U = -(\partial T/\partial U)_V(\partial U/\partial V)_T$$

and

$$(\partial T/\partial P)_U = -(\partial T/\partial U)_P(\partial U/\partial P)_T.$$

10. Show how Eq. (8.36) is obtained from Eqs. (8.34) and (8.35).

11. (a) Derive Eq. (8.37) for γ by the adiabatic expansion method.
 (b) Carry through the steps in the derivation of Eqs. (8.39) and (8.40) for γ as measured by the methods of Rüchardt and Rinkel.

12. Table 8.3 contains measured values of γ for several real gases.
 (a) If these gases were ideal, what would be the values of γ?
 (b) At what pressure does methane have a minimum value for γ?
 (c) Does γ for the other gases reach a minimum? Explain.

13. An experimental value for the speed of sound in dry air is 331.4 m/sec at 0°C. Compute a value for γ of air and compare it with the theoretical value for a gas containing diatomic molecules.

14. Prove that γ for a van der Waals fluid is given by the equation

$$\gamma = m s^2[RT + f(v, T)]^{-1},$$

where $f(v, T)$ consists of a series of small correction terms, the first of which is $2(bRT - a)/v$.

CHAPTER 9

Applications of Thermodynamic Methods to Other Systems

Because classical thermodynamics deals with macroscopic quantities and with large-scale processes, its methodology is rather gross and non-specific. Equations of state cannot be derived, and values of physical properties cannot be determined by thermodynamic analysis alone. Even so, there can be deduced general relations among quantities which characterize a system and also large-scale limitations on the processes which it can undergo. This we have seen in our study of gas systems. Here we shall extend these thermodynamic methods and apply them to a few other systems.

9.1. State Functions

The thermodynamic state of a closed system, we have learned, generally is described by several functions of no more than two or occasionally three independent variables. Suppose we select the entropy S and volume V to be two such variables. For an infinitesimal reversible process the first and second laws of thermodynamics yield the equation

$$dU = TdS - PdV, \qquad (9.1)$$

which indicates that U is a function of S and V. From this we get immediately

128

$$T = (\partial U/\partial S)_V \tag{9.2}$$

and

$$P = -(\partial U/\partial V)_S. \tag{9.3}$$

If an explicit relation for U can be found in terms of S and V by experimental, statistical, or other means, then Eq. (9.2) and Eq. (9.3) may be applied to evaluate T and P of the system. In addition, we can work out relations for other state functions in terms of S and V. Enthalpy H is simply

$$H = U + PV = U - V(\partial U/\partial V)_S. \tag{9.4}$$

Similarly, the Helmholtz function A and the Gibbs function G can be obtained from the equations

$$A = U - TS = U - S(\partial U/\partial S)_V \tag{9.5}$$

and

$$G = H - TS = U - S(\partial U/\partial S)_V - V(\partial U/\partial V)_S. \tag{9.6}$$

In the same way equations may be found for the Massieu and Planck functions and any others we may devise.

Once a pair of thermodynamic variables is selected as being independent, then every other one becomes a state function of the system. It is conventional to consider those variables having the dimensions of energy as state functions and rarely, if ever, as independent variables. The pair of independent variables generally is selected from P, V, and T, because these quantities are most readily measured.

Suppose we wish to replace S by T as an independent variable. We let S be a function of V and T; then

$$dS = (\partial S/\partial V)_T dV + (\partial S/\partial T)_V dT. \tag{9.7}$$

We now write

$$\begin{aligned} dU &= TdS - PdV \\ &= T(\partial S/\partial T)_V dT + [T(\partial S/\partial V)_T - P]\, dV. \end{aligned} \tag{9.8}$$

In this way S becomes a state function and T and V become the independent variables. Evidently,

$$(\partial U/\partial T)_V = T(\partial S/\partial T)_V, \tag{9.9}$$

which we recognize is the heat capacity of the system at constant volume, and

$$(\partial U/\partial V)_T = T(\partial S/\partial V)_T - P, \tag{9.10}$$

which we sometimes call the "internal pressure" of the system. This last equation, incidentally, can be obtained directly by dividing Eq. (9.1) throughout by dV and holding the temperature constant. Furthermore, if we compare Eq. (9.10) with Eq. (8.27), we see that $(\partial S/\partial V)_T$ must be equivalent to $(\partial P/\partial T)_V$. This equivalence is one of Maxwell's identities.

9.2. The Maxwell Identities

The functions U, H, A, and G all characterize the state of a system, and therefore their differentials are exact. Because of this condition we may apply Eq. (3.23) to each of them. From Eq. (9.1) we get

$$(\partial P/\partial S)_V = -(\partial T/\partial V)_S. \tag{9.11}$$

For an infinitesimal reversible process we note that

$$dH = dU + PdV + VdP$$
$$= TdS + VdP; \tag{9.12}$$
$$dA = dU - TdS - SdT$$
$$= -PdV - SdT; \tag{9.13}$$

and

$$dG = dH - TdS - SdT$$
$$= VdP - SdT. \tag{9.14}$$

From these exact differentials we obtain

$$(\partial V/\partial S)_P = (\partial T/\partial P)_S, \tag{9.15}$$
$$(\partial S/\partial V)_T = (\partial P/\partial T)_V, \tag{9.16}$$

and

$$(\partial S/\partial P)_T = -(\partial V/\partial T)_P. \tag{9.17}$$

Equations (9.11), (9.15), (9.16), and (9.17) are the four Maxwell identities. Similar relations may be developed for systems involving other thermophysical variables. These identities do not refer to a process, but rather they relate differential coefficients of a system which is in thermodynamic equilibrium. If we think of these coefficients as representing slopes of curves for thermodynamic processes, then the Maxwell identities tell us which of the slopes are equal.

These identities are valuable for eliminating the entropy function from equations. Thus we replace $(\partial S/\partial V)_T$ in Eq. (9.10) by its equivalent $(\partial P/\partial T)_V$ from Eq. (9.16) to obtain the energy equation

$$(\partial U/\partial V)_T = T(\partial P/\partial T)_V - P, \tag{9.18}$$

in which there is no reference to entropy. This energy coefficient may be evaluated for a specific system by introducing the equation of state of that system on the right side. The result is especially simple if the state equation has the form

$$P = Tf(V), \tag{9.19}$$

where $f(V)$ is an arbitrary function of the volume, for then $(\partial P/\partial T)_V$ equals

$f(V)$, and therefore $(\partial U/\partial V)_T$ equals zero. Furthermore, because $(\partial U/\partial P)_T$ equals $(\partial U/\partial V)_T(\partial V/\partial P)_T$ and $(\partial V/\partial P)_T$ generally does not vanish, it follows that $(\partial U/\partial P)_T$ also equals zero. That is, the internal energy of the system is not a function of volume or pressure, and consequently it must be a function only of temperature. An ideal gas has an equation of state like Eq. (9.19); hence its internal energy is independent of volume and pressure, a conclusion which agrees with that of Section 8.2.

9.3. Pressure in Blackbody Radiative Systems

If an evacuated chamber is heated to a uniform temperature T, its interior is conceived to be filled with radiant energy of density given by the Stefan fourth-power law [Eq. (3.8)]:

$$(\partial U/\partial V)_T = u_b = aT^4. \tag{9.20}$$

Equation (9.18) and Eq. (9.20) are now combined to obtain a partial differential equation in P and T:

$$T(\partial P/\partial T)_V - P = aT^4. \tag{9.21}$$

This equation is solved exactly like an ordinary differential equation of the same form, but here the integration "constant" actually is a function of volume. The solution is

$$P = \tfrac{1}{3}aT^4 + Tf(V). \tag{9.22}$$

For simplicity we may assume the pressure is independent of volume, and therefore $f(V)$ equals zero; thus

$$P = \tfrac{1}{3}u_b. \tag{9.23}$$

It is interesting to note, however, that both Eq. (9.18) and Eq. (9.23) are satisfied even if u_b has the more complicated form,

$$u_b = \alpha T^4 + \beta T^n V^{(n-4)/3}, \tag{9.24}$$

where n is any positive integer. This equation reduces to the fourth-power law if n equals 4. On the other hand, the second term would be completely negligible if n were to equal unity unless the temperature were near $0°K$ or the volume of the system were very small.

It has been customary, following Boltzmann, to assume the validity of Eq. (9.23) at the start and then to derive the fourth-power law by means of the energy equation. Maxwell had derived Eq. (9.23) from electromagnetic theory by 1871, but it was not verified experimentally until 30 years later.

Then Lebedew, in 1901, and, independently, Nichols and Hull, in 1903, made painstaking measurements of radiation pressures on the vanes of specially designed sensitive radiometers. But Stefan had announced the fourth-power law as early as 1879, after analyzing some experimental data which were obtained by Dulong and Petit, and Lummer and Pringsheim verified it over a wide range of temperatures by 1897, several years before the pressure of radiation was measured.

The existence of radiation pressure had been suspected ever since Kepler observed that the tail of a comet veers around to be always farther from the sun than the head, even while the comet recedes from the sun.[1] Radiation pressure is believed to play a dominant role in maintaining dynamic equilibrium within stars. Also, in the formation of the Earth and other planets, radiation pressure may have pushed small particles into each other's shadows to form aggregates. Probably it is not significant here on Earth unless the intensity becomes extremely high, as in nuclear explosive reactions. A radiation pressure of only 1 gm/cm² (approximately 0.001 atm) would require a blackbody temperature of 25,000°K.

9.4. Internal Energy of an Ideal Paramagnetic Substance

The discussion at the end of Section 9.2 may be generalized for an arbitrary system. To do this we replace $-P$ by the generalized force Y and V by the generalized displacement X to get

$$(\partial U/\partial X)_T = -T(\partial Y/\partial T)_X + Y. \qquad (9.25)$$

If now the equation of state for a specific system has the form

$$Y = Tf(X), \qquad (9.26)$$

then, by an argument exactly like that for the ideal gas, we can prove that the internal energy U of the system is not a function of Y or X, but only of temperature T. This result is immediately applicable to an ideal paramagnetic substance.

Imagine a system to consist of a long paramagnetic rod placed along the axis of a solenoid. The work required to increase the magnetization of this rod from M_i to M_f is given in Section 3.1 as the integral of $H dM$ between these limits, where H is the applied magnetic field intensity and M is the dipole moment of the system. For this system, therefore, Y equals H, and X equals M. We assume that the change in volume is negligible. If the rod is

---

[1] It is now believed that the tails are produced by high speed (a few hundred miles per second) electrons and protons from the sun, bombarding the comet as a "cosmic wind" blowing radially outwards.

a paramagnetic substance for which the dipole moment satisfies Eq. (3.12), it is said to be ideal. This equation has the form

$$M = B(H/T),$$

which may be solved for H:

$$H = Tf(M). \tag{9.27}$$

Because Eq. (9.27) is like Eq. (9.26) we conclude that the foregoing general result applies here and therefore that the internal energy of an ideal paramagnetic substance depends only on temperature. This we had assumed for the special case of the Curie law in problem 8.3.

9.5. *Elastomers*

Hitherto we have studied systems in which only one pair of thermodynamic variables enters into the work exchange between a system and its near-surround. Suppose now we investigate the *isothermal* elastic extension of a wire or rubber filament. In general, for these systems changes in both volume and length may occur when a stretching force is applied. The first law of thermodynamics for them is written

$$dU = TdS - PdV + FdL. \tag{9.28}$$

This equation is divided throughout by dL and temperature is held constant; solving for F we get

$$F = (\partial U/\partial L)_T + P(\partial V/\partial L)_T - T(\partial S/\partial L)_T. \tag{9.29}$$

The applied force thus equals the sum of an internal energy term, a volume term, and an entropy term. Ordinarily, within the elastic limits of common materials which satisfy Hooke's law, the entropy term is negligible. On the other hand, this term is the dominant one for rubber and rubberlike substances (elastomers) over wide ranges of extension. The volume term generally can be neglected, but it may play an important role for a few materials, and moreover it can have negative values.

A rubber specimen exhibits long-range extensibility. Its stress-strain curve is S-shaped rather than straight, as illustrated by the upper curve in Fig. 9.1. Some rubbers may be stretched 200–300% without a measurable change in volume. For them the volume term in Eq. (9.29) may be ignored. Under suitable conditions a loaded specimen contracts on being heated, contrary to the behavior expected of most substances. Furthermore, a rubber filament feels warmer than its near-surround immediately after it is quickly stretched, and it becomes perceptibly cooler if it is allowed to contract rapidly. These thermoelastic properties of rubber are called Gough-Joule effects after

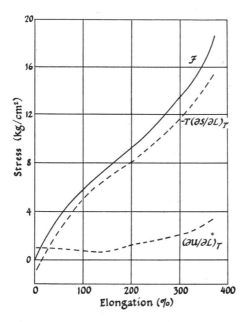

Figure 9.1. Stress-strain curve for rubber. Dotted curves show variations of the entropy and energy terms as computed from the stress-strain and thermal expansion data. [Adapted from R. L. Anthony, R. H. Caston, and E. Guth, "Equations of State for Natural and Synthetic Rubber-like Materials," *J. Phys. Chem.*, **46**, 826, 1942.]

Gough, a totally blind experimentalist, who first described them in 1802, and Joule, who investigated them some 50 years later.

The one characteristic all elastomers have in common is a structure of intertwined and cross-linked long molecular chains in more or less random orientation. Stretching a specimen brings about partial alignment of the chains and thereby decreases its entropy. It is for this reason that the entropy term in Eq. (9.29) is the dominant one for rubber and rubberlike substances and that the foregoing anomalous effects can occur.

Relations similar to the Maxwell identities may be found by the same method adopted in Section 8.2. We learn that $(\partial S/\partial L)_T$ equals $-(\partial F/\partial T)_L$; thus for isochoric processes Eq. (9.29) reduces to

$$F = (\partial U/\partial L)_T + T(\partial F/\partial T)_L. \qquad (9.30)$$

The isometric coefficient $(\partial F/\partial T)_L$ is rather difficult to measure directly, and therefore it is replaced by the product $-(\partial F/\partial L)_T(\partial L/\partial T)_F$, whose factors can be determined more easily from stress-strain and thermal expansion data. The entropy term is computed and then subtracted from the corresponding values of F to obtain the internal energy term. In Fig. 9.1 curves for the entropy and internal energy which add up to give the stress-strain curve are drawn on the same graph for comparison. The curve for the entropy term is described rather well by the James-Guth state equation for an ideal elastomer. The internal energy term is seen to become especially important only for large elongations.

9.6. Heat Capacities and Compressibilities of Solids and Liquids

In Section 8.6 we derived a general relation for the difference between the specific heat capacities at constant pressure and constant volume and applied it primarily to gas systems. For a solid the quantity $\beta^2 v / k_t c_p^2$ is nearly constant over a wide range of temperatures [for example, for copper it equals $(3.73 \pm 0.07) \times 10^{-6}$ mole/joule in the temperature range 50–1200°K]. Consequently, Eq. (8.29) becomes simply

$$c_p - c_v = A c_p^2 T, \tag{9.31}$$

in which A represents $\beta^2 v / k_t c_p^2$. This quantity may be computed once and for all from one complete set of values of β, v, k_t, and c_p for a solid at a convenient temperature, and thereafter Eq. (9.31) is useful for computing values of c_v which are difficult to measure directly. This form of the equation for $c_p - c_v$ was introduced by Nernst and Lindemann.

In order to measure isothermal compressibilities k_t of liquids and solids special high-pressure apparatus is needed. On the other hand, adiabatic compressibilities k_s can be readily determined in most laboratories by means of Eq. (8.41) from the density of the medium and the speed of sonic waves in it. All we need then is a suitable relation between k_t and k_s.

To develop such a relation we recall that

$$c_p = T(\partial s/\partial T)_p = -T(\partial s/\partial P)_T (\partial P/\partial T)_s$$
$$= T(\partial v/\partial T)_p (\partial P/\partial T)_s \tag{9.32}$$

and, furthermore, that

$$c_v = T(\partial s/\partial T)_v = -T(\partial s/\partial v)_T (\partial v/\partial T)_s$$
$$= -T(\partial P/\partial T)_v (\partial v/\partial T)_s$$
$$= T(\partial P/\partial v)_T (\partial v/\partial T)_p (\partial v/\partial T)_s. \tag{9.33}$$

The ratio of the two heat capacities then equals

$$\frac{c_p}{c_v} = \frac{(\partial P/\partial T)_s}{(\partial P/\partial v)_T (\partial v/\partial T)_s} = \frac{(\partial P/\partial v)_s}{(\partial P/\partial v)_T}. \tag{9.34}$$

If numerator and denominator of the right side of this equation are multiplied by $-v$, we obtain the ratio of the adiabatic to the isothermal bulk modulus; or, in terms of compressibilities, we get

$$c_p/c_v = k_t/k_s. \tag{9.35}$$

This result is perfectly general; it applies to gases as well as to liquids and solids. For an ideal gas, k_t equals P^{-1} and k_s equals $(\gamma P)^{-1}$, so by Eq. (9.35) c_p/c_v equals γ, as it should.

It is now convenient to combine Eqs. (8.29), (8.41), and (9.35) to obtain equations for γ and k_t. Thus

$$\gamma = c_p/c_v = 1 + \beta^2 S^2 T c_p^{-1} \qquad (9.36)$$

and
$$k_t = \rho^{-1}(S^{-2} + \beta^2 T c_p^{-1}), \qquad (9.37)$$

where ρ is the density of the medium and S is the speed of sonic waves in it. In table 9.1 are gathered from several sources[2] experimental values of c_p, ρ, β, and S for water, mercury, and methanol at 20°C. Values of γ, c_v, and k_t were computed by means of these equations. Experimental values of k_t for these liquids are entered in the last column of the table for comparison.

TABLE 9.1. *Heat Capacities and Compressibilities of Three Liquids at 20°C.*

Liquid	c_p $\left(\dfrac{\text{joules}}{\text{gm-deg}}\right)$	ρ (gm/cm³)	β (10^{-4} deg^{-1})	S (m/sec)	γ	c_v $\left(\dfrac{\text{joules}}{\text{gm-deg}}\right)$	k_t (comp.) (10^{-6} atm^{-1}	k_t (meas.) (10^{-6} atm^{-1}
Water	4.1859	0.9982	2.07	1494	1.0067	4.1579	45.59	46.2
Mercury	0.1391	13.546	1.8186	1450	1.1465	0.1213	4.062	4.078
Methanol	2.509	0.7913	11.99	1121	1.2110	2.074	122.9	127.0

Problems

1. The isothermal compressibility of water at 20°C and atmospheric pressure is 4.62×10^{-5} atm^{-1}, and its volume expansivity at this same temperature and pressure is 2.07×10^{-4} deg^{-1}. Compute a value for the internal pressure of water at 20°C and one atmosphere of pressure. This is approximately five times the numerical value of the measured tensile strength of water at this temperature.

2. Compare the internal pressure of mercury and methanol with that of water at 20°C and atmospheric pressure. Data for these substances are gathered in Table 9.1.

3. The Planck function ψ is defined by the equation

$$\psi = s - h/T,$$

so for an infinitesimal reversible process

$$d\psi = -(v/T)dP + (h/T^2)dT.$$

---

[2] *American Institute of Physics Handbook* (1957), *Handbook of Chemistry and Physics*, 35th ed., Smithsonian Physical Tables (1954).

From this derive the equation

$$(\partial u/\partial P)_T = -P(\partial v/\partial P)_T - T(\partial v/\partial T)_P,$$

and show how to obtain the energy equation from it.

4. Determine the four equations for a stretched rubber band corresponding to the Maxwell identities.

5. Derive the equations

$$PV^{4/3} = \text{constant}$$

and

$$VT^3 = \text{constant}$$

for a blackbody radiation system which undergoes a quasistatic adiabatic process.

6. (a) Give a qualitative explanation for the Gough-Joule effects in rubber.

(b) To a first approximation the James-Guth state equation for an ideal elastomer is

$$F = AT(\alpha - \alpha^{-2}),$$

where α equals L/L_0 and A is constant for a given specimen. Show that

$$(\partial \alpha/\partial T)_F = -\alpha(\alpha^3 - 1)/T(\alpha^3 + 2),$$

and from this result explain why a loaded rubber band should contract on being heated.

7. For copper at 27°C the specific heat at constant pressure c_p equals 24,600 joules/kgm-mole-deg. Compute values for the specific heat at constant volume c_v and the ratio γ for copper at this temperature.

8. Show that the Massieu function μ can be written in the form

$$\mu = s - u(\partial s/\partial u)_v$$

and the Planck function ψ in the form

$$\psi = s - u(\partial s/\partial u)_v - v(\partial s/\partial v)_u.$$

9. The radiation pressure for a *parallel* beam of light equals J/c, where J is the intensity of the radiation and c is the speed of light. If the intensity of sunlight at zenith outside the earth's atmosphere equals 1.40 kw/m², compute the total force exerted by the radiation on the Earth.

CHAPTER **10**

Phase Transformations

THE equilibrium states between a liquid and its vapor in a closed liquid-vapor system really do not represent static situations. The liquid is conceived to evaporate and the vapor to condense continually at equal rates such that the amounts of liquid and of vapor remain essentially constant. Suppose now that heat is supplied *slowly* in such a way as to maintain the temperature and pressure constant and uniform throughout the system. Slightly more vaporization than condensation occurs, resulting in a net transfer of mass from the liquid to the vapor phase and an increase in volume of the system. A similar situation holds for sublimation, melting, and other phase changes of this kind. As suggested in Section 6.8, all these phase transformations are accompanied by characteristic latent heats and abrupt changes in volume. They are known as phase transformations of the first kind.

On the other hand, there exist phase changes in which appear no clear evidence of latent heats or abrupt changes in volume. Instead, specific heat capacity, volume expansivity, and compressibility are the parameters which change discontinuously. Transformations of this kind include transitions from the ferromagnetic state of iron or nickel to the paramagnetic state at the Curie point, order-disorder transitions in certain alloys and compounds, the transition in some substances from the superconducting to the normal conducting state in the absence of an applied magnetic field, and the helium I-II transition at the λ-point. They are known as phase transformations of the second kind.

138

10.1. P-V Diagram for Liquid-vapor Systems

When values of equilibrium volume and applied pressure over a wide range of temperatures for a closed liquid-vapor system are measured and plotted on a P-V diagram, we obtain a family of characteristic isotherms, as illustrated in Fig. 10.1. Andrews first constructed such a family in 1863

Figure 10.1.   Family of P-V isotherms for 1 kg of carbon dioxide. The liquid and vapor saturation curves are the left and right branches of the dotted curve.

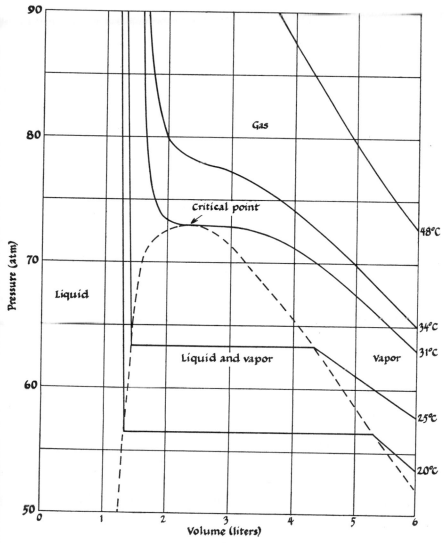

from experimental data on carbon dioxide and thereby demonstrated the physical continuity between the gaseous and liquid phases of a pure substance. Over the horizontal isobaric portion of an isotherm, liquid and vapor coexist in equilibrium. The pressure here is the vapor pressure of the pure substance at the temperature of the isotherm, and the temperature at which the vapor pressure equals one standard atmosphere is the normal boiling point (NBP) of the substance. As the volume in this isobaric portion is increased evaporation takes place until the liquid phase disappears. On the other hand, as it is decreased the vapor condenses until only the liquid phase remains.

As shown in Fig. 10.1, at a certain temperature there exists a critical isotherm whose horizontal isobaric portion is reduced to a point of inflexion, called the critical point. At this point the densities of the vapor and liquid phases are equal in value. It should be noted that the transition from vapor to liquid at pressures well above the critical value is continuous without the formation of a sharp boundary when the temperature and volume are decreased. Here we have simply a fluid system which becomes progressively more dense as it passes from a tenuous vapor to the liquid condition.

The locus of the end points of the isobaric straight-line portions of the isotherms forms two branches with the critical point at the apex, as shown by the dotted lines in Fig. 10.1. The branch on the left is the liquid saturation curve, and that on the right is the vapor saturation curve. Along an isobar between these saturation curves the densities, or specific volumes, of the liquid and vapor phases are constant.

Finally, although Andrews had suggested that the tenuous phase be called vapor below the critical temperature and gas above it, this division is entirely arbitrary and does not mean that any real distinction in physical properties is observed.

10.2. Explanation of the Liquid-vapor Isotherms for Real Substances

The slope of an isotherm at a temperature above the critical value is continuous over the entire experimental range of volumes, whereas the slope of an isotherm at a temperature below the critical value is discontinuous, as can be seen in Fig. 10.1. In 1871 James Thomson, brother of William Thomson (Lord Kelvin), pointed out that isotherms at subcritical temperatures may be derived from curves with continuous slopes, as illustrated in

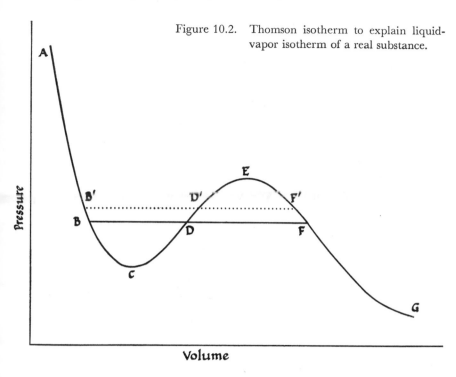

Figure 10.2.   Thomson isotherm to explain liquid-vapor isotherm of a real substance.

Fig. 10.2. The isobaric portion *BDF* of the actual isotherm represents stable dynamic equilibrium states intermediate between virtual equilibrium states along the curve *BCDEF*.

States along *CDE*, save that at *D*, are unattainable, for to arrive at any one of them the volume of the system must expand with increasing applied pressures or diminish with decreasing pressures—processes that are physically impossible. Under carefully controlled experimental conditions equilibrium states along *BC* and *FE* can be attained. Pure water vapor may be compressed isothermally beyond the point where condensation usually takes place without the formation of water droplets. This is the condition of supersaturation. Likewise, pure liquid water in a closed, clean glass tube may be subjected to pressures less than the vapor pressure without the formation of vapor. For that matter, if point *C* lies below the volume axis, tensions may be applied to the confined liquid before rupture takes place. Branches *BC* and *EF* represent unstable but available equilibrium states of the liquid-vapor system. Superheating of a liquid and the supercooling of a vapor are similar processes involving unstable equilibrium states.

As the temperature of the system is raised, the maximum and minimum points of its Thomson curves approach one another, and the isobaric por-

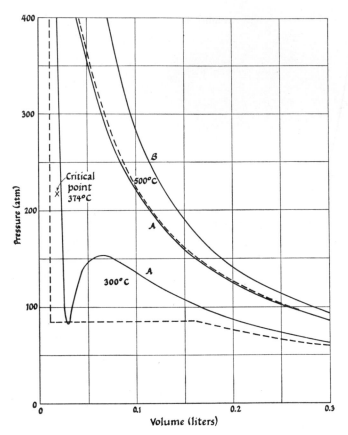

Figure 10.3. Comparison of isotherms for a van der Waals fluid and an ideal gas with those for water vapor at temperatures of 300°C and 500°C. Dashed curves from steam tables; full lines from theory. *AA*, ideal van der Waals fluid at 300°C and 500°C; *B*, ideal gas at 500°C.

tions of its experimental curves become shorter until the critical point is reached. At this point both the slope $(\partial P/\partial V)_T$ and the rate of change of the slope $(\partial^2 P/\partial V^2)_T$ vanish. By means of these two conditions and the state equation itself, three relations between the temperature, pressure, and specific volume at the critical point are obtained. From them values of T_c, P_c, v_c and the critical compressibility factor $P_c v_c/RT_c$ can be computed. For a van der Waals fluid at the critical point

$$\left(\frac{\partial P}{\partial v}\right)_{T_c} = \frac{2a}{v_c^3} - \frac{RT_c}{(v_c - b)^2} = 0,$$

$$\left(\frac{\partial^2 P}{\partial v^2}\right)_{T_c} = -\frac{6a}{v_c^4} + \frac{2RT_c}{(v_c - b)^3} = 0,$$

and

$$(P_c + a/v_c^2)(v_c - b) = RT_c,$$

from which we find

$$T_c = 8a/27bR, \qquad P_c = a/27b^2,$$

$$v_c = 3b, \qquad P_cv_c/RT_c = \tfrac{3}{8}.$$

For a real substance the critical compressibility factor is less than $\tfrac{3}{8}$, as suggested by the few experimental values entered in the last column of Table 10.1.

In Fig. 10.3 are plotted the experimental isotherms of water at 300°C and 500°C and the curves representing the van der Waals equation at these same temperatures. In addition, a curve for an ideal gas at 500°C is drawn. From this little evidence it appears that the van der Waals equation is a reasonably good approximation for the actual liquid-vapor state equation of water at temperatures above the critical value and at low densities. Even near the critical point it is fairly satisfactory for a qualitative description of the changes of state. Furthermore, the tenuous phase of water is far from an ideal gas even at 500°C.

TABLE 10.1.   *Critical Point Data For Several Substances.* *

Substance	Mol. wt. (gm)	Temperature (°C)	Pressure (atm.)	Density (gm/cc)	P_cv_c/RT_c
Ammonia	17.03	132.35	111.3	0.235	0.242
n Butane	58.12	152.01	37.47	0.228	0.274
Carbon dioxide	44.01	31.04	72.85	0.468	0.274
Carbon monoxide	28.01	−140.2	34.5	0.3010	0.294
Carbon tetrachloride	153.84	283.2	44.97	0.558	0.272
Deuterium (normal)	4.029	−234.81	16.43		
Diethyl ether	74.12	194.6	35.6	0.265	0.259
Ethyl alcohol	46.07	243.	63.0	0.276	0.248
Helium 3	3.017	−269.82	1.15		
Helium 4	4.004	−267.95	2.26	0.0693	0.306
Hydrogen (normal)	2.016	−239.92	12.80	0.03102	0.305
Methane	16.04	−82.5	45.8	0.162	0.290
Nitrogen	28.02	−146.9	33.54	0.3110	0.292
Oxygen	32.00	−118.38	50.14	0.41	0.308
Sulfur dioxide	64.07	157.5	77.79	0.524	0.269
Water	18.02	374.2	218.3	0.326	0.227

* Adapted from Table 4c-1, *American Institute of Physics Handbook*, p. 4–21, (McGraw-Hill, New York, 1957).

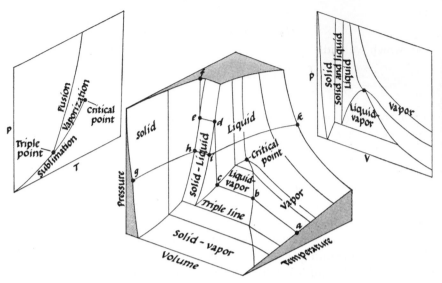

Figure 10.4.   *P-V-T* surface for an arbitrary substance and its projections in the *P-T* and *P-V* planes. [After F. W. Sears, *Thermodynamics*, Addison-Wesley, Reading, Mass., 1953.]

10.3. P-V-T Surfaces

Instead of plotting a family of *P-V* diagrams from the same data we may construct a *P-V-T* surface on which the *P-V* diagrams are represented by lines, as illustrated in Fig. 10.4. In addition to regions where liquid and vapor can exist in equilibrium as separate single phases or together in a two-phase system, there are shown here regions where the solid phase alone can exist and where the solid together with the vapor or liquid phase also can exist in equilibrium. When the *P-V* diagrams are projected on a *P-V* plane, therefore, they are more complete than those in Fig. 10.1. Note that along the triple line the solid, liquid, and vapor phases coexist in equilibrium and that in the projection on the *P-T* plane this line forms a point, the triple point, at the juncture of the sublimation, vaporization, and fusion curves. The vaporization curve, which is the projection of the liquid and vapor saturation curves on the *P-T* plane, starts at the triple point and terminates in the critical point; and the sublimation curve, which is the projection of the solid and vapor saturation curves on the *P-T* plane, starts in the neighborhood of 0°K and terminates in the triple point. The fusion curve, which is the projection of the solid and liquid saturation curves on the *P-T* plane, starts at the triple point and seems to extend indefinitely toward higher pressures without the

appearance of a solid-liquid critical point. However, the fusion
curve may terminate if another
liquid or solid phase can exist.
Helium and water are good examples.

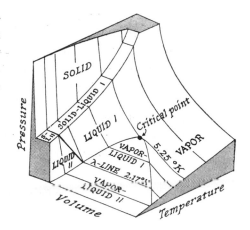

Figure 10.5.   P-V-T surface for helium. [After F. W. Sears, *Thermodynamics,* Addison-Wesley, Reading,
Mass, 1953.]

The P-V-T surface for helium, as illustrated in Fig. 10.5, reveals two unusual properties: helium has two liquid phases, and it has no solid-liquid-
vapor triple point. As it is compressed, helium vapor condenses to liquid

Figure 10.6.   P-V-T surface for pure water as constructed by Verwiebe from measurements by Bridgman.

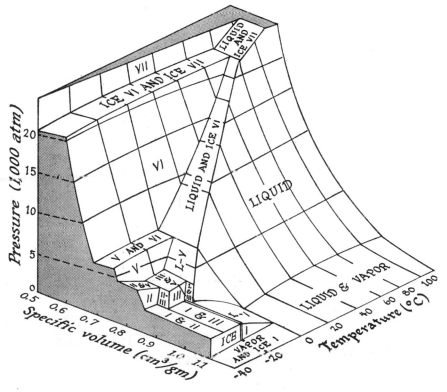

helium I between its critical temperature of 5.25°K (2.3 atm) and a temperature of 2.17°K (0.0508 atm) where liquid helium II is formed. This transition temperature is the first triple point or λ-point where the two liquid phases and helium vapor coexist in equilibrium. The λ-point temperature falls in value with increasing pressure until the second triple point is reached at 1.8°K (30 atm). Here the two liquid phases and solid helium coexist in equilibrium. Solid helium does not form at pressures lower than about 25 atm, but it can exist above the critical temperature of 5.25°K. These and other curious properties of helium are discussed more fully in Chapter 19.

Figure 10.7.   *P-T* or phase diagram for water.

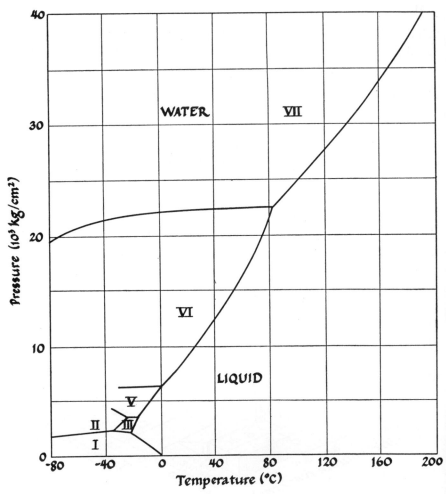

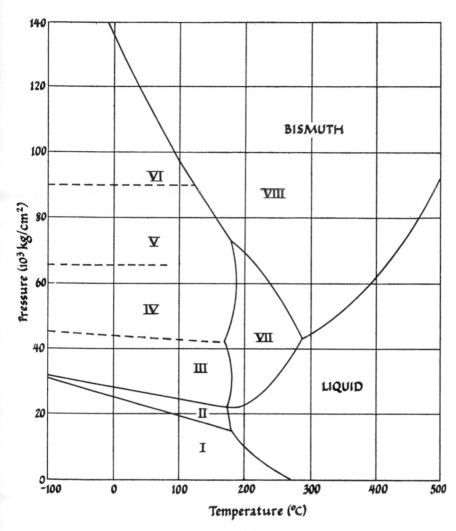

Figure 10.8.   *P-T* or phase diagram for bismuth.

The P-V-T surface for pure water was constructed by Verwiebe from measurements by Bridgman and is reproduced in Fig. 10.6. Six ice phases have been observed: ices I (common ice), II, III, V, VI, and VII. Two other ices, IV and VIII, were found to be unstable. Note that expansion takes place if liquid water freezes to ice I, but contraction occurs for the other ice forms. There are seven triple points, as illustrated in Fig. 10.7; the data for them are given in Table 10.2. A similar diagram for bismuth is shown in Fig. 10.8.

TABLE 10.2.   *Triple-point Data for Water Stuff.*

Triple Point	Pressure (kg/cm²)	Temperature (°C)	Δv (cm³/gm)	Latent Heat (joules/gm)	Phase Change
vapor-liquid-ice I	0.006203	+0.010	206,287	−2500	v–*l*
			206,287	−2833	v–I
			−0.090	333.4	I–*l*
Liquid-ice I-ice III	2115	−22.0	0.1352	234	I–*l*
			0.1818	21.6	I–III
			0.0466	−212	*l*–III
Ice I-ice II-ice III	2170	−34.7	0.1963	8.8	I–III
			0.2178	−42.2	I–II
			0.0215	−51	III–II
Liquid-ice III-ice V	3530	−17.0	0.0241	−257	*l*–III
			0.0788	−261	*l*–V
			0.0547	−3.9	III–V
Ice II-ice III-ice V	3510	−24.3	0.0145	−70.5	III–II
			0.0546	−3.9	III–V
			0.0401	66.6	II–V
Liquid-ice V-ice VI	6380	+0.16	0.0527	−293	*l*–V
			0.0916	−294	*l*–VI
			0.0389	−1	V–VI
Liquid-ice VI-ice VII	22,400	+81.6	0.0330	−354	*l*–VI
			0.0910	−354	*l*–VII
			0.0580	∼0	VI–VII

10.4. Thermodynamic Equations for Phase Transformations

When a closed system undergoes a reversible quasistatic process the specific value of its Gibbs function changes by the infinitesimal amount

$$dg = vdP - sdT. \qquad (10.1)$$

Here we have applied Eq. (9.14) to one mole. For processes at constant pressure and temperature we see that dg equals zero. Consequently, for transformations from one phase to another we conclude that the specific

Gibbs functions of the two phases are equal; the process is, so to speak, "isogibbsic." That is, for any equilibrium state of a two-phase system the specific Gibbs function for one phase equals that for the other. Furthermore, at a triple point the specific Gibbs function of the three phases are equal to one another. The distinction between phase transformations of the first and second kinds now can be made in terms of the first and second derivatives of the Gibbs function.

By Eq. (10.1), v equals $(\partial g/\partial P)_T$ and s equals $-(\partial g/\partial T)_p$. But for a phase transformation of the first kind the specific volume changes discontinuously, and there exists a latent heat. Because the latent heat equals $T(s_f - s_i)$ the specific entropy also changes discontinuously. Thus the first-order derivatives of the specific Gibbs function with respect to pressure and temperature change discontinuously during a phase transformation of the first kind. These results are suggested in the upper graphical constructions in Fig. 10.9.

From the defining equations for specific heat, volume expansivity, and compressibility we find

Figure 10.9.   Illustrating conditions for phase transformations of the first and second order. *A*, phase 1; *B*, phase 2. [After M. W. Zemansky, *Heat and Thermodynamics*, McGraw-Hill, New York, 1957.]

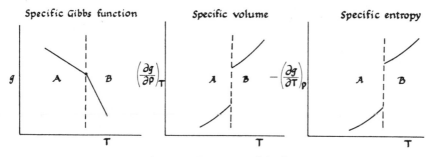

Phase transformations of the first kind

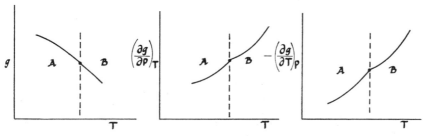

Phase transformations of the second kind

$$c_p/T = (\partial s/\partial T)_p = -(\partial^2 g/\partial T^2)_p,$$

$$\beta v = (\partial v/\partial T)_p = \partial^2 g/\partial T \partial P,$$

and

$$k_t v = -(\partial v/\partial P)_T = -(\partial^2 g/\partial P^2)_T.$$

Thus for a phase transformation of the second kind the second derivatives of the specific Gibbs function change discontinuously whereas the first derivatives do not. These results are suggested in the lower graphical constructions of Fig. 10.9.

Because of the discontinuities in the derivatives of the Gibbs function, phase transformations of the first and second kinds often are called first- and second-order phase transitions. Let us now derive equations for dP/dT which are applicable to these processes.

Consider a two-phase system for a pure substance in equilibrium at temperature T and pressure P. When an infinitesimal increase in pressure and temperature occurs the change in specific Gibbs function for each phase is given by Eq. (10.1):

$$dg' = v'dP - s'dT$$

and

$$dg'' = v''dP - s''dT.$$

After this change the system still is in equilibrium, so the specific Gibbs functions of the two phases must again be equal. It follows that dg' equals dg''. We equate and solve for dP/dT. The result is

$$dP/dT = (s'' - s')/(v'' - v').$$

The difference in specific entropies, we recall, equals the latent heat of this first-order phase transition divided by the temperature T; therefore,

$$dP/dT = l/T(v'' - v'). \tag{10.2}$$

Again we have obtained the Clapeyron equation. As pointed out in Section 6.8, the sign of dP/dT depends on whether v'' is greater or less than v'.

Latent heats may be measured either directly, by determining the amount of heat required to transform a unit mass of a pure substance from one phase to the other, or indirectly, by means of Eq. (10.2) and experimental values of specific volumes and slopes of vapor-pressure curves.

For second-order transitions both l and $v'' - v'$ equal zero, so dP/dT must be evaluated in some other way. In this instance we observe that

$$dv = (\partial v/\partial T)_p dT + (\partial v/\partial P)_T dP$$

$$= v\beta dT - vk_t dP. \tag{10.3}$$

Because v' equals v'' throughout the transformation it follows that dv' equals dv'', and therefore

$$\beta' dT - k'_t dP = \beta'' dT - k''_t dP$$

from which

$$dP/dT = (\beta'' - \beta')/(k''_t - k'_t). \tag{10.4}$$

In a similar manner,

$$ds = (\partial s/\partial T)_p dT + (\partial s/\partial P)_T dP$$
$$= T(\partial s/\partial T)_p (dT/T) - (\partial v/\partial T)_p dP$$
$$= c_p dT/T - \beta v dP. \tag{10.5}$$

Because s' equals s'' for second-order transitions it also follows that ds' equals ds'', and therefore

$$c'_p dT/T - \beta' v' dP = c''_p dT/T - \beta'' v'' dP.$$

But v' and v'' are equal; let them be represented by v. Then we find

$$dP/dT = (c''_p - c'_p)/vT(\beta'' - \beta'). \tag{10.6}$$

Equations (10.4) and (10.6) are known as Ehrenfest's equations.

10.5. *Thermodynamic Potentials*

Let us return to a further examination of the Thomson isotherm shown in Fig. 10.2. We are now in a position to answer the question: What determines the pressure at which the isotherm is cut by the horizontal isobar *BDF*? Consider an *arbitrary* isobar $B'D'F'$ (dotted line in Fig. 10.2). As the pressure is reduced we discover a value for it, say at *BDF*, such that the Gibbs functions for states *B* and *F* are equal. At higher pressures the Gibbs functions at points B' are less than those at D' and F'; at lower pressures the Gibbs functions at points F' are less than those at B' and D'. Thus the Thomson curve is cut by an isobar such that the Gibbs functions at B' and F' are equal and less than the one at D'. The Gibbs function then has a minimum value.

To demonstrate this consider a pure substance in a closed system to be in thermal and mechanical equilibrium, but not in chemical equilibrium. Let an infinitesimal quantity of heat $d'q$ be supplied to a unit mass of the system from a thermal reservoir at temperature T. The entropy of the reservoir changes by $-d'q/T$ and that of the system by ds. From the second law of thermodynamics,

$$ds - d'q/T \geq 0,$$

or

$$d'q - Tds \leq 0. \tag{10.7}$$

But from the first law of thermodynamics,

$$d'q = du + Pdv,$$

so for an isobaric isothermal process Eq. (10.7) is written

$$d(u + Pv - Ts) = dg \leq 0. \qquad (10.8)$$

As we have already discovered, the equality sign applies for two or three phases *in equilibrium*. The inequality sign indicates that the specific Gibbs function is greater than the equilibrium value for states nearby and presumably decreases as the system approaches equilibrium. In general, changes in the thermophysical variables take place spontaneously until a state of chemical equilibrium is reached where the Gibbs function has a minimum value.

Instead of holding P and T constant we might have held V and T constant. For such processes dv equals zero, and therefore in place of Eq. (10.8) we get

$$d(u - Ts) = da \leq 0. \qquad (10.9)$$

The specific Helmholtz function also reaches a minimum value for states of equilibrium. This result is useful in thermophysical statistics.

Because the Helmholtz and Gibbs functions play a role in thermodynamics similar to that played by potential energy in the approach to equilibrium of a conservative mechanical system, they have been called thermodynamic potentials. American chemists often apply the term "work function" to A and "free energy" to G, whereas many physicists call A "free energy." This confusion can be avoided by adopting the names Helmholtz and Gibbs for the two functions and by avoiding the symbol F for either of them.

Problems

1. The Dieterici equation of state for a mole of gas is

$$P(v - b) \exp{(a/RTv)} = RT.$$

Solve for the critical temperature, pressure, and specific volume in terms of the constants a, b, and R, and show that the critical value of the compressibility factor equals $2/e^2$.

2. Compute a value for the maximum tension which liquid water at 27°C can support, assuming that the van der Waals equation of state applies.

3. Make reasonable estimates of the critical compressibility factors for deuterium

and helium 3 from the data in Table 10.1, and compute values for the density of these elements at their critical points.

4. Let the vapor pressure on a Thomson curve be the average pressure P' over that portion of the curve between specific volumes v_1 and v_2 such that

$$\int_{v_1}^{v_2} (P - P')dv = 0.$$

(a) If the Thomson curve is described by the van der Waals equation, derive a set of equations from which the vapor pressure may be computed.
(b) Find a value for the vapor pressure of water at 373°K by means of these equations.

5. Describe the phase changes that take place in a pure substance which traverses the isothermal path *abcdef* on the P-V-T surface of Fig. 10.4. Likewise, describe the phase changes for the isobaric path *ghik* and for the isochoric path through the triple point.

6. A closed system consists of two phases of a single pure substance in equilibrium. For an infinitesimal quasistatic transfer of substance from one phase to the other,

$$dE = \Sigma_i \mu_i dn_i = 0,$$

where μ_i is the chemical potential and n_i is the number of moles in the *i*th phase. Prove that the chemical potentials of the substance in the two phases are equal.

7. In a two-phase system there are n moles of a pure substance for which a mole fraction x is in one phase and therefore $1 - x$ is in the other phase. Let v_1 and v_2 represent the specific volumes of these phases. Prove that the change in volume under isothermal conditions is directly proportional to the number of moles transferred from one phase to the other.

8. Suppose the average molar volume v of a two-phase system, consisting of a pure substance, equals the total volume divided by the number of moles in the system. Show that the mole fraction x of the substance in one phase is

$$x = (v - v_1)/(v_2 - v_1)$$

and the mole fraction in the other phase is

$$1 - x = (v - v_2)/(v_2 - v_1),$$

where v_1 and v_2 are the specific volumes for the two phases.

9. A sample of bismuth is in its liquid phase at a temperature of 200°C and a pressure of 20,000 kgm/cm². It is carried through the following reversible cycle: an isobaric decrease in temperature to 100°C, an isothermal reduction in pressure to 15,000 kgm/cm², an isobaric increase in temperature to 200°C, and finally an isothermal increase in pressure to the initial state. Describe the phase constitution throughout the cycle, and indicate whether the volume increases or decreases at each phase change.

10. Determine dP/dT for the fusion curve of helium as a function of temperature, and construct a graph for it from the data in Table 10.3.

TABLE 10.3. *Data For the Melting of Helium.**

Temperature (°K)	Pressure (kg/cm²)	Entropy (joule/mole-deg)		Volume (cc/mole)	
		Solid	Fluid	Solid	Fluid
5	196	0.96	7.10	16.21	17.14
10	595	2.01	8.36	13.45	14.13
15	1150	2.76	9.45	12.08	12.65
20	1800	3.60	10.63	11.10	11.61
25	2540	4.35	11.80	10.25	10.72

* Adapted from Table 4d-11, *American Institute of Physics Handbook* (McGraw-Hill, New York, 1957).

11. At 2.17°K the specific volume of liquid helium equals 6.84 cm³/gm and the specific heats are 5.0 joules/gm-deg for helium I and 12.1 joules/gm-deg for helium II. At this temperature the experimental value of the slope for the λ-line equals −81 atm/deg. From these data compute the change in volume expansivity to be expected, and compare it with the experimental value of −0.06 deg⁻¹. Also compute a value for the change in isothermal compressibility.

CHAPTER **11**

Molecular Thermophysics

FOR many centuries philosophers had speculated about the fundamental structure of matter. In order to explain the diverse observed natural
phenomena, frequently a microstructure of minute particles had been
postulated. But not until the seventeenth century were the elements of the
modern atomic theory first developed and applied in a qualitative fashion.
By the middle of the nineteenth century these ideas were formulated into a
unified quantitative theory. The theory developed rapidly until, by the end
of the century, the atomic structure of matter had become well established
and the kinetic theory was widely accepted. The electron had been identified
by Thomson in 1896, and the corpuscular nature of electricity became
reasonable. Even energy was shown to be quantized, by 1900, through the
investigations of Planck. The hypothesis that matter, electricity, and radiation appeared in small indivisible units was considered highly plausible by
many scientists at the beginning of the twentieth century, but little indisputable experimental evidence had been accumulated in support of it.

11.1. The Kinetic Theory

Every piece of matter now is conceived to consist of a very large number
of molecules which are arranged often in a fairly regular array in solids,
much less regularly in liquids, and completely at random in gases. Each
molecule usually is a complex of atoms that, in turn, contain electrons and

155

nuclei. Kinetic theory, however, has been more closely identified with molecules and with aggregates of molecules than with atoms, although it has been applied to many other systems from the electron gas to cosmological star clusters with some success. The visible "proof" of the kinetic theory of matter is found in observations on Brownian motion. With a newly invented achromatic objective on his microscope the botanist Robert Brown saw (in 1827) particles, such as pollen and soot grains, exhibit an unceasing irregular agitation when suspended in a liquid. At first the motions were ascribed to "vital forces," but fifty years after Brown's discovery Wiener and Delsaulx, and later Gouy, suggested that random motions were caused by bombardment from the invisible molecules of the liquid. Quantitative verification of this hypothesis came with the theoretical work of Einstein in 1905 and with the experimental measurements of Perrin in 1909. Not only are the molecules of material systems in unceasing agitation, but also photons in radiative systems and electrons or other charged particles in electrical systems are continually in motion.

The internal energy of any large-scale material system consists primarily of the random translational, rotational, and vibrational energies of all the molecules in it. Not all this energy vanishes at 0°K. As the temperature of the system is raised, the added energy increases the motions of the molecules so that agitations about points of equilibrium in solids give place to restricted translatory movements in liquids and finally to relatively large translations in gases.

We shall begin our development of the kinetic theory with a study of ideal gas systems. The results of this study apply rather well to real gases at low densities and elevated temperatures, to the electron gas at low densities, and to substances in weak solutions.

11.2. The Ideal Gas

In molecular thermophysics a gas is conceived to be an aggregate of molecules with a random distribution among available values of speeds and positions within a given region. It is an ideal gas if it satisfies the following conditions:

(1) The molecules are very small compared with the average distance between them.

(2) The molecules exert no influence on one another unless they collide, and they travel along straight paths between collisions if no external forces act on them.

(3) All collisions of molecules with one another and with the walls of the container are perfectly elastic.

(4) At any moment, as many molecules have velocities in one direction as in another, and the distribution of the molecules among speeds is independent of direction. All speeds are assumed to be available from zero to an upper limit. However, no molecule can have a speed approaching an infinite value, for then its energy would be inconsistent with the total energy of the gas of which it is a part.

(5) Any given volume of gas contains a very large number of molecules, and the molecular density is uniform, if no external forces are acting on the system. These conditions are assumed to apply even to an element of volume dV; that is, dV is sufficiently small to be a mathematical infinitesimal in equations but is large enough in a physical sense to contain very many molecules. This assumption may be seriously questioned, however, if it is applied to gases at very low molecular densities. One cubic micron of any gas at 0°C and a standard atmosphere contains about 30 million molecules, but in the best vacuums attainable in the laboratory there may be only 20–30 molecules per cubic centimeter.

The fundamental aspects of kinetic theory can be developed for an ideal gas without a knowledge of the exact form of the velocity distribution function of the molecules. For this purpose simple definitions of average speed, mean square speed, and mean free path are sufficient. The average speed is given by the equation

$$\bar{v} = \int_0^{v_{max}} v\mathrm{f}(v)dv, \qquad (11.1)$$

and the mean square speed by

$$\overline{v^2} = v_{rms}^2 = \int_0^{v_{max}} v^2\mathrm{f}(v)dv, \qquad (11.2)$$

where $\mathrm{f}(v)dv$ represents the fractional number of molecules per unit volume with speeds in the range v to $v + dv$. The root mean square speed v_{rms} is proportional to the average speed $\bar{v}$, as may be ascertained by considering all the speeds changed by the same factor. The definition of mean free path is deferred until Chapter 12.

11.3. Number of Molecules Striking a Unit Area Per Unit Time

Our first problem is to develop a relation for the number of molecules which strike a unit area of the container wall per unit time or for half the number which pass through a unit area anywhere within the gas per unit time. The result of this analysis is applicable to such phenomena as molecular evaporation, thermionic emission, and bacterial growth.

The ideal gas is in thermal, mechanical, and chemical equilibrium, and no external forces act on it. With the passage of time, molecules of all available speeds may be conceived to impinge on a small area S of the container wall from every possible direction. We shall first set down the number of these molecules with speeds in the range v to $v + dv$ which are headed for S from a given direction and which reach it during a short time interval τ. Then we shall integrate the expression over all the possible directions and available speeds to obtain the total number of molecules which strike area S during the time interval τ.

Construct a slanting parallelepiped of slant height $v\tau$ at angle θ with the normal to area S, as shown in Fig. 11.1. The number of molecules with speeds in the range v to $v + dv$ within this parallelepiped at any instant equals $nvf(v)dvS\tau \cos \theta$, where n represents the total number of molecules in a unit volume. Only a small fraction of these molecules, however, are traveling directly to-

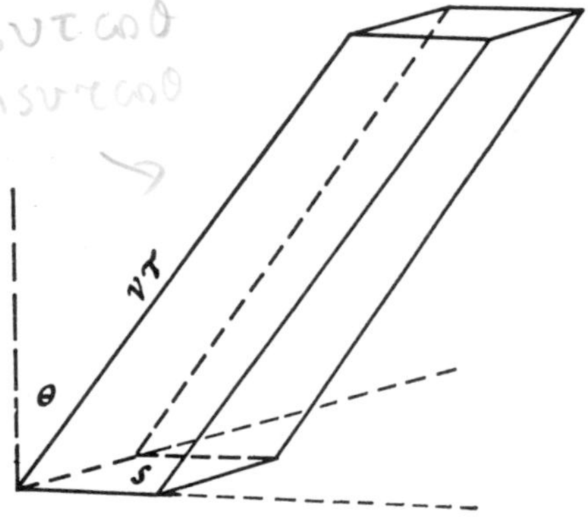

Figure 11.1. Construction for determining the number of molecules which strike a unit area per unit time.

ward S. In order to determine this fraction, let the velocity of each molecule be represented by a vector, and imagine that all the velocity vectors are moved parallel to themselves to a common origin. The head ends of these vectors of lengths from v to $v + dv$ then are distributed *uniformly* in a spherical shell of radius v and of thickness dv. This uniformity of distribution follows from our fourth condition for an ideal gas. An element of area on the surface, in spherical polar coordinates, equals $v^2 \sin \theta d\theta d\varphi$, and the total area is $4\pi v^2$. The fraction of the total number of molecules with speeds in the range v to $v + dv$ and with the angular direction θ, φ is equal to the ratio of this element to the total area, namely $\sin \theta d\theta d\varphi / 4\pi$.

At any instant the number of molecules in the parallelepiped which are traveling with speeds in the range v to $v + dv$ directly toward S equals

$$nvf(v)dvS\tau \cos \theta \cdot \tfrac{1}{4}\pi^{-1} \sin \theta d\theta d\varphi. \tag{11.3}$$

This expression is integrated over φ from 0 to 2π, over θ from 0 to $\frac{1}{2}\pi$, and over all the available speeds in order to obtain the total number of molecules that strike area S during time interval τ. On dividing the result by $S\tau$ and on introducing the average speed as given by Eq. (11.1), the number of molecules striking a unit area per unit time is found to be

$$\nu = \tfrac{1}{4}n\bar{v}. \tag{11.4}$$

11.4. Gas Pressure

Suppose we wish to find a relation for the pressure exerted by an ideal gas on the walls of its container. We recall that by definition pressure is equal to the normal component of force per unit area, and that by Newton's second law of motion any force equals a time rate of change of momentum. In order to obtain a relation for gas pressure we shall compute the total change of momentum experienced by the molecules striking a unit area per unit time.

Because all collisions of the molecules are perfectly elastic, by our third condition for an ideal gas, the entire change in momentum of each molecule is normal to the wall surface and is equal to $2mv \cos \theta$, where m is the mass of a single molecule. This change in momentum is multiplied by the number of molecules with speeds in the range v to $v + dv$ (in the parallelepiped of Fig. 11.1) which are traveling directly toward area S at any instant as given in Eq. (11.3). The resulting expression then is integrated over φ from 0 to 2π and over θ from 0 to $\frac{1}{2}\pi$, and over all the available speeds. On dividing it by $S\tau$ and on introducing the mean square speed as given in Eq. (11.2), we find the pressure exerted by the ideal gas to equal

$$P = \tfrac{1}{3}mn\overline{v^2}. \tag{11.5}$$

Note that mn equals the density ρ of the ideal gas and that $\frac{1}{2}m\overline{v^2}$ is the average translational kinetic energy ϵ of a molecule in the gas, so

$$P = \tfrac{1}{3}\rho\overline{v^2} = \tfrac{2}{3}n\epsilon. \tag{11.6}$$

These several relations for gas pressure were first derived during the middle part of the nineteenth century by Joule and Clausius.

Since $n\epsilon$ is the internal energy per unit volume, by Eq. (11.6) the pressure in the ideal gas equals two-thirds the energy density. This result should be compared with the relation for radiation pressure in terms of radiant energy density (Eq. 9.23).

11.5. The Avogadro Number and Boltzmann Constant

One mole of any real gas at 273.15°K and a standard atmosphere is observed to occupy a volume of 22.41 liters. Or, equal volumes of pure gases under standard conditions of pressure and temperature are found to have masses which are proportional to their molecular weights. These observations led Avogadro to enunciate an hypothesis that subsequently was amply confirmed: Equal volumes of gases under like conditions of temperature and pressure contain equal numbers of molecules.

From a variety of experimental measurements the number of molecules in one gram-molecular weight of a gas has been found to equal $(6.0248 \pm 0.0003) \times 10^{23}$. This is the Avogadro number. Note that one gram molecular weight of a gas contains this number of molecules regardless of the temperature and pressure until dissociation occurs and, furthermore, that the Avogadro number is applicable to liquids, solids, and substances in solution.

The quotient of the universal gas constant R divided by the Avogadro number is another universal constant of significance throughout thermophysics. It is represented by k and is called the Boltzmann constant. Its value is $(1.38041 \pm 0.00007) \times 10^{-23}$ joule/deg Kelvin, and it has the dimensions of entropy.

11.6. Temperature in Kinetic Theory

Because the Boltzmann constant k is the universal gas constant per molecule, we write the state equation for an ideal gas in the form

$$P = nkT, \qquad (11.7)$$

where n is the number of molecules in a unit volume. This equation and Eq. (11.5) may now be combined and solved for temperature:

$$T = m\overline{v^2}/3k. \qquad (11.8)$$

This temperature is assumed to be identical with the thermodynamic temperature, provided the ideal gas is in thermodynamic equilibrium. It is convenient, however, sometimes to define an effective temperature given by Eq. (11.8) for an ideal gas even when the gas is not in equilibrium.

11.7. Equipartition of Energy and Specific Heats

From Eq. (11.6) and Eq. (11.7) we see that ϵ equals $\frac{3}{2}kT$. One-third of this energy per molecule may be associated with each of the mutually perpendicular velocity components in a three-dimensional coordinate system; the molecules then are said to have three translational degrees of freedom. The degree-of-freedom concept is extended in elementary kinetic theory to the rotational motion of a molecule. If the molecules of an ideal gas have f rotational and translational degrees of freedom, the internal energy of the gas equals the product of the total number of molecules within the gas and $\frac{1}{2}fkT$. Thus the internal energy of an ideal gas is a function of temperature only. Compare this result with similar conclusions in Sections 8.2 and 9.2.

Each mole of an ideal gas has an internal energy

$$u = \tfrac{1}{2}fRT, \qquad (11.9)$$

and therefore its molar heat capacity at constant volume is

$$c_v = du/dT = \tfrac{1}{2}fR, \qquad (11.10)$$

and its molar heat capacity at constant pressure is

$$c_p = c_v + R = (1 + \tfrac{1}{2}f)R. \qquad (11.11)$$

Finally, the ratio of the two heat capacities γ is

$$\gamma = 1 + 2/f. \qquad (11.12)$$

The numbers of translational and rotational degrees of freedom for monatomic, diatomic, and triatomic gases are 3, 5, and 6, and the corresponding values of γ are 1.667, 1.400, and 1.333, respectively. These theoretical conclusions are in approximate agreement with the experimental observations given in Table 8.3 (column *a*).

If molecular vibrations and electronic transitions within molecules are considered in addition to the translational and rotational motions, then the molar heat capacity c_p is increased by a small term which is a function of temperature. The exact form of this term depends on the specific molecule and is rather complicated. It cannot be derived by classical equipartition methods; instead, quantum statistics is applied. For carbon monoxide, as an illustration, the equation

$$c_p = \tfrac{7}{2}R + \tfrac{1}{2}R(3080/T)^2[\cosh{(3080/T)} - 1]^{-1} \qquad (11.13)$$

holds up to 2000°K. Although hydrogen is diatomic, as can be seen in

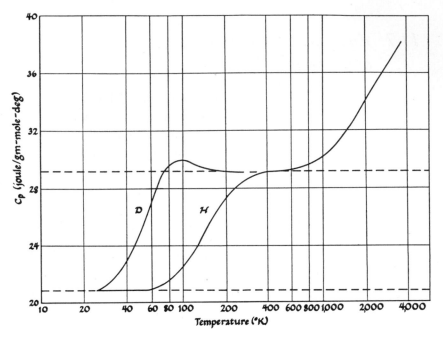

Figure 11.2.   Molar heat capacity at constant pressure for normal hydrogen H and normal deuterium D.

Fig. 11.2, it is exceptional in that at low temperatures its c_p falls from $\frac{7}{2}R$ to approximately $\frac{5}{2}R$, a value appropriate to a monatomic gas. This effect is associated with certain peculiar rotational properties of molecules at low temperatures and would appear in other diatomic gases as their temperature is lowered if they did not liquefy first.

11.8. Molecular Effusion and Thermal Transpiration

Imagine two chambers connected by one or more capillaries so small that gas molecules may wander through them almost individually. During the passage the molecules may suffer many collisions with the walls, but very few with other gas molecules. We may expect the mean rate of transfer of the gas to be proportional to $\bar{v}$ and therefore to the square root of $\overline{v^2}$. From Eq. (11.8) we see that this speed is proportional to the square root of T/M, where M is the molecular weight of the gas. Consequently, the rate of molecular effusion is inversely proportional to the square root of the molecular weight of a gas. This is Graham's law. Ramsey made application of it in 1895 when he first separated helium from nitrogen by repeated fractionation through unglazed clay pipe stems. It is applied today in one method for separating the uranium isotopes U^{235} and U^{238}. Uranium hexafluoride gas UF_6 is manufactured from naturally occurring uranium and then allowed to effuse through fine capillaries in a ceramic barrier. Although the mass difference between the two isotopes is small, the gas may be enriched in U^{235} to high concentrations by passage through a series of such barriers.

For thermal transpiration, which was discussed from a macroscopic point of view in Section 8.5, the two chambers are maintained at different constant temperatures. The number of molecules striking a unit area of the separating porous diaphragm per unit time is given by Eq. (11.4). Of these a small fraction will enter the pores and effuse to the other side. If we combine Eq. (11.5) with Eq. (11.4) and remember that

$$\bar{v} \propto v_{rms} \propto T^{1/2},$$

we find that the rate of entry of molecules into the pores on each side of the diaphragm is proportional to $PT^{-1/2}$. If the pores are small holes and the diaphragm is very thin, we would expect counter-effusion to occur until a state of dynamic equilibrium becomes established in which the rates of entry on either side of the diaphragm are equal. For this state,

$$P_1/P_2 = (T_1/T_2)^{1/2}. \tag{11.14}$$

This is the equation for thermal transpiration which Reynolds found to hold at low gas pressures. Later work suggests that it begins to fail when the distance traveled by a molecule between collisions becomes comparable to the size of the pores.

From Eq. (11.14) we find that dP/dT equals $P/2T$ or $R/2v$, where v is the specific volume; therefore the heat of transport q^* in Eq. (8.20) is simply

$$q^* = -\tfrac{1}{2}RT. \tag{11.15}$$

We can interpret this result to mean that each molecule during its passage has essentially one less degree of freedom than it would have in the bulk gas. It liberates $\tfrac{1}{2}kT$ units of energy on entering a pore on one side of the diaphragm and absorbs an equal amount of energy as it emerges on the other side.

11.9. Maxwell's Derivation of f(v)

In order to derive an explicit form for the distribution function $f(v)$ according to Maxwell (1860), we shall assume that a monatomic ideal gas has a uniform temperature and pressure and is not subject to external forces. Let n be the number of molecules in a unit volume, and suppose that the velocity v of any one of them has the components v_x, v_y, and v_z in rectangular coordinates. The number of molecules per unit volume with velocity v_x between v_x and $v_x + dv_x$ is now given by $nf(v_x)dv_x$. Similarly, the number with velocities between v_y and $v_y + dv_y$ is $nf(v_y)dv_y$, and the number with velocities between v_z and $v_z + dv_z$ is $nf(v_z)dv_z$.

Velocities v_x, v_y, and v_z are at right angles to one another and independent, so the number of molecules with velocities simultaneously between v_x and $v_x + dv_x$, v_y and $v_y + dv_y$, and v_z and $v_z + dv_z$ is $nf(v_x)f(v_y)f(v_z)dv_xdv_ydv_z$. If we imagine the velocity vectors of all the molecules moved to a common origin (see Fig. 11.3), then the element of volume $dv_xdv_ydv_z$ in this velocity space may be replaced by $v^2 \sin\theta d\theta d\varphi$. Since the distribution function is independent of angular direction, we may integrate over the total solid angle immediately to get $4\pi v^2 dv$ for the element of volume. The product $f(v_x)f(v_y)f(v_z)$ must be solely a function of v; hence we write

$$f(v_x)f(v_y)f(v_z) = F(v^2), \qquad (11.16)$$

where

$$v^2 = v_x^2 + v_y^2 + v_z^2. \qquad (11.17)$$

The components of velocity for each molecule must satisfy both Eq. (11.16) and Eq. (11.17) at the same time. In these equations we may consider v^2 to be a parameter which can vary over all positive numbers.

Because of symmetry the functions $f(v_x)$, $f(v_y)$, and $f(v_z)$ should have the same form. To find it we apply Lagrange's method of undetermined multi-

Figure 11.3.   Random distribution of velocity vectors for molecules having speed v in a gas which is in thermal equilibrium. This two-dimensional diagram illustrates what is done for the three-dimensional random distribution of molecules.

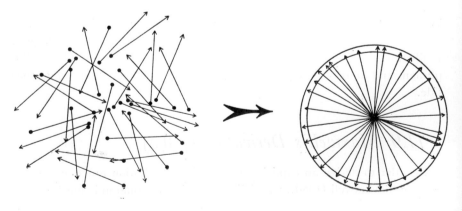

pliers. A small variation in the velocity components for any one value of the parameter v^2 leads, by differentiation of Eq. (11.16) and Eq. (11.17), to the equations

$$\frac{f'(v_x)}{f(v_x)}\,\delta v_x + \frac{f'(v_y)}{f(v_y)}\,\delta v_y + \frac{f'(v_z)}{f(v_z)}\,\delta v_z = 0 \qquad (11.18)$$

and

$$v_x\delta v_x + v_y\delta v_y + v_z\delta v_z = 0. \qquad (11.19)$$

In essence, if we fix the value of v, then v_x, v_y, and v_z are no longer independent, for they must satisfy Eq. (11.17). Furthermore, their variations are not independent either, for they must satisfy Eq. (11.19). In one method of solution we multiply Eq. (11.19) throughout by an arbitrary factor β and add the result to Eq. (11.18). This factor is independent of v_x, v_y, and v_z and is evaluated by solving for $\overline{v^2}$. It is called, however, an undetermined multiplier.

The equation we get by the foregoing procedure is

$$\left[\frac{f'(v_x)}{f(v_x)} + \beta v_x\right]\delta v_x + \left[\frac{f'(v_y)}{f(v_y)} + \beta v_y\right]\delta v_y + \left[\frac{f'(v_z)}{f(v_z)} + \beta v_z\right]\delta v_z = 0. \qquad (11.20)$$

First we evaluate the multiplier β by equating one of the coefficients to zero. Since the variations in the remaining two velocity components are completely independent we set each of their coefficients equal to zero in order that the sum vanish. Consider

$$\frac{f'(v_x)}{f(v_x)} + \beta v_x = 0. \qquad (11.21)$$

We multiply through by dv_x and integrate; thus

$$f(v_x) = A \exp\left(-\tfrac{1}{2}\beta v_x^2\right), \qquad (11.22)$$

in which A is the integration constant. In order to determine A we recall that the integral of $nf(v_x)dv_x$ over all available values of v_x should equal n. Because of the sharpness of this function we assume that no serious error arises if the integration is extended from $-\infty$ to $+\infty$, even though the actual limiting values of v_x cannot be so large:

$$\int_{-\infty}^{\infty} f(v_x)dv_x = A \int_{-\infty}^{\infty} \exp\left(-\tfrac{1}{2}\beta v_x^2\right)dv_x = 1. \qquad (11.23)$$

This definite integral equals $(2\pi/\beta)^{1/2}$, and therefore A equals its reciprocal. The functions $f(v_y)$ and $f(v_z)$ are like Eq. (11.22) with this same value for A, and $F(v^2)$ is simply the product of these three functions. Thus we see that $f(v)$ is given by the equation

$$f(v) = 4\pi v^2 F(v^2) = 4\pi(\beta/2\pi)^{3/2}v^2 \exp\left(-\tfrac{1}{2}\beta v^2\right), \qquad (11.24)$$

where we have replaced $v_x^2 + v_y^2 + v_z^2$ by v^2. When $f(v)$ is multiplied by ndv

the product equals the number of molecules with speed v between v and $v + dv$.

11.10. Values of β, $\bar{v}$, v_{rms}, and the Most Probable Speed

In order to determine the average value of v^p, Eq. (11.24) is multiplied by $v^p dv$ and the integration is carried out for speeds from 0 to ∞. The results for v and v^2 are

$$\bar{v} = \int_0^\infty v f(v) dv = (8/\pi\beta)^{1/2} \qquad (11.25)$$

and

$$\overline{v^2} = \int_0^\infty v^2 f(v) dv = 3/\beta. \qquad (11.26)$$

Thus we see that the ratio of v_{rms} to $\bar{v}$ is $(3\pi/8)^{1/2}$; the root mean square speed is proportional to the average speed, as we noted at the end of Section 11.2.

By comparing Eq. (11.26) with Eq. (11.8) we find

$$\beta = m/kT, \qquad (11.27)$$

and therefore

$$\bar{v} = (8kT/\pi m)^{1/2}. \qquad (11.28)$$

Figure 11.4.   Maxwellian distribution of speeds for nitrogen at 0°C. Most probable speed $v_{mps} = 401$ m/sec; average speed $\bar{v} = 453$ m/sec; root-mean-square speed $v_{rms} = 492$ m/sec.

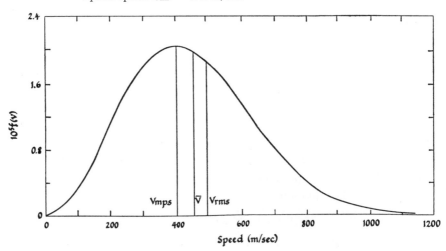

Finally, the distribution function becomes

$$f(v) = 4\pi(m/2\pi kT)^{3/2}v^2 \exp(-\tfrac{1}{2}mv^2/kT). \qquad (11.29)$$

Note that the argument of the exponential factor contains the ratio of the kinetic energy of a molecule to systemic energy kT.

In Fig. 11.4 the function $f(v)$ is plotted against v for nitrogen at $0°C$. Values of $\bar{v}$ and v_{rms} also are indicated for this particular distribution. The speed at which the maximum occurs is the most probable speed, for more molecules in the system have this value of speed than any other. To obtain its magnitude we equate $df(v)/dv$ to zero and solve for v in the usual way for finding maxima. The most probable speed equals $(2/\beta)^{1/2}$ or $(2kT/m)^{1/2}$. The most probable speed, mean speed, and root mean square speed are in the ratio $1.41/1.60/1.73$.

11.11. *Experimental Verification of the Maxwellian Distribution*

Maxwell's derivation of the distribution function contains steps which are questionable. The most serious of these is the assumption that molecules may have speeds which are indefinitely large. More elaborate and rigorous treatments for an ideal gas *in equilibrium*, however, all lead to the maxwellian distribution. Moreover, it turns out to be the only possible one, as was

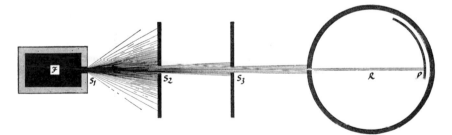

Figure 11.5.   A molecular beam apparatus for studying velocity distributions.

demonstrated by Boltzmann. But the indisputable test of its validity comes from several beautifully executed experiments.

The first direct experiment was conducted on silver by Sterns in 1920. Subsequently the method has been modified and elaborated by Compton and co-workers, by Eldridge, by Zartmann, by Ko, and by Miller and Kusch.

A schematic diagram of the essential features in the apparatus for this experiment is given in Fig. 11.5. Molecules effuse from hot vapor in a furnace

F, through slits S_1, S_2, S_3 and into an evacuated region R, where faster moving molecules in the beam can gain on the slower ones. In this way the molecules become spread out into a velocity spectrum. Finally, the molecules are caught on a plate P which moves rapidly across the beam to register a distribution pattern. An analysis of such a pattern indicates that the molecules in the vapor within the furnace have Maxwell's normal distribution of speeds.

In Fig. 11.6 are reproduced one set of experimental points and theoretical curves for bismuth as published by Ko in 1934. Ordinate values are proportional to the number of molecules deposited at distance x (the abscissa) from the zero point along the plate, and these values of x are proportional to the molecular speeds. Zartmann had made similar measurements in 1931, but Ko improved the apparatus and

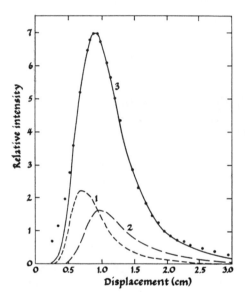

Figure 11.6.   Velocity distribution for bismuth vapor at 1148°K. [Adapted from C. C. Ko, "The Heat of Dissociation of Bi_2 Determined by the Method of Molecular Beams," *J. Franklin Inst.* **217**, 173, 1934.]

obtained such good results that he could determine the relative amounts of Bi and Bi_2 in the bismuth vapor from the shape of the experimental curve. Curves 1 and 2 in Fig. 11.6 are the maxwellian distributions for Bi and Bi_2 at 1148°K, and the third curve is their weighted sum. At this temperature about 60% of the vapor is monatomic bismuth. The discrepancies at the two ends Ko ascribed largely to diffuse molecules, although a slight peak near the upper end appears to arise from the presence of a small amount of Bi_8 in the vapor.

Miller and Kusch (1955–1956) constructed an improved molecular beam apparatus, especially in the design of the slit system, which almost eliminates diffusing molecules. By means of it they obtained velocity distributions of atoms in potassium and thallium vapors and of molecules in several alkali halide vapors, all in excellent agreement with theory. In Fig. 11.7 are repro-

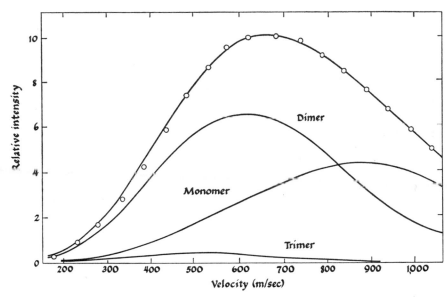

Figure 11.7.   Velocity distribution for lithium chloride molecules in a vapor at
971°K. The curve through experimental points is the sum of the
monomer, dimer, and trimer theoretical distributions which are required to produce a best fit. [Adapted from R. C. Miller and P. Kusch,
"Molecular Composition of Alkali Halide Vapors," *J. Chem.
Physics* **25**, 860, 1956.]

duced their curves for two runs on lithium chloride which indicate how well
molecular compositions can be analyzed by this method. The concentrations
of monomer, dimer, and trimer in the vapor are in the ratios 1/1.10/0.06.
The heat of vaporization may be found from the experimental values of
vapor pressure as described in Section 6.8, and polymer dissociation energies
may be computed from the distribution data and partial pressures. For
further details the original articles should be consulted.

In 1947 Estermann, Simpson, and Stern described a free-fall experiment
for determining velocity distributions in vapors. A schematic diagram of the
apparatus is shown in Fig. 11.8. Atoms from a vapor in the oven effuse
through the narrow horizontal slit S_1 and thereafter follow parabolic trajectories in an evacuated space as suggested by the dotted lines (much
exaggerated). Only those atoms whose trajectories pass through a second
horizontal slit S_2 are able to reach detector D. The detector consists of a
horizontal, hot tungsten wire, which can be moved downward, and a surrounding collecting cylinder. If a cesium atom, for example, passes through
S_2 and strikes the wire, which is maintained positive relative to the cylinder,

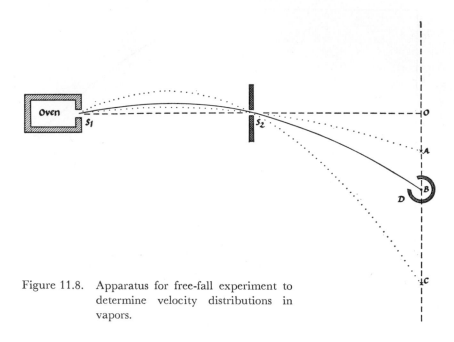

Figure 11.8.   Apparatus for free-fall experiment to
                determine velocity distributions in
                vapors.

it becomes ionized, immediately evaporates, and is then collected by the
negative cylinder. A large number of these ions produces a measurable
current. At any one position of the wire the current is proportional to the
number of cesium atoms with a particular value of speed, and as the wire is
dropped below the direct path S_1S_2O it ionizes atoms of lower and lower
speeds. Thus a plot of ion current against wire distance from O represents
the velocity distribution of cesium atoms in the molecular beam. The theoretical curve in Fig. 11.9 fits the experimental data rather well.

Not only do the foregoing results prove the existence of maxwellian dis-

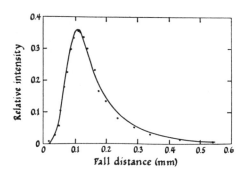

Figure 11.9.   Comparison of theoretical curve with experimental
data for the free-fall of cesium
atoms. [Adapted from I. Estermann, O. C. Simpson, and O. Stern,
"The Free Fall of Atoms and the
Measurement of the Velocity Distribution in a Molecular Beam of
Cesium Atoms," *Phys. Rev.* **71**,
238, 1947.]

tributions of molecular velocities in vapors under near-equilibrium conditions, but, contrariwise, the existence of these distributions demonstrates that
vapors over hot, and even molten, metals and salts behave like ideal gases.
We had assumed such behavior in deriving equations for vapor pressures
over liquids and solids; now we have experimental evidence for it.

11.12. Thermionic Emission

When a piece of metal is heated within an evacuated chamber to a sufficiently high temperature it emits electrons and becomes surrounded by an
electron gas having a negative space charge. This space charge is detected
and measurements are made on it with appropriate electrical instruments
and probes. The electron gas is conceived to exist in a condensed phase
within the metal and in a rarefied phase outside it. A relation between the
temperature of the metal surface and the rate of electron emission may be
derived if the rarefied phase is treated like a monatomic ideal gas in dynamic
equilibrium with its condensed phase in spite of its space charge.

We assume that the number of emitted electrons from a unit area per
second during thermionic emission equals the number of electrons which
strike the unit area per second when the condensed and rarefied phases are
in dynamic equilibrium. Then the thermionic current density j is equal to
the product of the electronic charge e and v of Eq. (11.4), in which n represents the density and $\bar{v}$ the average speed of the electrons in the rarefied
phase,

$$j = \tfrac{1}{4}ne\bar{v}. \qquad (11.30)$$

From Eq. (11.28) $\bar{v}$ equals $(8kT/\pi m)^{1/2}$, and from Eq. (11.7) n equals P/kT.
These values of $\bar{v}$ and n are now substituted into Eq. (11.30) and the natural
logarithm of j is found:

$$\ln j = \ln P - \tfrac{1}{2} \ln T + \text{constant}. \qquad (11.31)$$

All quantities which do not vary here have been lumped together under
"constant."

In order to evaluate $\ln P$ we consider the rarefied and condensed electron
gas to behave very much like a vapor-solid system and thermionic emission
to be similar to the sublimation process. For it the heat of transformation l_e
equals the amount of thermal energy required to transform one mole of
electron gas from the condensed to the rarefied phase. By experimental and
other means l_e is found to be given by

$$l_e = l_0 + c_p T, \qquad (11.32)$$

in which l_0 is the heat of transformation at 0°K and c_p is the molar heat capacity of the electron gas in its rarefied phase. Because the electron gas is monatomic, c_p equals $\frac{5}{2}R$. Nonthermodynamic evidence suggests that the heat capacity of the electron gas in its condensed phase is negligible. An equation of exactly the same form as Eq. (6.14) may now be derived for the "vapor pressure" P of the electron gas:

$$\ln P = -(l_0/RT) + \tfrac{5}{2} \ln T + \text{integration constant.} \qquad (11.33)$$

Finally, we combine Eq. (11.31) and Eq. (11.33) by eliminating $\ln P$ and by replacing the sum of the "constants" by $\ln A$. We find

$$\ln (j/T^2) = \ln A - l_0/RT. \qquad (11.34)$$

This is the Richardson-Dushman equation for thermionic emission from a metal.

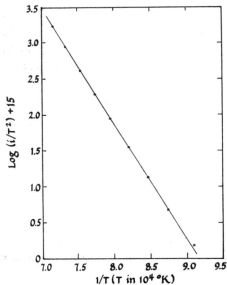

It is convenient to replace l_0 by $N_0 e\varphi$, in which N_0 is the Avogadro number, e is the electronic charge and φ is the thermionic work function of the emitting surface. The work function is the work required to remove a single electron from just inside a neutral metal across the surface to a point far outside. Usually it has a value of a few electron-volts, and surface impurities have a marked effect on it. The coefficient A depends on a number of factors, such as the reflectivity of the surface for electrons, the temperature coefficient of the work function, and impurities on the surface. Equation (11.34) now may be rewritten in terms of φ as

Figure 11.10.   Richardson plot for a thoriated tungsten surface. The work function equals 3.2 electron-volts.

$$\ln (j/T^2) = \ln A - e\varphi/kT, \qquad (11.35)$$

where k is the Boltzmann constant. A Richardson plot of thermionic emission data for a thoriated tungsten surface is shown in Fig. 11.10. The tungsten surface is partially covered with a monolayer of thorium atoms, which reduces its work function to a value intermediate between the work functions for thorium and for tungsten.

11.13. *Maxwellian Distribution of Speeds in the Electron Gas*

The distribution of speeds among electrons in an electron gas is best investigated by means of a negatively charged probe which repels electrons. Suppose the probe is maintained at negative potential V relative to a cathode source of thermionic electrons. Then only those electrons with a component of velocity normal to the surface of the probe in excess of a critical value v_c, given by the equation

$$\tfrac{1}{2}mv_c^2 = eV, \qquad (11.36)$$

can be collected and measured in the probe circuit. We now solve for the number of these electrons which strike a unit area of probe surface per second by applying the method of Section 11.3. Equation (11.3) is transformed to one for normal components of velocity and then integrated over φ from 0 to 2π, over θ from $-\tfrac{1}{2}\pi$ to $+\tfrac{1}{2}\pi$, and over all speeds greater than v_c. The result is multiplied by electronic charge e to obtain the current density to the probe:

$$j = ne(kT_e/2\pi m)^{1/2} \exp(-eV/kT_e). \qquad (11.37)$$

The temperature T_e of the electron gas may be found by plotting $\ln j$ against retarding potential V. If the graph is a straight line with a negative slope, we conclude that the electron gas does indeed have a maxwellian distribution of speeds. Electron temperature T_e may be computed from the slope value. If it should very nearly equal the temperature of the cathode, this would be additional evidence for the correctness of our conclusion. Extensive measurements of this kind have been made. They support the assumption we made in Section 11.12 that an electron gas behaves like an ideal gas under quasi-equilibrium conditions.

Problems

---

1. Compute the number of molecules in a cubic millimeter of gas at 0°C and at pressures of 76 cm, 1 mm, 1 μ, 1 mμ and 1$\mu\mu$ of mercury. How much pressure exists in an extremely rarefied gas containing an average of only one molecule per cubic centimeter? Is the concept of "pressure" meaningful here?

2. How much volume does one mole of water vapor occupy at 20°C and a standard atmosphere of pressure? How much volume does one mole of liquid water occupy at the same temperature and pressure? How many water molecules are in the vapor and in the liquid? Compare the average translational kinetic energy of a vapor molecule with the energy required to transfer a molecule from the liquid to the vapor phase.

3. Derive the Dalton law of partial pressures from kinetic theory.

4. Suppose the distribution function $f(v)$ for molecular speeds is quadratic, namely

$$f(v) = Av(v_0 - v)/v_0^3,$$

in which v_0 is the maximum speed attainable and v can have any value between 0 and v_0. Evaluate A, and then determine the average speed, mean square speed, and most probable speed in terms of v_0.

5. In a two-dimensional gas the force per unit length is analogous to pressure. Derive an equation like Eq. (11.5) for it.

6. How large is a pin-hole through the thin wall of a high-vacuum system at 27°C if the observed rate of pressure increase due to the air leak is approximately 0.1 mm/hr? Assume that every air molecule which reaches the pin-hole passes into the system.

7. The molecules of a gas in an oven at temperature T have a normal distribution among speeds. Find the average kinetic energy of molecules which escape through a small hole of area S in the wall of the oven, and show that it is greater than the average kinetic energy of molecules within the oven by the factor $\sqrt{4/3}$. Note that the number of molecules with speeds between v and $v + dv$ which strike unit area per unit time equals $\frac{1}{4}nvf(v)dv$.

8. Spectral lines have a finite width due largely to a Doppler effect in which hot-gas atoms with components of velocity along the line of sight give rise to small changes in frequency of emitted radiation. Show that the intensity across the line is $I_0 \exp(-mc^2x^2/2kT)$, where I_0 is the intensity at the center of the line, x is the distance from it in wavelength units, c is the speed of light, and T is the temperature of the gas.

9. Suppose area S in Fig. 11.1 represents a portion of a piston moving with speed u along its axis, and furthermore suppose u is very much less than the molecular speeds.

    (a) Show that the loss in kinetic energy experienced by a molecule on colliding with S is $2mvu \cos \theta$ even though the collision is perfectly elastic.

    (b) From this result show that the total loss of molecular kinetic energy per unit area and per unit time from many molecules striking the piston is Pu, in which P is the pressure given by Eq. (11.5). We recall that Pu, is the rate at which mechanical work is being done on a unit area of the piston.

    (c) Explain why we should expect the temperature of the gas to fall during an adiabatic expansion.

10. Because thermophysical systems near the Earth's surface are in a uniform force field the pressure in them decreases with altitude according to the relation

$$dp = -\rho g dz,$$

in which ρ is the density at altitude z, and g is the gravitational acceleration.

(a) Prove that $\rho = \rho_0 \exp(-mgz/kT)$ under isothermal conditions, where ρ_0 is the density at altitude zero and m is the mass of a particle.

(b) If the number of particles within a small volume of cross-section S and height Δz at two different altitudes z_1 and z_2 are counted, show that

$$\ln \Delta n_1 - \ln \Delta n_2 = (mg/kT)(z_2 - z_1).$$

(Observations by Perrin on minute suspended particles confirmed this equation.)

11. At what temperature does the additional term in c_p for carbon monoxide, as given in Eq. (11.13), equal 1% of c_p? Is this term more significant at higher or lower temperatures?

12. If the work function of a metal surface is a linear function of temperature, how does this affect the coefficient A in the Richardson equation? How does the reflectivity of the surface affect A? Develop the equation for $\ln(j/T^2)$ with these corrections included in it.

CHAPTER **12**

Mean Free Path and
Transport Processes

WE have learned that a mole of gas in equilibrium at uniform pressure and temperature actually contains a very large number of molecules in continual and rapid motion. This unceasing activity increases in violence as the temperature is raised. The kinetic energy of translation and rotation for all the molecules constitutes a large fraction of the internal energy of the gas. We can now see why the temperature of a gas can be changed not only by heating it but also by doing work on it. Each of these processes increases the average kinetic energy of the molecules, whose distribution among speeds therefore is changed by increasing the value of the temperature parameter in the maxwellian distribution function. The kinetic theory value of temperature, we see, characterizes the state of the system.

Furthermore, an increase in the number of molecules per unit volume of the gas raises the pressure. Consequently, a gas system is in internal mechanical equilibrium only if the molecular density is uniform throughout. The value of molecular density also characterizes the state of the system.

Suppose we impose on a gas system a small gradient in temperature or pressure. The system is no longer in equilibrium, and adjustments take place within it such that it approaches equilibrium. From the kinetic theory point of view the molecules move about and redistribute themselves by their unceasing activity until the temperature and pressure are again uniform throughout the gas.

In order to study such nonequilibrium conditions we assume that a maxwellian distribution can be found for each small region of the gas. That is, we break up the system into many small regions and suppose that the equations for equilibrium apply to each one. If the gradients are too large, this procedure cannot be followed, and wholly new methods must be invented.

Here we shall first develop the concepts of mean free path and collision cross-section and then apply them to the transport of momentum, energy, or mass through a gas in which a small gradient of momentum, temperature, or pressure exists. In this way we shall gain some insight into a few of the fundamental flow processes insofar as they apply to gases.

12.1. Mean Free Path and Collision Cross-section

With each molecule in a gas system, which is at uniform temperature and pressure, we can associate not only a speed but also a free path whose length extends from one collision point to the next. For an ideal gas the path is straight, and the free path lengths of all the molecules satisfy a distribution law much like that for speeds. It is convenient to define a mean free path $\bar{\lambda}$ by the equation

$$\bar{\lambda} = \int_0^{\lambda_{max}} \lambda f(\lambda) d\lambda, \qquad (12.1)$$

where $f(\lambda)d\lambda$ represents the fractional number of molecules with free paths in the range λ to $\lambda + d\lambda$. We can also define a mean free path $\bar{\lambda}_v$ for all the molecules with speeds in the range v to $v + dv$ by the equation

$$\bar{\lambda}_v = \int_0^{\lambda_{v\,max}} \lambda_v f(\lambda_v) d\lambda_v, \qquad (12.2)$$

where $f(\lambda_v)d\lambda_v$ represents the fractional number of molecules with speeds in the range v to $v + dv$ and with free paths between λ_v and $\lambda_v + d\lambda_v$. We shall now make the assumption that $\bar{\lambda}_v$ equals $\bar{\lambda}$. In effect, this means that we consider the free paths to be independent of molecular speeds and $f(\lambda_v)$ to equal $f(\lambda)$.

The straightforward definition of mean free path given by Eq. (12.1) rarely has been applied directly, and this has introduced difficulties. If the time between two successive collisions is τ, then $\bar{\lambda}$ equals the mean value of $v\tau$ for all the molecules in the system. It has been found convenient, however, to replace this mean value by the product of the average speed and the average time between collisions, and these, in turn, by the root mean square speed and the reciprocal of the mean collision frequency. This final "mean free path" is but remotely related to the mean free path of Eq. (12.1). We shall not follow the usual practice, but rather we shall apply the straightforward definition directly.

Let the distance between centers of two colliding molecules be represented by σ. Because molecules are neither hard nor spherical, and may even be of different kinds in a given system, σ can have a range of values. For simplicity we shall assume that all the molecules in a system are replaced by identical hard spheres for which σ has only one value. If necessary, our results can then be modified to account for any "softness" and asphericalness in the molecules and for other differences.

A molecule will have a collision cross-section $\pi\sigma^2$, and therefore it will sweep out a free-path volume $\pi\sigma^2\lambda$ between one collision and the next. The total destined free-path volume associated with all the molecules in a unit volume of ideal gas at any instant is

$$n \int_0^{\lambda_{max}} \pi\sigma^2\lambda f(\lambda)d\lambda = \pi\sigma^2 n\bar{\lambda}, \qquad (12.3)$$

and this should not exceed the unit volume. We expect it to be less since not all the volume is traversed by molecular free paths. Let the total free-path volume equal q; then

$$\bar{\lambda} = q/\pi n\sigma^2. \qquad (12.4)$$

Several values between 0.6 and 0.8 have been proposed for q, but its value depends on which of the definitions is selected for mean free path and on whether σ really is a constant. For our discussion we shall adopt Maxwell's value of 0.707.[1]

The concept of collision cross-section is useful in studies of recombination of ions in gaseous discharge, of electron and ion bombardment, and especially of nuclear reactions. The nuclear reactor operates at relatively low temperatures because slow thermoneutrons have sufficiently high collision cross-sections to maintain the nuclear reactions in it.

Viscosity, thermal conduction, and diffusion are three transport phenomena that are functions of the mean free path. They may be studied by essentially similar methods, involving the transfer of excess momentum, energy, and mass from layer to layer of the gas.

---

[1] This computation may be found in books on kinetic theory; for example, Present, R. D., *Kinetic Theory of Gases*, Sections 3-2 and 5-2 (McGraw-Hill, New York, 1958).

12.2. *Viscosity in Gases*

Experimental observations suggest that the coefficient of viscosity for a gas is independent of pressure and increases with temperature over rather wide ranges of values. These curious results can be understood in terms of the kinetic theory, for the viscous drag within a streaming gas arises from the transfer of excess momentum by the molecules from one layer to another.

Let a gas be moving to the left in streamlines. It is conceived to be divided into several layers, such as 1, 2, 3, 4 of Fig. 12.1. Suppose layer 1 moves faster than layer 2, layer 2 moves faster than layer 3, and so on. A molecule may leave a point such as A, A', A'' and move from layer 2 into layer 3 before it experiences a collision at B, B', B''. Because layer 2 is moving faster than layer 3, the molecule carries on the average a little excess momentum from one layer to the other. At the same time another molecule carries a slightly deficient amount of momentum on the average from layer 3 into layer 2. The rate with which momentum is exchanged between the layers equals a force, namely the viscous drag.

In order to evaluate the viscous drag within an ideal gas, we multiply the number of molecules with speed v and free path λ which travel in the angular direction θ,φ by the rate of transfer of momentum per molecule, and then

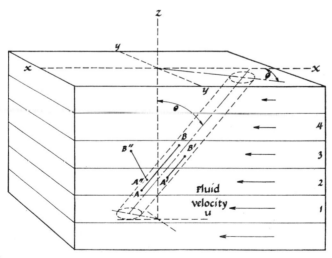

Figure 12.1.   Molecules at A, A', A'' in layer 2 move to B, B', B'' in layer 3 from one collision event to the next.

integrate the resulting expression over all possible angles and over all free paths and speeds.

Let du/dz represent the velocity gradient normal to the direction of motion of the gas. A molecule, whose free path makes an angle θ with the layers, carries an excess of momentum $-m(du/dz)\lambda \cos\theta$ from layer 2 into layer 3, as shown at AB and $A'B'$ in Fig. 12.1. But the number of molecules with speed v and free path λ which move from layer 2 into layer 3 per unit time within a parallelepiped of cross-sectional area ΔS equals

$$dn = (1/4\pi)nf(\lambda)d\lambda vf(v)dv\Delta S \cos\theta \sin\theta d\theta d\varphi. \qquad (12.5)$$

This relation is obtained in exactly the same manner as was Eq. (11.3). The total rate of change of momentum for all the molecules with speed v and free path λ, which are *exchanged* between layers 2 and 3 in the direction θ,φ, equals *twice* the product of the excess momentum per molecule and the number of molecules given by Eq. (12.5). The resulting expression then is integrated over φ from 0 to 2π, and over θ from 0 to $\frac{1}{2}\pi$, and over all speeds and free paths. The viscous drag is

$$F = -\tfrac{1}{3}mn\bar{\lambda}\bar{v}\Delta S(du/dz), \qquad (12.6)$$

where du/dz is assumed to be constant and implicitly is a negative quantity. If the coefficient of viscosity η is defined by

$$\eta = \tfrac{1}{3}mn\bar{\lambda}\bar{v}, \qquad (12.7)$$

Eq. (12.6) reduces to the relation for viscous drag which is commonly ascribed to Newton. The numerical factor $\frac{1}{3}$ is altered to some extent if the more common definition of $\bar{\lambda}$ is introduced and if Jeans' persistence of velocities[2] during a collision is taken into account.

Because $\bar{\lambda}$ is inversely proportional to the molecular density n, as can be seen in Eq. (12.4), it follows that η is independent of n, and therefore it is independent of the gas pressure. On the other hand, η is proportional to the square root of the Kelvin temperature through the average speed $\bar{v}$. These results have been amply confirmed by experimental observations over wide ranges of temperatures and pressures. The fact that the viscosity of a gas increases with temperature is surprising, for, at first sight, it would appear that increasing the temperature should reduce somehow the effectiveness of the intermolecular forces and thereby decrease the viscosity. This is the effect observed in liquids. For gases, however, we see that the viscosity depends almost entirely on interchanges of momentum between the moving layers of fluid.

---

[2] Jeans, J., *An Introduction to the Kinetic Theory of Gases*, p. 147 (Macmillan, New York, 1940).

12.3. Values of Average Speeds, Mean Free Paths, and Collision Diameters

If a gas is in dynamic equilibrium, the motions of its molecules are described by several physical parameters which may be computed from the temperature, viscosity, density, and molecular weight of the gas. From Eq. (11.28) we can write

$$\bar{v} = (8RT/\pi M)^{1/2}, \tag{12.8}$$

in which R is the gas constant and M is the molecular weight. From Eq. (12.7) we get

$$\bar{\lambda} = 3\eta/\rho\bar{v}; \tag{12.9}$$

finally, by combining these equations with Eq. (12.4) and substituting 0.707 for q we find

$$\sigma^2 = (2/3\pi\eta)(MkT/\pi N_0)^{1/2}, \tag{12.10}$$

in which N_0 represents the Avogadro number. Although other values for the numerical factors in Eq. (12.9) and Eq. (12.10) have been computed by more elaborate means, we shall not introduce them here. The "surfaces" of molecules are rather fuzzy, and the collision process is more complex than we have assumed. For these reasons, only approximate values of $\bar{\lambda}$ and σ can be computed, and the foregoing equations are quite satisfactory.

Table 12.1 contains experimental values of M, η, and ρ for several gases at 0°C and one atmosphere of pressure. The computed average speeds range

T A B L E   12.1.   *Average Speeds and Mean Free Paths for Several Gases at 0°C and One Atmosphere.*

Molecule	M (kgm/mole)	η (newton-sec/m²)	ρ (kgm/m³)	$\bar{v}$ (km/sec)	$\bar{\lambda}$ (mμ)	$\bar{\nu}$ (sec⁻¹)
A	39.94	21.0×10^{-6}	1.784	0.380	93	5.2×10^9
CH_4	16.03	10.2	0.717	0.600	71	10.7
CO	28.01	16.6	1.250	0.454	88	6.6
CO_2	44.00	13.7	1.977	0.362	58	8.0
H_2	2.016	8.42	0.090	1.694	166	13.0
He	4.002	18.6	0.178	1.207	260	5.9
N_2	28.02	16.6	1.250	0.454	88	6.6
Ne	20.18	29.7	0.900	0.538	184	3.7
NH_3	17.03	8.89	0.771	0.583	59	12.5
O_2	32.00	19.1	1.429	0.425	95	5.7

from approximately 0.2 mile/sec to 1 mile/sec at 0°C, and the mean free path lengths are of the order 1000 Å at atmospheric pressure. If the temperature is increased to 2200°C without changing the volume of the gas, the average speeds are tripled but the mean free paths are unaffected. If the pressure is reduced isothermally from one atmosphere to 10^{-4} mm Hg, the speeds are not changed, but the mean free paths are increased nearly eight-million times. Molecules of residual air would have mean free paths about 70 cm long. At pressures a million times less, collisions between gas molecules are rare and relatively unimportant for experimental work.

In Table 12.2 are entered values of σ as computed from the data in Table 12.1 by means of Eq. (12.10) and also values of molecular diameters from other sources for comparison. The numbers in the d (spectra) columns are

TABLE 12.2.   *Approximate Diameters of Gas Molecules in Ångstroms.*

Mole-cule	σ (viscosity)	d (van der Waals)	d (spectra)	Mole-cule	σ (viscosity)	d (van der Waals)	d (spectra)
A	3.00	2.94	1.34	He	1.80	2.65	0.60
CH_4	3.44	3.23	2.29	N_2	3.10	3.12	2.15
CO	3.10	3.16	2.24	Ne	2.14	2.38	0.64
CO_2	3.81	3.23	3.22	NH_3	3.73	3.08	2.07
H_2	2.25	2.76	1.80	O_2	2.99	3.00	2.10

values of the maximum diameters (not center-to-center distances) estimated from spectral data. The van der Waals values of diameters are computed from the constant b in the van der Waals equation of state.

It is not surprising to find the several values of molecular diameters in disagreement. Atoms and molecules are not hard spheres and therefore do not have very sharp boundaries. Furthermore, collisions are not simple re-bounds since they involve intermolecular forces which act at a distance. Molecules with large relative velocities approach each other more closely than do those with small relative velocities. But at low temperatures usually they do not approach so closely as to disrupt their electronic configurations and produce ionization. From these considerations we should expect the van der Waals diameters to be in better agreement with values of σ than diameters found from data on electronic and band spectra. Actually, the spectral values generally should be significantly less because they are related to the structure of the molecules and not to molecular interactions.

12.4. *Thermal Conductivity in Gases*

For this discussion the gas is considered to be in a steady dynamic state with a temperature gradient of dT/dz in the z-direction only. The gas is divided into layers at right angles to the direction of this temperature gradient. The diagram in Fig. 12.1 represents the situation, but now the gas is not streaming, as was assumed earlier. Here we assume that layer 1 is at a higher temperature than layer 2, layer 2 is at a higher temperature than layer 3, and so on. As a molecule travels from a layer at slightly higher temperature into a layer at slightly lower temperature and experiences a collision, it transports an excess of energy $-\frac{1}{2}fk(dT/dz)\lambda \cos\theta$ from one layer to the other. Similarly, a deficiency of energy per molecule of the same amount is transported from the layer of lower temperature to the layer of higher temperature. The total rate of transfer of energy between adjacent layers for all molecules with speed v and free path λ traveling in the θ,φ direction is equal to twice the product of this excess energy per molecule and the number of molecules given in Eq. (12.5). The resulting expression is integrated over φ from 0 to 2π, over θ from 0 to $\frac{1}{2}\pi$, and over all speeds and free paths. Thus the rate of heat conduction through the gas in the z-direction is

$$dQ/d\tau = -\tfrac{1}{6}fnk\bar{\lambda}\bar{v}\Delta S(dT/dz). \qquad (12.11)$$

But from elementary physics we recall that the Fourier law for unidirectional heat conduction in a medium is

$$dQ/d\tau = -\sigma_t A dT/dz, \qquad (12.12)$$

in which σ_t is the thermal conductivity of the medium, A is the cross-sectional area through which conduction takes place, and dT/dz is the temperature gradient along the conductor. By comparison of these equations we find

$$\sigma_t = \tfrac{1}{6}fnk\bar{\lambda}\bar{v} \qquad (12.13)$$

for an ideal gas with f degrees of freedom. Here, too, the thermal conductivity is independent of pressure and proportional to the square root of the absolute temperature. Experimental observations confirm these conclusions fairly well.

The ratio σ_t/η may be obtained from Eqs. (12.7) and (12.13). The Boltzmann constant is replaced by R/N_0 and mass m by M/N_0; then

$$c_v = \tfrac{1}{2}fR = \sigma_t M/\eta. \qquad (12.14)$$

From the first of these equations we find that the molar heat capacity at constant volume should equal 12,200 joules/kgm-mole-deg Kelvin for monatomic gases, 20,300 joules/kgm-mole-deg Kelvin for diatomic gases, and

24,400 joules/kgm-mole-deg Kelvin for polyatomic gases in which only translational and rotational degrees of freedom are counted. These predicted values for monatomic and diatomic gases are in good agreement with the observed values, as may be seen in the sixth column of Table 12.3.

TABLE 12.3.   *Test of Eq. (12.14) for Several Gases at 0°C.*

Gas	σ_t $\left(\dfrac{\text{joule}}{\text{m-sec-deg}}\right)$	M (kgm/mole)	η (newton-sec/m²)	$c_t(\sigma_t M/\eta)$ $\left(\dfrac{\text{joule}}{\text{mole-deg}}\right)$	c_v (obs.) $\left(\dfrac{\text{joule}}{\text{mole-deg}}\right)$	Difference $\left(\dfrac{\text{joule}}{\text{mole-deg}}\right)$
A	0.0162	39.94	21.0 × 10⁻⁶	30,800	12,700	18,100
Air	0.0237	28.93	17.2	39,900	20,800	19,100
CH₄	0.0301	16.03	10.2	47,300	26,800	20,500
C₂H₄	0.0166	28.05	8.36	55,700	33,600	22,100
CO	0.0227	28.01	16.6	38,300	20,700	17,600
CO₂	0.142	44.00	13.7	45,600	27,800	17,800
H₂	0.174	2.016	8.42	41,600	20,300	21,300
He	0.142	4.002	18.6	30,600	12,600	18,000
N₂	0.0237	28.02	16.6	40,000	20,900	19,100
Ne	0.0463	20.18	29.7	31,500	12,700	18,800
NH₃	0.0215	17.03	8.89	41,200	28,400	12,800
O₂	0.0239	32.00	19.1	40,000	20,900	19,100

From the second of Eqs. (12.14) values of c_v may be computed by inserting experimental data for σ_t, M, and η. The results are in marked disagreement with the observations, as is evident by comparing the fifth and sixth columns of Table 12.3. Curiously, the difference is nearly a constant for all the gases in the table with the exception of ammonia. Eucken proposed that $k_t M/\eta$ for polyatomic gases should be multiplied by the factor $4(9\gamma - 5)^{-1}$, in which γ is the ratio of the specific heat capacities c_p/c_v. Although this factor does bring about closer agreement for most of the polyatomic gases, it lacks a sound theoretical basis, and it is inadequate to account for the discrepancy in values of c_v for ammonia. The problem of the monatomic gases is discussed briefly in Section 12.6.

12.5. Diffusivity in Gases

Here a concentration gradient of molecular density dn/dz is assumed to exist in the z-direction. As in the previous sections, the ideal gas is divided into layers at right angles to the gradient. The excess number of molecules traveling from the more-dense to the adjacent less-dense layer in a unit volume is $\lambda \cos \theta (dn/dz)$. On the average, the mass conveyed from one layer to the other per molecule is obtained by multiplying by m and dividing by n. The total mass transported between adjacent layers for all molecules with speed v and free path λ and with direction of travel θ, φ is equal to twice the product of the transferred excess mass per molecule and the number of molecules given in Eq. (12.5). The resulting expression is integrated over the usual ranges of angles, free paths, and speeds. The rate of diffusion of molecules is

$$dN/d\tau = -\tfrac{1}{3}\bar{\lambda}\bar{v}\Delta S dn/dz. \qquad (12.15)$$

If the coefficient of diffusion D is defined by

$$D = \tfrac{1}{3}\bar{\lambda}\bar{v}, \qquad (12.16)$$

Eq (12.15) has the form of Fick's law for the rate of diffusion. Note that the coefficient of viscosity is equal to the product of the gas density and the coefficient of diffusion, and that the coefficient of thermal conductivity equals $\tfrac{1}{2}fnkD$. The coefficient of diffusion is subject to the same errors that affect the coefficients of viscosity and thermal conductivity.

12.6. Results from the Chapman-Enskog Theory

As implied in the introduction to this chapter, the foregoing results apply to gases which are under conditions only slightly different from equilibrium. The molecules are assumed to be rigid spheres and only first-order effects are taken into account. But a more rigorous treatment of the kinetic theory of dilute gases has been developed by Chapman and Enskog. In it an integro-differential equation due to Boltzmann is solved by a perturbation method, and the results are then applied to obtain expressions for the fluxes of energy, momentum, and mass and for the transport coefficients. The computations are too long and involved to include in this book, but they may be found in Chapter 7 of *Molecular Theory of Gases and Liquids* by Hirschfelder, Curtiss, and Bird (Wiley, New York, 1954).

From the Chapman-Enskog theory we find that mass transfer results not only from a concentration gradient, but also from a temperature gradient (thermodiffusion); similarly, we find that energy transfer results not only from a temperature gradient, but also from a concentration gradient (diffusion temperature). These and other cross-effects, which cannot be described in terms of simple kinetic theory, emerge naturally in the more rigorous treatment. They are discussed from an entirely different point of view in Chapter 20 under irreversible flow processes.

Mean free path, which plays a fundamental role in the simple kinetic theory of transport phenomena, does not appear explicitly in the Chapman-Enskog theory of gases. Instead all the transport coefficients involve a set of integrals which come from a detailed study of molecular encounters under the action of intermolecular forces. Applications of these general results are limited to some extent by our incomplete knowledge of these forces. Even so, first-order results indicate that the equations for the transport coefficients are identical in form with those in terms of collision cross-section from simple theory, but that they are multiplied by different numerical factors. Thus η is given by the equation

$$\eta = (5/16\Omega_\eta)(MkT/\pi N_0)^{1/2}. \tag{12.17}$$

Here the coefficient is $(5/16)$ instead of $(2/3)$ as in Eq. (12.10). When Eq. (12.17) is applied to hard spherical molecules, the collision cross-section for viscosity, Ω_η, is set equal to $\pi\sigma^2$. Similarly, the equations for the coefficients of thermal conductivity and diffusion are

$$\sigma_t = (25c_v/32M\Omega_t(MkT/\pi N_0)^{1/2} \tag{12.18}$$

and

$$D = (3/8\rho\Omega_D)(MkT/\pi N_0)^{1/2}, \tag{12.19}$$

in which the collision cross-sections Ω_t and Ω_D generally differ from one another and from Ω_η. The expressions for these several cross-sections depend on the specific intermolecular force law which is assumed to apply. (The results for coulombic interactions are given in Chapter 21.) On the other hand, Ω_t and Ω_D also equal $\pi\sigma^2$ for hard spherical molecules.

From Eqs. (12.17) and (12.18) we note that for a monatomic gas consisting of hard spherical molecules the molar specific heat capacity is related to thermal conductivity and viscosity by the equation

$$c_v = \tfrac{2}{5}(\sigma_t M/\eta). \tag{12.20}$$

According to this more rigorous theory, the values of $\sigma_t M/\eta$ for argon, helium, and neon as given in Table 12.3 should be multiplied by 0.40. This factor thus accounts for the major discrepancy between the theoretical and experimental results for the monatomic gases in Table 12.3.

12.7. Distribution of Free Paths and Mean Collision Frequency

Up to this point we have not had to introduce an explicit function for the distribution of free paths in a gas at uniform temperature and pressure, nor for a gas when a gradient of temperature, pressure, or velocity exists in it, provided the gradient is not too large. If we wish to study other problems, such as the frequency with which molecular collisions occur or the average distance a molecule travels in a specified time interval, we will need to know how the molecules are distributed among free paths.

At a given instant, we conceive each molecule in a gas to have associated with it a vector which has the magnitude of the free-path length of the molecule and the direction of its velocity vector. For a normal distribution of gas molecules the free-path vectors are assumed to have as random a distribution in magnitude and direction as do the velocity vectors. By exactly the same method which was applied to obtain the maxwellian distribution of speeds, we may derive a similar equation for the distribution of free paths. The result is

$$f(\lambda_x) = (\alpha/2\pi)^{1/2} \exp\left(-\tfrac{1}{2}\alpha\lambda_x^2\right) \tag{12.21}$$

for the distribution of one component and

$$f(\lambda) = 4\pi(\alpha/2\pi)^{3/2}\lambda^2 \exp\left(-\tfrac{1}{2}\alpha\lambda^2\right) \tag{12.22}$$

for the distribution of the resultant free paths, where

$$\lambda^2 = \lambda_x^2 + \lambda_y^2 + \lambda_z^2, \tag{12.23}$$

and α is a parameter characterizing the distribution. The value of $\bar{\lambda}$ in terms of α now can be found by integrating $\lambda f(\lambda)d\lambda$ over all values of λ:

$$\bar{\lambda} = (8/\pi\alpha)^{1/2}. \tag{12.24}$$

Little error is introduced in taking the limits of λ from 0 to ∞, provided the gas is neither too dense nor too rarefied. The value of $\bar{\lambda}$ should be not only much greater than the molecular diameter but also much smaller than the size of the gas container.

A free path begins and ends with a collision, and the molecule requires a finite time to travel it. These transit times should be as randomly distributed as the speeds and free paths, unless there exists a correlation between free-path lengths and speeds. The reciprocal of the transit time equals the effective rate of collision, and its mean value over a large number of molecules is the mean collision frequency.

A different way of looking at molecular chaos is to observe a single molecule in a gas, which is at constant pressure and temperature, over a long period of time—so long that the molecule suffers a very large number of collisions. Its speeds and free paths between collisions are assumed also to satisfy the normal distributions. It follows that the average speed and mean free path found by averaging the speeds and free paths of the single molecule, which suffers many collisions over a long period of time, ought to equal the average speed and mean free path found by averaging the speeds and free paths which many similar molecules of the gas have at a single instant of time. Furthermore, the mean collision frequency of the single molecule over a long time equals that associated with the free paths of the many molecules at any one moment.

The mean collision frequency of a molecule can be found therefore by integrating $(v/\lambda)f(v)f(\lambda)dvd\lambda$ over all values of λ and v; the result is

$$\bar{\nu} = 4\bar{v}/\pi\bar{\lambda}. \tag{12.25}$$

Often, it is assumed that this frequency equals simply $\bar{v}/\bar{\lambda}$, which is about 25% less than the value given in Eq. (12.25). Values of $\bar{\nu}$ for several gases are given in the last column of Table 12.1.

Suppose a molecule experiences many collisions during a specified time interval τ. How far is it from its starting point at the end of this time? If the free paths are all independent of one another, the problem is simply one of random flight. Each free path is resolved into its components λ_x, λ_y, and λ_z. The separate components in the three directions are added together, and then the resultant displacement is computed in the usual way:

$$r^2 = (\lambda_{x1} + \lambda_{x2} + \lambda_{x3} + \cdots)^2 + (\lambda_{y1} + \lambda_{y2} + \lambda_{y3} + \cdots)^2$$
$$+ (\lambda_{z1} + \lambda_{z2} + \lambda_{z3} + \cdots)^2$$

$$= \lambda_{x1}^2 + \lambda_{x2}^2 + \cdots + 2\lambda_{x1}\lambda_{x2} + \cdots + \lambda_{y1}^2 + \lambda_{y2}^2 + \lambda_{y3}^2 + \cdots$$
$$+ 2\lambda_{y1}\lambda_{y2} + \cdots.$$

If a very large number of collisions occur on the average, there will be as many negative cross-terms as positive ones and they will cancel. Finally,

$$r^2 = \lambda_1^2 + \lambda_2^2 + \lambda_3^2 + \cdots = \bar{\nu}\tau\overline{\lambda^2}$$

$$= 4\tau\bar{v}\overline{\lambda^2}/\pi\bar{\lambda} = \tfrac{3}{2}\tau\bar{\lambda}\bar{v}). \tag{12.26}$$

Here we have applied Eq. (12.25) and have replaced $\overline{\lambda^2}$ by its equivalent $(3\pi/8)(\bar{\lambda})^2$. From the data in Table 12.1 we find that the rms displacement of an argon atom during one second in the pure gas at 0°C and one atmosphere of pressure equals approximately 7.5 mm. For the hydrogen atom it is a little more than 2 cm under similar conditions. Meanwhile about ten-billion collisions have occurred!

12.8. Attenuation in a Molecular Beam

Imagine a beam of molecules, all of the same velocity, injected into a gas with normal distributions of speeds and free paths. Let us follow a group containing N_0 of them at the start. As the group moves along, collisions take place such as to remove molecules from it. Suppose there are N molecules left after the group has moved a distance z. As it moves through the next infinitesimal distance dz we assume that an additional number of molecules

dN is lost from the beam. The number lost is equal to the number of collisions which occur in distance dz, and this in turn is proportional to the number of molecules N remaining in the beam. We write

$$dN = -p_v N dz, \qquad (12.27)$$

from which we find

$$N = N_0 e^{-p_v z}. \qquad (12.28)$$

The proportionality constant p_v we name the collision probability coefficient for speed v, because the right side of Eq. (12.27) may be interpreted as the probability for the loss of dN molecules out of N traveling with speed v through distance dz. Equation (12.28) is called a survival equation, for it gives the number of molecules remaining in the group after traveling the distance z.

From another point of view, dN with a positive sign represents the number of molecules which have traveled a distance greater than z, but less than $z + dz$, before experiencing a collision. The average distance of travel for all N_0 molecules from the starting point until collisions take place therefore may be found by multiplying $-z/N_0$ into Eq. (12.27), where N is replaced by means of Eq. (12.28), and then by integrating the result over the complete range of values for z from 0 to ∞. By this means we find that p_v equals the reciprocal of the mean distance of travel $\bar{z}$. It is common practice to regard $\bar{z}$ as equivalent to $\bar{\lambda}$. Actually, because all the molecules under study have the same speed, $\bar{z}$ is more nearly equivalent to $\bar{\lambda}_v$. We may conceive the original group to consist of all the molecules in a mass of gas which have suffered a collision during a very short interval of time (almost instantaneously) and all of which acquire the same speed. Then z and dz are distances measured along each of the paths, and $\bar{z}$ is the average path length. Only if the distribution of free paths among these molecules is identical with the distribution of free paths among all molecules having the same speed will we find $\bar{z}$ equal to $\bar{\lambda}_v$, and therefore (from our discussion in Section 12.1) equal to $\bar{\lambda}$, the mean free path.

Problems

1. A cubic centimeter of nitrogen is confined in a small cubical chamber at atmospheric pressure and a temperature of $300°K$.
   (a) How many collisions per second are experienced by any one molecule?

(b) How many molecules collide with the walls of the chamber during one second?

2. The effect of temperature on the viscosity of water vapor between 100°C and 600°C is represented rather well by the Sutherland semi-empirical equation

$$\eta = AT^{1/2}/(1 + B/T),$$

in which $A = 1.501 \times 10^{-5}$ poise-deg$^{-(1/2)}$ and $B = 446.8°K$. What is the ratio of the effective collision cross-sections for viscosity at 100°C and 600°C? If the Sutherland equation were to apply outside this range of temperatures, at what temperatures would the effective cross-section be one-half that at 100°C and twice that at 100°C?

3. What is the collision frequency of an oxygen molecule at 300°K and atmospheric pressure? What is it at 300°K and a pressure of 10^{-6} atm? At 300°K and 10^{-10} atm?

4. The coefficient of viscosity and density for xenon at 0°C are 21.01×10^{-6} newton-sec/m² and 5.851 kgm/m³. Compute values for the average speed, mean free path, collision diameter, and collision frequency of the xenon atoms. Do this also for molecules of water vapor at 100°C where the coefficient of viscosity equals 12.55×10^{-6} newton-sec/m² and the density equals 0.598 kgm/m³.

5. The coefficient of diffusion for carbon dioxide at 0°C equals 13.9×10^{-6} m²/sec. Determine a value for the collision cross-section Ω_D of carbon dioxide and compare it with Ω_t and Ω_η.

6. Evaluate $\overline{\lambda^2}$ in terms of α, where α equals $8/\pi(\overline{\lambda})^2$.

7. Aluminum is evaporated in a small furnace under a bell-jar. Its atoms immediately pass through a small aperture and then travel to a clean glass plate which is to be aluminized. The distance between the aperture and the glass plate is 40 cm. What should the pressure under the bell-jar be in order that 90% of the aluminum atoms which leave the aperture reach the plate?

CHAPTER 13

Statistical Thermodynamics

Statistical thermophysics is divided roughly into studies of systems in equilibrium and studies of transport and flow phenomena. We shall limit the discussion in this chapter largely to systems in equilibrium, although some attention will be paid to rates of approach to equilibrium. At first glance this study appears to cover the same ground as thermodynamics, and frequently it is called statistical thermodynamics. Why then introduce statistics and make the subject more complicated? The answer is not difficult to find. By postulating the existence of a suitable microstructure for a system, consisting of many microsystems which may be more or less complex in themselves, and by applying the methods of probability to the distribution of these microsystems among microstates with respect to energy, it is possible to correlate the resulting formulas with those of thermodynamics. From |them we may then derive equations of state, such as that for an ideal gas; we may evaluate certain indeterminate constants of thermodynamics such as appear in the equation for the entropy of an ideal gas; and we may determine explicit relations for the thermodynamic functions, such as the Helmholtz function. Perhaps more important than these specific results is the new insight and clear understanding of thermodynamic concepts gained by the introduction of the statistical point of view.

A gas containing N molecules is a system within which each molecule is a microsystem. Although a molecule is complex, this complexity need not concern us at the moment. All N molecules are supposed to be identical, save for the energy associated with each one. The fundamental question in statistical thermodynamics then is how many microsystems (molecules) are there

191

on the average in each accessible energy state consistent with a specified value for the total energy of the system (gas). Under equilibrium conditions this array of numbers represents a normal distribution of the microsystems. We ask essentially for the number, or else the fraction of the total number, of microsystems on the average in each energy state at a given instant of time. This problem may be approached in another way. We may observe the energy of a single microsystem of the normal distribution over and over again for a long time and finally ask for the number of observations, or the fraction of the total number of observations, that the given microsystem occupied each accessible energy state consistent with the specified value for the total energy of the system.[1] In either case it is numbers or fractions that are evaluated. The assumption then is made that the most probable value of a physical quantity $\overline{Q}$ is equal to the sum of $f_i Q_i$ over all the states, where f_i is the fraction of the microsystems on the average in the i state and Q_i is the value of the quantity for that state.

The analysis is especially difficult if energy terms are introduced as a result of interactions between the microsystems, for then the total energy of the system is no longer simply the sum of the energies of the microsystems. On the other hand, in order for the microsystems to acquire a normal distribution a slight interaction must occur between them, but it is assumed to be negligible in evaluating the total energy. The results of the statistical analysis then are especially applicable to gases and crystals. In crystals the microsystems are assumed to occupy more or less fixed positions and to acquire a normal distribution among the energy states through an intermediary minute amount of free particles which convey energy from microsystem to microsystem.

We may imagine the microsystems to exist in a phase space, each point of which represents a microstate. By phase space we mean a six-dimensional space having position coordinates x, y, z and momentum coordinates p_x, p_y, p_z. For analytical purposes an element of volume around a point in this space is sufficiently small that all the microsystems within it are assumed to be in microstates infinitesimally close to that of the given point. Sometimes it is

---

[1] The statement expressing the equivalence of the results from the two methods of attacking the problem is called the ergodic hypothesis. This hypothesis is rather difficult to justify, but its study has led to many important contributions in theoretical physics. Its validity is seriously questioned by Tolman and Fowler, for it implies that each microsystem must pass through every accessible energy state in a continuous fashion, and this seems almost an impossibility. Tolman suggests that the assumption of equal *a priori* probabilities for different regions of equal extent in phase space, wherein the systems are conceived to exist, is more valuable for statistical studies than is the ergodic hypothesis. It is a consequence of Liouville's theorem, which is discussed briefly in Section 13.5.

convenient to think of the phase space as being broken up into compartments, each of which contains microsystems all occupying the same microstate.

Many of the difficulties inherent in the foregoing approach to statistical thermophysics may be avoided if the entire system is considered to be a single macrosystem among infinitely many replicas of it in as many energy states, all characterized by the same value of absolute temperature. This assembly of systems, or ensemble, was first introduced and studied by Gibbs. In it we do not worry about interactions between microsystems or precisely how the microsystems are distributed within a macrosystem. Any one arrangement of the microsystems among the microstates is a complexion of the macrosystem, and this complexion may be represented by a single point in a hyperphase space of $6N$ dimensions.

13.1. *Thermophysical Probability*

In mathematics, biology, psychology, and sociology the probability for the occurrence of an event equals the ratio of the number of times the event occurs on the average to the total number of times available for its occurrence. In classical statistical thermophysics the probability for a microsystem to exist in a microstate equals the ratio of the number of microsystems in that state on the average to the total number of microsystems available. Probability has significance in both situations only if the distributions result from random processes. The definitions then are very similar. The analogy can be carried a little further if we examine a specific system. Consider a nonloaded coin to be a microsystem which may occupy either of two microstates: heads up or tails up. The coin may be tossed many times and its aspect noted each time, or the coin and many others exactly like it may be tossed once and the number of coins in the heads-up and in the tails-up microstates noted. Observation justifies our surmise that the coins are very nearly equally divided between the heads-up and tails-up microstates. The *a priori* probability for the coin to land in one or the other microstate is $\frac{1}{2}$.

Suppose now that the system consists of two identical nonloaded coins. It may exist in any one of three microstates: heads–heads, tails–tails, or heads–tails. The heads–tails aspects will occur twice as often as either heads–heads or tails–tails, and therefore the *a priori* probabilities associated with the three microstates are $\frac{1}{4}$, $\frac{1}{4}$, and $\frac{1}{2}$. If the coins can be distinguished from one another, the number of distinct complexions is materially increased, for now an interchange of the two coins produces a new complexion. The *a priori* probability associated with each microstate having one of the heads–heads, tails–tails, or heads–tails aspects is reduced to $\frac{1}{8}$, $\frac{1}{8}$, and $\frac{1}{4}$, respectively. The several complexions of a system of three similar but distinguishable coins are shown in Fig. 13.1. The *a priori* probabilities for a single microstate with the heads–heads–heads, tails–tails–tails, heads–heads–tails, and heads–tails–tails aspects are $\frac{1}{48}$, $\frac{1}{48}$, $\frac{1}{16}$, and $\frac{1}{16}$.

The foregoing discussion may be extended to systems consisting of any number of coins. The *a priori* probability for the occurrence of n_1 heads–up and n_2 tails-up aspects among n identical nonloaded coins is

$$W = (n!/n_1!n_2!)(\tfrac{1}{2})^n, \tag{13.1}$$

where $n_1 + n_2$ equals n. Any symbol such as $n!$ represents the product of the integers from one through n and is called n-factorial. If the coins can be distinguished from each other, the probability w for a single complexion is $W/n!$. In arriving at Eq. (13.1) we have supposed that the heads-up aspect is as likely to occur as the tails-up aspect. However, if the coins are loaded— all exactly alike so the chance for heads is g_1, and for tails is g_2, where $g_1 + g_2$ equals unity—then the probability w associated with each complexion is

$$w = g_1^{n_1}g_2^{n_2}/n_1!n_2!. \tag{13.2}$$

For systems consisting of microsystems with more than two aspects, such as loaded dice, Eq. (13.2) may be generalized

$$w = g_1^{n_1}g_2^{n_2}\cdots g_i^{n_i}\cdots g_l^{n_l}/n_1!n_2!\cdots n_i!\cdots n_l! \tag{13.3}$$

Here l represents the number of microstates, so

$$\Sigma_1^l\, n_i = n, \tag{13.4}$$

and

$$\Sigma_1^l\, g_i = 1. \tag{13.5}$$

For the following discussion n_i is assumed to be very large.

We now ask: Under what conditions will w have its maximum value? Our intuition suggests that n_i should equal ng_i. Let us see if this is a reasonable answer by maximizing w subject to the condition that n is constant. The computation is somewhat easier if we maximize $\ln w$ rather than w directly. By Stirling's formula[2]

$$\ln n_i! = n_i \ln n_i - n_i + \tfrac{1}{2}\ln(2\pi n_i) + \ln(1 + 1/12n_i + \cdots), \tag{13.6}$$

which reduces to

$$\ln n_i! \cong n_i \ln n_i - n_i \tag{13.7}$$

[2] The derivation of Stirling's formula may be found in mathematical treatises; for example, Whittaker, E. T., and G. N. Watson, *Modern Analysis*, 4th ed., p. 251 (The University Press, Cambridge, 1935). The validity of the approximation may be tested by demonstrating that $\ln n_i!$ equals $n_i \ln n_i - n_i$ to less than 1% even for such a small value of n_i as 100.

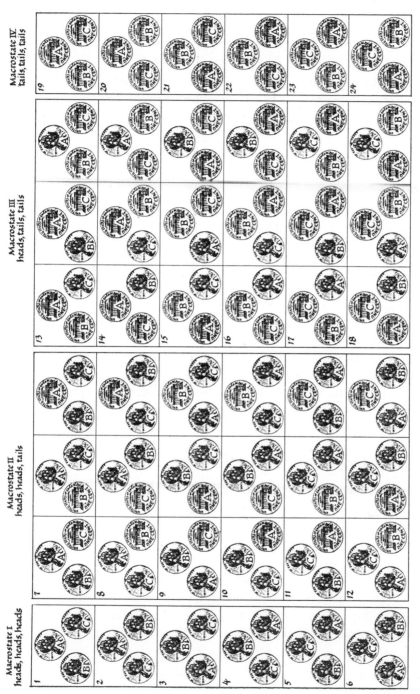

Figure 13.1. The 48 complexions of a system of three similar but distinguishable coins.

if n_i is sufficiently large. Then we can write

$$\ln w = \ln W/n! = -\Sigma_1^l \ln n_i! + \Sigma_1^l n_i \ln g_i$$
$$= n - \Sigma_1^l n_i \ln n_i + \Sigma_1^l n_i \ln g_i. \qquad (13.8)$$

Let n_i vary by a very small amount and equate the variation in $\ln w$ to zero. Because of the meaning of $\ln w$ we are assured that this computation yields the condition for an absolute maximum value for w and therefore for W too;

$$\delta \ln w = -\Sigma_1^l \delta n_i(\ln n_i - \ln g_i) = 0, \qquad (13.9)$$

where n is constant, so

$$\delta n = \Sigma_1^l \delta n_i = 0. \qquad (13.10)$$

From this equation we see that all the n_i except one are arbitrary. Eliminate n_1 between Eqs. (13.9) and (13.10). Thus

$$\Sigma_2^l \delta n_i[\ln (n_i/g_i) - \ln (n_1/g_1)] = 0 \qquad (13.11)$$

is satisfied for all arbitrary variations δn_i only if the expression in brackets vanishes for every term. That is, the ratio n_i/g_i must be a constant for all states from 1 through l. The value of this constant may be determined now by means of Eqs. (13.4) and (13.5), and it is found to equal n. Our surmise that n_i should equal ng_i is justified.

For an assembly of coins where g_1 is the weight of the heads-up and g_2 is the weight of the tails-up aspect, the most likely distribution consists of g_1n heads and g_2n tails. Therefore, if the coins are not loaded, they are equally divided between the heads-up and tails-up aspects.

13.2. Accessibility of Microstates

Although there may be an infinite number of microstates in which the microsystems may be placed, ordinarily only relatively few of them are available because of limitations on one or more thermophysical coordinates of the macroscopic system. Classically we suppose the number of *accessible* microstates is so small that a very large number of microsystems occupies each of the microstates. Then Stirling's approximation may be applied to the factorial of each occupation number. The principal quantity that limits the accessibility of microstates in physical systems is the total energy. To the conditions expressed in Eqs. (13.4) and (13.5) we add

$$U = \Sigma_1^l n_iU_i, \qquad (13.12)$$

where U_i is the energy associated with the ith microstate and n_i is the occupation number.

If the total energy of a system is constant, the variation δU equals zero, so

$$\Sigma_1^l U_i \delta n_i = 0 \qquad (13.13)$$

is an additional relation between the δn_i. It may be combined with Eq. (13.10) to eliminate δn_2 from Eq. (13.11). However, it is somewhat easier to carry out the analysis by means of Lagrange's method of undetermined multipliers (see Section 11.9). Multiply Eq. (13.10) by α and Eq. (13.13) by β and add them to Eq. (13.9). The result is

$$\Sigma_1^l \delta n_i(\alpha + \beta U_i - \ln n_i + \ln g_i) = 0. \qquad (13.14)$$

We can select the multipliers in such a way that two of the l terms in this sum vanish. Since the δn_i in the remaining $l - 2$ terms are completely independent of one another we are at liberty to assign any values we please to them. Suppose only one has a non zero value and all the others are zero. Then Eq. (13.14) reduces to a single term,

$$\delta n_i(\alpha + \beta U_i - \ln n_i + \ln g_i) = 0.$$

Because δn_i is not zero its coefficient must vanish, and therefore

$$n_i = g_i \exp (\alpha + \beta U_i). \qquad (13.15)$$

This equation for occupation number applies to each state of the system, since the foregoing assignment of values for the δn_i was completely arbitrary. By substituting these values of n_i back into Eqs. (13.4) and (13.12) we may evaluate the multipliers α and β. We find

$$\frac{n_i}{n} = \frac{g_i \exp \beta U_i}{\Sigma_1^l g_i \exp \beta U_i} = \frac{1}{\beta} \frac{\partial}{\partial U_i} [\ln \Sigma_1^l g_i \exp \beta U_i]_\beta, \qquad (13.16)$$

where the average energy per microsystem is

$$\frac{U}{n} = \frac{\Sigma_1^l g_i U_i \exp \beta U_i}{\Sigma_1^l g_i \exp \beta U_i} = \frac{\partial}{\partial \beta} [\ln \Sigma_1^l g_i \exp \beta U_i]_{\text{all } U_i}. \qquad (13.17)$$

Although β is implicitly determinable as a function of U/n it is more significant to consider U/n as a function of β. Later we shall identify β with the reciprocal of the absolute temperature of the system. Equation (13.16) represents the normal distribution of microsystems among the microstates of energies U_i and weights g_i; it is the canonical distribution of Maxwell and Boltzmann.[3]

The bracketed expression in Eqs. (13.16) and (13.17) we shall represent

---

[3] In physical statistics it is common practice to assign numbers greater than unity to the weight factors in the following way. The phase space which is accessible to the system is divided into a very large number of small cells G of equal volume such that there would be G_i of these cells in the ith state. Then $g_i = G_i/G$. Therefore, in terms of the weight factors G_i the classical probability of Maxwell and Boltzmann becomes $W_{M-B} = WG^n$, and the canonical distribution may be written in terms of the G_i's instead of the g_i's.

hereafter by F. It is the logarithm of the partition sum or weighted Zustand-summe:

$$F = \ln \Sigma_1^l \, g_i \exp \beta U_i = \ln Z. \tag{13.18}$$

Perhaps Z is the most important function in all of statistical thermophysics, for it appears time and again in statistical equations. In it the summation may be replaced by an integration where the energies of the microstates form a continuous spectrum.

If n_i is eliminated from Eq. (13.8) by means of Eq. (13.16), the resulting expression reduces to

$$\ln w = nF - n \ln n + n - \beta U$$
$$= \beta(E - U), \tag{13.19}$$

The combination of symbols $nF - n \ln n + n$ has been replaced by the product of β and an energy function E which is related to U, as may be discovered by finding its derivative with respect to β, holding all the U_i constant:

$$(dE/d\beta)_{\text{all } U_i} = -\beta^{-2}(nF - n \ln n + n) + \beta^{-1}n(\partial F/\partial \beta)_{\text{all } U_i}$$
$$= -\beta^{-1}(E - U). \tag{13.20}$$

If this equation is rearranged to give U in terms of E, it bears a curious resemblance to the thermodynamic relation

$$U = A - T(\partial A/\partial T)_V. \tag{13.21}$$

The resemblance is even more striking if β^{-1} is replaced by the parameter λ, so

$$U = E - \lambda(\partial E/\partial \lambda)_{\text{all } U_i}. \tag{13.22}$$

The fact that all U_i are held constant in developing Eq. (13.22) is interpreted to mean that no work is done to alter the accessible microstates, and this corresponds to holding the volume constant in the thermodynamic treatment. The analogy between Eqs. (13.21) and (13.22) becomes complete if the Helmholtz function A is identified with E and if λ is proportional to the absolute temperature T. As will become clear later, it is convenient to introduce $-k$ for the proportionality constant; thus

$$\lambda = \beta^{-1} = -kT, \tag{13.23}$$

and

$$A = -nkT(F - \ln n + 1)$$
$$= -nkT[1 - \ln n + \ln \Sigma_1^l \, g_i \exp (-U_i/kT)]. \tag{13.24}$$

The relation between statistical thermodynamics and classical thermodynamics is found only by a suitable analogy. In the end it is the success of the statistical point of view in furthering our understanding of thermophysical problems that matters.

Now we recall that S equals $-(\partial A/\partial T)_V$ and P equals $-(\partial A/\partial V)_T$; thus we find

$$S = kn[F - \ln n + 1 + T(\partial F/\partial T)_V] \qquad (13.25)$$

and

$$P = nkT(\partial F/\partial V)_T. \qquad (13.26)$$

All we need do is to evaluate F for a particular system in terms of T and V in order to determine explicit relations for A, S, and P.

From the equations for U/n and $\ln w$, namely Eqs. (13.17) and (13.19), we now see that Eq. (13.25) reduces to

$$S = k \ln w,$$

an equation first proposed by Boltzmann. He had argued that since both entropy and probability increase and reach maximum values as a system becomes less ordered, the simplest relation between them would be a proportionality between entropy and the logarithm of the probability. Frequently this relation serves as the starting point for developing thermodynamic equations.

13.3 Partition Function of a Monatomic Ideal Gas

We have introduced some of the fundamental concepts of statistical thermophysics and have related certain quantities in it to temperature, entropy, and the Helmholtz function. Let us now apply these ideas to determine an explicit relation for the partition function of a monatomic ideal gas, and therefore F, in terms of the macroscopic thermodynamic coordinates.

Each molecule is a microsystem in the ideal gas. Energy U_i of the ith microstate for this monatomic system is the kinetic energy

$$U_i = \tfrac{1}{2}mv_i^2 = p_i^2/2m, \qquad (13.27)$$

where p_i represents the linear momentum of the molecules in the ith microstate. Because the speeds, and therefore the momenta and energy, form continuous spectra, the summation in the partition function is replaced by an integration. This integration extends over the three position and the three momentum coordinates of a system in phase space. Let an element of volume be represented by $d\tau$; then for a monatomic molecule

$$Z = c \int_\tau \exp\left(-p^2/2mkT\right)d\tau, \tag{13.28}$$

where the weights of all the accessible microstates are assumed to be proportional to equal volume elements $d\tau$. The proportionality constant c depends on the unit of volume in the phase space.

The integration of Eq. (13.28) over the positional coordinates is simply the total space volume V accessible to the monatomic system, and the integral for each of the three momentum coordinates is of the form

$$\int_{-\infty}^{\infty} \exp\left(-p_x^2/2mkT\right)dp_x = (2\pi mkT)^{1/2}. \tag{13.29}$$

Although the momentum cannot be infinite if the total energy of the gas is a constant finite value, the exponential is so sharp that no serious error is made in extending the limits of the integral to infinity. Therefore, the partition function for the monatomic ideal gas is

$$Z = cV(2\pi mkT)^{3/2}, \tag{13.30}$$

and its Helmholtz function is

$$A = -nkT \ln\left[cVen^{-1}(2\pi mkT)^{3/2}\right]. \tag{13.31}$$

Relations for the entropy, internal energy, and other thermodynamic variables of the gas now may be set down.

The statistical entropy of the ideal monatomic gas is

$$S = nk \ln\left[cVe^{5/2}n^{-1}(2\pi mkT)^{3/2}\right]. \tag{13.32}$$

Here we have an equation similar to that for the thermodynamic entropy of the ideal gas, but the constant appears to be more explicit. The implications of this result are discussed in the following section. If the foregoing relations for A and S are introduced into $A + TS$, the internal energy of the monatomic ideal gas comes out to equal $\frac{3}{2}nkT$, in agreement with the analysis of Section 11.6. The pressure within the gas may now be found from Eq. (13.26); it is simply nkT/V. By statistical methods we have derived the state equation for an ideal gas. Apparently no recourse has been made to experimental observations, as is so necessary in classical thermodynamics. Actually these results for the entropy, internal energy, and pressure of an ideal gas can agree with earlier results only if k is interpreted to be the Boltzmann constant. It is here, in a sense, that experimental observation is brought to bear on the problem.

13.4. The Liouville Theorem and Equal Probability in Phase Space

In Section 13.3 the statistical weights were assumed to be proportional to the elements of volume in phase space. We need to justify this assumption and to develop its implications.

Suppose a group of microsystems occupies an increment of volume in phase space at a given instant of time. Each microsystem in the group moves through a continuous series of microstates in the phase space as its momentum and position change due to collisions and other processes. If there is a large number of microsystems in the group and if they form a subsystem with a normal distribution, the volume of the increment must remain constant in time even though it may be drawn out into a completely filamentous net. The density of the microsystems therefore is constant. These principles of constant extension-in-phase and constant density-in-phase are two ways of stating the Liouville theorem.[4] If the volume occupied by the group of micro-systems in phase space were altered, even though the total energy and space volume of the system remain constant, the distribution would be changed from the normal one. On the other hand, whenever a microsystem in a normal distribution moves from one microstate to another, a second micro-system must enter the vacated microstate. Fundamentally, there occurs a continual interchange of microsystems among the microstates such as to maintain the normal distribution. This is essentially the principle of detailed balance.

A group of microsystems occupies equal elements of phase space for equal lengths of time; otherwise the density-in-phase does not remain constant. That is, the chance for a microsystem to be in one element or another of phase space is equally probable. The statistical weight for an element of phase space therefore is proportional only to the volume of that element. This we assumed in the foregoing discussion.

13.5. The Maxwellian Distribution of Speeds in a Gas

We replace g_i in Eq. (13.16) by $cd\tau$, n_i by dn, and U_i by $\frac{1}{2}m(v_x^2 + v_y^2 + v_z^2)$. As before, the integration over the position coordinates may be performed

---

[4] For a proof of the theorem see Kittel, C., *Elementary Statistical Physics*, p. 9 (Wiley, New York, 1958).

immediately so long as U_i depends only on momentum. We substitute $m^3 dv_x dv_y dv_z$ for the differential element $dp_x dp_y dp_z$, and the relation for the partition function of an ideal gas, Eq. (13.30), for the summation in the denominator. The final expression then may be written

$$dn = n(2\pi kT/m)^{-3/2} \exp \left[-\tfrac{1}{2}m(v_x^2 + v_y^2 + v_z^2)/kT\right]dv_x dv_y dv_z$$

$$= 4\pi n(2\pi kT/m)^{-3/2}v^2 \exp \left(-\tfrac{1}{2}mv^2/kT\right)dv, \qquad (13.33)$$

which we recognize to be the maxwellian distribution of speeds in an ideal gas.

13.6. Harmonic Oscillators

The partition sum of Section 13.2 need not be restricted to the essentially free particles of a monatomic ideal gas, as described in Sections 13.3 and 13.5. Consider an assembly of nearly independent harmonic oscillators with energies that are multiples of $h\nu$, where h is the Planck constant and ν is the fundamental frequency of the oscillators. Furthermore, suppose the accessible energy states differ by *integral* multiples of $h\nu$. For generality let us assume that

$$U_i = (a + i)h\nu, \qquad (13.34)$$

where i represents any positive integer and a is a constant which gives a measure of the energy when i equals zero. The phase space is divided into equal volume elements such that $g_1 = g_2 = \cdots = g_i = \cdots = g$. Then the partition sum for the harmonic oscillators is

$$Z = \Sigma_0^\infty g_i e^{\beta U_i} = g e^{a\beta h\nu} \Sigma_0^\infty e^{i\beta h\nu}$$

$$= g e^{a\beta h\nu}/(1 - e^{\beta h\nu}). \qquad (13.35)$$

From this result relations for the average energy per oscillator, the entropy, and the Helmholtz function may be developed by means of the equations in Section 13.2.

Only the relation for the energy per oscillator is given here in order to identify the assembly of oscillators with the blackbody radiative system. We find

$$U/n = (\partial F/\partial \beta)_{\text{all } U_i} = ah\nu + h\nu/[e^{h\nu/kT} - 1], \qquad (13.36)$$

where $-1/kT$ has been substituted for β.

From quantum mechanics we know that the first term on the right with a equal to $\tfrac{1}{2}$ and that the first term on the right represents the zero-point energy possessed by the harmonic oscillator at absolute zero degrees. Ordinarily at elevated temperature this term is omitted from the expression for U/n, and then we have the Planck equation for the spectral distribution in blackbody radiation. The assembly of harmonic oscillators with an infinite number of energy states that differ by whole quanta is a useful construct for studying the blackbody radiative system. The statistics that apply to this assembly were first developed by Bose for radiative systems and were applied by Einstein to ideal gas systems. They differ from the Maxwell-Boltzmann statistics largely by the condition that all microsystems are identical and cannot be distinguished from one another, so no new complexion arises when a rearrangement of the microsystems is made among the energy states.

A second type of harmonic oscillator, the Fermi oscillator, differs from the foregoing Planck oscillator by having only two energy states, 0 and U', so

$$Z = g + g e^{\beta U'}, \tag{13.37}$$

where again we have assumed the phase space is divided into equal volume elements. The average energy per oscillator then is

$$U/n = U'/[e^{U'/kT} + 1], \tag{13.38}$$

which has exactly the same form as the average energy for a system satisfying the Fermi-Dirac statistics.

The development of the Bose-Einstein and Fermi-Dirac statistics will be postponed until Chapter 17.

Problems

1. A pair of unloaded dice is tossed. What is the probability that seven spots will show? What is the probability that four spots will show on one die and three on the other?

2. (a) Show that $\exp(-\alpha)$ of Eq. (13.15), as it applies to a monatomic ideal gas, is proportional to the $\frac{5}{2}$ power of the temperature and inversely proportional to the pressure.

   (b) For helium and molecular hydrogen, c in Eq. (13.30) equals h^{-3}, where h is Planck's constant. Evaluate $\exp(-\alpha)$ per molecule for helium and hydrogen at their normal boiling points. Only if $\exp(-\alpha)$ is very much larger than unity may Maxwell-Boltzmann statistics be applied to a gas. Is this permissible for helium, hydrogen or heavier gases?

3. Find a general equation for the Gibbs function G in terms of F, the logarithm of the partition sum. Set down the Gibbs function for a monatomic ideal gas. Since the chemical potential μ equals the specific Gibbs function of a pure gas, show that α in Eq. (13.15) equals μ/kT.

4. (a) Derive a value for the partition function of a two-dimensional monatomic gas which is confined to surface area D.

   (b) Obtain an equation for the Helmholtz function of this gas, and by means of it find the state equation.

5. Consider an isothermal gas in a uniform gravitational field, such as might exist over limited ranges of altitude above the earth's surface. The energy of the ith molecule at height z_i from an arbitrary level of zero potential then is the sum of a potential energy and a kinetic energy term; namely

$$U_i = mgz_i + \tfrac{1}{2}mv_i^2,$$

in which m is the mass of the molecule and g is the gravitational acceleration. Show that the partition function Z for this gas has the form

$$Z = \exp F = cD(kT/mg)(2\pi mkT)^{3/2},$$

where D is the cross-sectional area of a column of the gas, and then determine the distribution function for the molecules in terms of altitude z. This result reduces to the law of atmospheres,

$$p = p_0 \exp(-mgz/kT),$$

if n is replaced by p/kT, where p is atmospheric pressure at height z above the zero-potential level at pressure p_0.

6. A system consists of 2000 particles distributed between two nondegenerate energy states $U_1 = kT_0$ and $U_2 = 2kT_0$.

   (a) Find the most probable distribution-in-energy in classical statistics if the total energy of the system is 2800 kT_0.

   (b) Obtain the equation for the entropy of this system as a function of the total energy, and plot an $S - U$ diagram in units of k and kT_0.

   (c) Determine the temperature of the system when its total energy has each of the following values: 2800 kT_0, 3000 kT_0, and 3200 kT_0. Interpret the results.

CHAPTER 14

Brownian Motion and
Random Fluctuations

Iᶠ the number of molecules in a closed gas system is sufficiently large and if enough time has elapsed, the mass and energy densities of the gas seem to approach uniform constant values with near certainty. The final state of the system, from a macroscopic point of view, is one of complete thermodynamic equilibrium. But suppose that at one instant more molecules have components of velocities in one direction than in the reverse; then the system no longer would be in equilibrium, and the densities would tend toward nonuniformity. Although this condition is not likely to prevail, there is no reason for excluding it as a possibility. Furthermore, it is more apt to occur in systems containing relatively few molecules per unit volume.

Suppose a gas system is divided into subsystems each containing exactly N molecules. Let Z represent a physical property of one of these subsystems at any instant, such as energy E or momentum M in one direction. Because of interactions between subsystems, Z changes almost continually. On the average, however, its value equals the ratio of Z for the whole system divided by the number of subsystems, or the product of N into the average value of Z per molecule, which we shall represent by $\bar{z}$. We write

$$Z - \bar{Z} = \Sigma_i(z_i - \bar{z}), \qquad (14.1)$$

where $\bar{Z}$ equals $N\bar{z}$, and the summation extends over the N molecules. If the deviations $Z - \bar{Z}$ were averaged over all the subsystems, the result would be zero. Instead of doing this, let us solve for the mean square deviation $\langle (Z - \bar{Z})^2 \rangle$[1] In this way we have a measure of the fluctuations in Z. First we note that

$$(Z - \bar{Z})^2 = \Sigma_{i,j}(z_i - \bar{z})(z_j - \bar{z}). \qquad (14.2)$$

Here we have been careful to include all the cross-terms, for i can refer to one molecule and j to another in the subsystem. The motions of the molecules are completely independent, save during collisions, but z_i and z_j range over the same set of values. Consequently, for all pairs of molecules we find

$$\langle (z_i - \bar{z})(z_j - \bar{z}) \rangle = \langle z_i - \bar{z} \rangle \langle z_j - \bar{z} \rangle = 0, \qquad (14.3)$$

and therefore only the N terms in which i equals j are left. Thus

$$\langle (Z - \bar{Z})^2 \rangle = \Sigma_i \langle (z_i - \bar{z})^2 \rangle. \qquad (14.4)$$

In other words, the mean square deviation of Z from the average for a subsystem equals the sum of the mean square deviations of z from the average for the N individual molecules.

The right side of Eq. (14.4) is expanded and $\overline{z^2}$ is assumed to have the same value for all subsystems; hence,

$$\langle (Z - \bar{Z})^2 \rangle = N[\overline{z^2} - (\bar{z})^2]. \qquad (14.5)$$

The averages $\bar{z}$ and $\overline{z^2}$ may now be evaluated by applications of the distribution law.

Suppose both sides of Eq. (14.5) are divided by $(\bar{Z})^2$; we get

$$\left\langle \left(\frac{Z - \bar{Z}}{\bar{Z}} \right)^2 \right\rangle = \frac{1}{N} \left[\frac{\overline{z^2} - (\bar{z})^2}{(\bar{z})^2} \right]. \qquad (14.6)$$

The relative mean square deviation is inversely proportional to N. Ordinarily, $(\bar{z})^2$ and $\overline{z^2}$ are of the same order of magnitude, so the relative mean square deviation is extremely small if N is very large. We conclude that the energy, momentum, and other physical properties of a system normally differ almost imperceptibly from their mean values. That is, the distribution function has a very sharp maximum, a conclusion in agreement with assumptions we have already made about it.

14.1. Energy and Momentum Fluctuations

If E represents the energy of a subsystem at any instant and U represents its average internal energy, then, from Eq. (14.5),

$$\langle (E - U)^2 \rangle = N[\overline{\epsilon^2} - (\bar{\epsilon})^2]. \qquad (14.7)$$

---

[1] The symbol $\langle Q \rangle$, meaning $\bar{Q}$, is useful for representing average values if Q is rather complicated.

We recall that $\bar{\epsilon}$ equals $\frac{3}{2}kT$ and note that

$$\overline{\epsilon^2} = (kT)^{-(3/2)}(2/\sqrt{\pi}) \int_0^\infty \epsilon^{5/2} \exp{(-\epsilon/kT)}d\epsilon$$
$$= \tfrac{15}{4}(kT)^2 \qquad\qquad (14.8)$$

by application of the maxwellian distribution law in which we replace $\frac{1}{2}mv^2$ by ϵ. Finally,

$$\overline{\epsilon^2} - (\bar{\epsilon})^2 = (\tfrac{15}{4} - \tfrac{9}{4})(kT)^2 = \tfrac{3}{2}(kT)^2; \qquad\qquad (14.9)$$

therefore,

$$\langle (E - U)^2 \rangle = \tfrac{3}{2}N(kT)^2 \qquad\qquad (14.10)$$

and

$$\langle (E - U)^2/U^2 \rangle = \tfrac{2}{3}N\ ^1. \qquad\qquad (14.11)$$

By a similar analysis we find that the mean square deviation of the momentum of a subsystem in one direction equals $\frac{1}{2}NmkT(\pi - 1)/\pi$, and its relative value is $(\pi - 1)N^{-1}$. If N is large, the relative values of the mean square deviations of both energy and momentum in one direction are minute. If N is small, they can become significantly large.

Suppose N is small and the volume occupied by one subsystem is replaced by a particle. This particle now is subjected to all the random collisions formerly experienced by the subsystem, and its motions are equivalent to those of a single massive molecule. It exhibits the same unceasing agitation as the surrounding molecules and, consequently, moves hither and thither in an erratic manner. This motion is a manifestation of molecular random flight on an enlarged scale; it is the brownian motion which was described in Section 11.1.

14.2. Theory of Brownian Motion

In 1906 Einstein[2] and Smoluchowski[3] separately derived essentially the same equation for brownian motion by different methods. Then, in 1908, Langevin[4] gave an elementary proof which we reproduce here.

From instant to instant a small particle in a fluid is pushed about by molecular forces arising from the rate of change of excess momentum at the surface of the particle. At the same time this motion is retarded by forces of viscous interactions, which are assumed to be proportional to particle velocity. The vector sum of these forces is equated to the product of the mass and acceleration of the particle; thus for the y-component we get

[2] Einstein, A., *Ann. d. Physik*, **19**, 371 (1906).
[3] Smoluchowski, M., *Akad. Sci. Cracovie Bull.*, **7**, 577 (1906).
[4] Langevin, P., *Comptes Rendus*, **146**, 503 (1908).

$$\underset{\underset{\downarrow}{\text{xs mol. force}}}{Y} - b\dot{y} = m\ddot{y}. \tag{14.12}$$

This equation is multiplied throughout by displacement y and, after appropriate substitutions for $\dot{y}y$ and $\ddot{y}y$, it is averaged over all suspended particles in the fluid. We find that $\dot{y}y$ equals $\frac{1}{2}d(y^2)/d\tau$ and

$$\ddot{y}y = \tfrac{1}{2}(d/d\tau)[d(y^2)/d\tau] - \dot{y}^2, \tag{14.13}$$

so

$$Yy - \tfrac{1}{2}bd(y^2)/d\tau = \tfrac{1}{2}m(d/d\tau)[d(y^2)/d\tau] - m\dot{y}^2. \tag{14.14}$$

When this equation is averaged over the particles, $\overline{Yy}$ vanishes, because changes in force Y and displacement y are completely irregular and independent, and for a large number of particles as many negative as positive terms appear in the summation. Furthermore, $\tfrac{1}{2}\overline{m\dot{y}^2}$ equals $\tfrac{1}{2}kT$ by the principle of equipartition of energy. Let p represent $d(y^2)/d\tau$; then

$$-\tfrac{1}{2}bp = \tfrac{1}{2}m(dp/d\tau) - kT. \tag{14.15}$$

This is a differential equation of the first order and degree; its solution is

$$p = (2kT/b) + C\exp(-b\tau/m). \tag{14.16}$$

From Stokes' law for spherical particles the coefficient b equals $6\pi\eta r$, in which η is the coefficient of viscosity of the fluid and r is the radius of the particle. The mass of a particle with a radius of $0.1\ \mu$ is of the order 10^{-17} kgm, and from Table 12.3 η is of the order 10^{-5} newton-sec/m²; hence b/m is roughly $6\pi \times 10^{-5} \times 10^{-7}/10^{-17}$ or 2×10^6 sec⁻¹, a very large number. Only for a microsecond or less is the exponential term significant, and thereafter it may be neglected.

If now the exponential term is neglected and p is replaced by $d\overline{y^2}/d\tau$, a first-order differential equation is obtained. Its solution is

$$\overline{y^2} = (2kT/b)\tau, \tag{14.17}$$

where τ is the time interval (greater than a few microseconds) during which the y-component of the mean square displacement changes by the amount $\overline{y^2}$. This is the Einstein equation for brownian motion.

The quantity $\overline{y^2}$ may be interpreted as the y-component of the mean square displacement for the particle in random flight during time τ. Such flight was described for a molecule in Section 12.7. The particle experiences millions of very small displacements in a random manner, as suggested by the diagram in Fig. 14.1. Actually, this represents the two-dimensional projection of the three-dimensional path of the particle. In terms of mean free path, $\overline{y^2}$ equals $\tfrac{1}{2}\tau(\overline{\lambda}\overline{v})$.

In an experiment the position of several similar particles may be photographed at two instants separated by time interval τ. The y-components of the displacements of these particles are then read from the photograph, squared, and averaged to obtain $\overline{y^2}$. Alternatively, the y-coordinate value for the positions of the single particle at successive equal time intervals τ are recorded, and the consecutive differences are squared and averaged to obtain a value for $\overline{y^2}$.

The classical method of testing the Einstein equation is to solve it for the Avogadro number. If b is replaced by $6\pi\eta r$ and k by R/N_0, then

$$N_0 = R\mathsf{T}\tau/3\pi\eta r\overline{y^2}. \qquad (14.18)$$

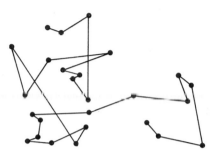

Figure 14.1. A particle executing brownian motion.

Perrin,[5] from 1900 to 1912, carried out the first extensive quantitative experiments for measuring N_0 in this way. By observing the brownian motions of granules in emulsions of gamboge or mastic over a wide range of sizes, he demonstrated that the mean square displacement $\overline{y^2}$ is proportional to time τ and therefrom determined a value for N_0 approximately equal to the accepted value of today. Also he showed that the values of y satisfy an exponential distribution law like Eq. (12.21). Nordlund[6] (1913) and Westgren[7] (1919) confirmed these results by measurements on colloidal suspensions of mercury, gold, silver, and selenium. Westgren's value for N_0 is $(6.05 \pm .03) \times 10^{23}$, which is in excellent agreement with the accepted value, $(6.0248 \pm .0003) \times 10^{23}$ molecules per gram-mole. In 1909 Ehrenhaft[8] and de Broglie[9] independently published similar observations on particles suspended in gases, and in 1910 Millikan[10] reported on his oil-drop experiment. These measurements furnish additional evidence to substantiate Einstein's assumption that a particle, whatever its size, moves with a mean translational energy depending only on the temperature of the medium in which the particle is suspended, and consequently they help establish the validity of the kinetic theory of matter.

[5] Perrin, J. B., *Atoms* (Constable, London, 1920).
[6] Nordlund, I., *Ark. f. Mat. Ast. och Fysik*, **9**, 1 (1913).
[7] Westgren, A., *Ark. f. Mat. Ast. och Fysik*, **13**, 1 (1919).
[8] Ehrenhaft, F., *Phys. Zeits.*, **10**, 308 (1909).
[9] de Broglie, M., *Comptes Rendus*, **148**, 1163, 1315 (1909).
[10] Millikan, R. A., *Science*, **32**, 436 (1910).

14.3. Rotational Brownian Motion

By an analysis similar to that for linear brownian motion Einstein[2] derived an equation for the mean square angular displacement of a spherical particle undergoing rotational brownian motion. It is

$$\overline{\theta^2} = kTr/4\pi\eta r^3, \qquad (14.19)$$

in which r is the radius of the particle. For rotation about the geometrical axis of a long thin cylinder of length l and cross-sectional radius r, the denominator in Eq. (14.19) is replaced by $2\pi\eta l r^2$. For rotation of the thin cylinder about transverse axes through its center, the denominator is replaced by $\frac{1}{8}\pi\eta l^3$. Equation (14.19) has been tested by measurements on nearly spherical grains of mastic or urea which are large enough to be seen under the microscope. Such observations were made by Perrin[5] in 1908. But it is more convenient to employ a system with only one degree of freedom where the brownian motion is restricted to rotations about a single axis.

The moving system of a suspension d'Arsonval galvanometer has one mechanical degree of freedom, so random fluctuations in angular displacement about the vertical axis can take place and give rise to an unsteady zero reading. Here, damping consists of three effects: viscous drag of the air, mechanical damping due to the imperfect elasticity of the suspension, and electromagnetic damping when the coil is connected into a closed circuit. Even if all the air is removed, brownian motion still can occur. It must be clearly understood that this motion in part is inherent in the suspended coil and is *not necessarily caused* by the bombardment of gas molecules.

For the galvanometer suspension the total energy at any instant is given by the equation

$$E = \tfrac{1}{2}c\theta^2 + \tfrac{1}{2}I\dot{\theta}^2, \qquad (14.20)$$

where c is the restoring torque per unit angle of twist and I is the rotational inertia of the system. Now a general statement for the principle of equipartition of energy is the following: If the energy of a system can be written as the sum of terms, each of which is proportional solely to the square of a system variable, than the average value of each term equals $\frac{1}{2}kT$. For the suspension,

$$\tfrac{1}{2}c\theta_{\text{rms}}^2 = \tfrac{1}{2}I\overline{\dot{\theta}^2} = \tfrac{1}{2}kT, \qquad (14.21)$$

or the mean square angular displacement equals kT/c. As the sensitivity of the galvanometer is increased, by making the suspension finer and thereby decreasing the value of c, evidently the random excursions of the mirror become larger. Equation (14.21) gives us another relation from which the

Avogadro number may be computed. Kappler[11] (1931) obtained a value of $(6.06 \pm 0.06) \times 10^{23}$ molecules per gram-mole by this method.

In order to detect a small electric current the galvanometer should produce a deflection significantly greater than the θ_{rms} for rotational brownian motion of the suspension at the ambient temperature. Suppose the galvanometer is connected into a circuit which has a total resistance equal to its critical external damping resistance, namely

$$R_c = \square^2 \Phi^2 \tau_0 / 4\pi I, \qquad (14.22)$$

as found by solving the equation of motion for the galvanometer. Here, $\square$ equals the number of turns on the deflecting coil, Φ represents the total flux threading the coil when it is at right angles to the field, τ_0 is the natural period of mechanical oscillation for the suspension, and I is the rotational inertia of the system. The period τ_0 equals $2\pi(I/c)^{1/2}$, and, at equilibrium with minimum current i_m in the coil, the deflecting torque $\square \Phi i_m$ just balances the restoring torque $c\theta_m$, so

$$\theta_m = \square \Phi i_m / c. \qquad (14.23)$$

If now we set θ_m equal to $\xi\theta_{\mathrm{rms}}$, where ξ is a small number, then on combining the several relations we find

$$i_m = \xi(\pi kT / R_c \tau_0)^{1/2}. \qquad (14.24)$$

For a galvanometer with a period of 4 sec and a critical damping resistance of 125 ohms at a room temperature of 290°K, $(\pi kT / R_c \tau_0)^{1/2}$ equals 5×10^{-12} amp. Finally, because only one out of 16,000 random deflections of the galvanometer suspension will exceed $4\theta_{\mathrm{rms}}$, it is highly probable that a deflection greater than this is not due to chance. Thus we can set ξ equal to 4 and conclude that the minimum detectable current should be approximately 2×10^{-5} microampere.

Even though the random fluctuations in angle of deflection become large when the torque constant of the suspension is decreased, as can be seen in Eq. (14.21), the minimum detectable current can be made as small as we please simply by increasing the period of the system, as is indicated in Eq. (14.24). The mechanical stability of the fine suspension and the patience of the observer are the principal limiting factors.

The foregoing equations have been verified experimentally by Jones and McCombie.[12] They magnified the deflections of an ordinary galvanometer, with a period of approximately 2 sec and a sensitivity of 0.01 amp/mm, by means of an optical lever. Fluctuations of a galvanometer suspension when the coil is unconnected and when it is in a nearly critically damped circuit

[11] Kappler, von Eugen, *Ann. d. Physik*, **409**, 233 (1931).
[12] Jones, R. V., and C. W. McCombie, *Phil. Trans. A*, **244**, 205 (1951).

are represented by the traces in Fig. 14.2. Whereas on open circuit the damping is small and the system tends to oscillate at its natural frequency, such that the trace has a periodic structure superposed on the random fluctuations, for the critically damped circuit the system is aperiodic and the deflections appear to be completely random.

The periodic structure in the trace of Figure 14.2(a) can be reduced by increasing the pressure and, therefore, the molecular density of the atmosphere around the suspension. Although rotational brownian motion is inherent in the suspension, as we have intimated, its appearance and general

(a)

(b)

Figure 14.2.   Fluctuations of a galvanometer suspension: (a) when the coil is on open circuit; (b) when it is connected into a nearly critically damped circuit.

character are markedly altered by changing the number of collisions per unit time which take place between it and the gas molecules.

14.4. Current Fluctuation and Johnson Noise

The mean square displacement of a system due to brownian motion, whether linear or angular, is directly proportional to its Kelvin temperature, and therefore the motion is said to be thermal. When a Fourier analysis is made of the random displacements of a system over a period of time a broad spectrum of frequencies is obtained in which each component is independent of every other. A similar resolution is found for noise in sound studies, and therefore by analogy we say brownian motion produces thermal noise in a system.

Consider the galvanometer coil and suspension once again. Interactions occur not only between it and the gas molecules, but also between it and radiation from the surroundings. Suppose the gas is completely removed and the temperature of the galvanometer is reduced to nearly 0°K. Even if this could be done, the suspension would still fluctuate because of brownian motion of the electrons in the external circuit to which the galvanometer coil is connected. That is, random currents appear in a closed circuit at temperature T and thereby give rise to random deflections of the galvanometer suspension. Here we have a manifestation of the thermal noise in the external circuit.

Let us apply these ideas to an electrical circuit having resistance R, inductance L, and capacitance C at temperature T. Because of the random motions of the electrons in the circuit, we assume there exists a corresponding fluctuating emf e which satisfies the circuit equation

$$L(di/d\tau) + Ri + q/C = e. \qquad (14.25)$$

The total energy in this circuit at any instant is

$$E = \tfrac{1}{2}Li^2 + \tfrac{1}{2}q^2/C. \qquad (14.26)$$

If the principle of equipartition of energy is applied to this system as a whole, we get

$$\tfrac{1}{2}L\overline{i^2} = \tfrac{1}{2}\overline{q^2}/C = \tfrac{1}{2}kT. \qquad (14.27)$$

These equations also may be solved for the Avogadro number. On the other hand, although they give us mean square values of the total fluctuations in current and charge, they tell us nothing about the frequency distribution of these fluctuations. And when a circuit, such as an amplifier, is to be operated near the limit of its sensitivity a knowledge of its "noise spectrum" is indispensable.

Imagine a Fourier analysis of the current fluctuations in the circuit has been performed. Sinoidal current waves are obtained over a continuous range of frequencies and with randomly distributed values of amplitudes. The question now posed is: how much energy exists in any specified frequency range or bandwidth! This problem was first studied experimentally by Johnson[13] and theoretically by Nyquist.[14]

To answer the question we postulate that current i_f and charge q_f for each sinoidal component at frequency f arises because of an emf e_f given by $V_f \exp(j\omega\tau)$, where ω equals $2\pi f$. For this component Eq. (14.25) is written in the form

$$L(d^2q_f/d\tau^2) + R(dq_f/d\tau) + q_f/C = V_f \exp(j\omega\tau). \qquad (14.28)$$

In order to solve this equation we make two plausible assumptions about V_f: its mean square value $\overline{V_f^2}$ is independent of frequency, and, because there is no correlation between the amplitudes, the average values of the cross-products $\overline{V_f V_{f'}}$ equal zero. Equation (14.28) now is solved for the mean square value of the fluctuating charge in the short frequency range between $f - \tfrac{1}{2}\Delta f$ and $f + \tfrac{1}{2}\Delta f$; the result is

[13] Johnson, J. B., *Phys. Rev.*, **32**, 97 (1928).
[14] Nyquist, H., *Phys. Rev.*, **32**, 110 (1928).

$$\overline{q_f^2} = \frac{\overline{V^2}}{(\omega^2 L - 1/C)^2 + \omega^2 R^2}, \qquad (14.29)$$

where the subscript on $\overline{V^2}$ has been omitted because for a given bandwidth $\overline{V^2}$ does not depend on frequency. For an infinitesimal change in frequency therefore we write the mean square charge as $\overline{q_f^2}df/\Delta f$. If this expression is integrated over the complete range of frequencies from 0 to ∞, we should obtain the total mean square fluctuation in charge $\overline{q^2}$ given by Eq. (14.27); thus

$$\tfrac{1}{2}kT = \tfrac{1}{2}\overline{q^2}/C = \frac{1}{2C\Delta f}\int_0^\infty \overline{q_f^2}df = \frac{\overline{V^2}}{4\pi C\Delta f}\int_0^\infty \frac{d\omega}{(\omega^2 L - 1/C)^2 + \omega^2 R^2}. \qquad (14.30)$$

The definite integral can be shown[15] to equal $\pi C/2R$, and therefore

$$\overline{V^2} = 4RkT\Delta f. \qquad (14.31)$$

Although $\overline{V^2}$ is independent of frequency, its magnitude does depend on the range of frequencies over which the averaging is done. It is the mean square value of voltage fluctuations which generate Johnson noise. The corresponding value of $\overline{i_f^2}$ equals $\overline{V^2}/Z^2$, where Z, the impedance of the circuit, depends on the frequency.

Let us compute a value for the rms Johnson emf developed in a 400,000 ohm resistor at 290°K for a bandwidth from 100 to 17,000 cps. We have

$$V_{rms} = (4RkT\Delta f)^{1/2}$$
$$= (4 \times 4 \times 10^5 \times 1.38 \times 10^{-23} \times 290 \times 16,900)^{1/2}$$
$$= 10.2 \times 10^{-6} \text{ volt, or about 10 microvolts,}$$

and the corresponding rms current equals approximately 25×10^{-6} micro-amp. These fluctuations would be significant for a high-gain amplifier in which the 400,000 ohm resistor is in the grid circuit.

In conclusion, it should be noted that whereas the total mean square value of the fluctuations depends only on L and C, as seen in Eq. (14.27), the distribution of voltage fluctuations among frequencies involves only R, as seen in Eq. (14.31). Furthermore, the power dissipated in the circuit as a result of these fluctuations equals $\overline{V^2}/R$, which is proportional to the temper-

---

[15] To solve the integral let $\omega = x(LC)^{-(1/2)}$; thus

$$(C^3/L)^{1/2}\int_0^\infty \frac{-d(1/x)}{(x - 1/x)^2 + R^2C/L} = (C^3/L)^{1/2}\int_0^\infty \frac{dx}{(x - 1/x)^2 + R^2C/L}.$$

The integral on the right is obtained by replacing x by $1/x$. Half the sum of these integrals is now evaluated:

$$\tfrac{1}{2}(C^3/L)^{1/2}\int_0^\infty \frac{d(x - 1/x)}{(x - 1/x)^2 + R^2C/L} = \tfrac{1}{2}(C^3/L)^{1/2}\int_{-\infty}^\infty \frac{dy}{y^2 + R^2C/L} = \pi C/2R.$$

ature of the circuit and the bandwidth but does not depend on the location of the band in the spectrum.

14.5. *Theory of Fluctuations about an Average*

From our studies of brownian motions and molecular fluctuations we see that we are dealing with statistical phenomena. In this section therefore we shall apply statistical methods in developing a suitable theory for fluctuations about an average.

Suppose there exist n similar items distributed at random among s possible regions which, for convenience, we shall call cells in an item-space. These items may be n measurements of a physical quantity spread over s ranges of values, n molecules dispersed among s energy states, or some other comparable distribution. The average number of items per cell $\bar{r}$ equals n/s. What is the probability that a group of r items will be found in a given cell?

If we assume that the probability of finding one item in the given cell is $1/s$, then the probability of finding a particular group of r items in this cell, and the remaining $n - r$ items outside it, is $(1/s)^r(1 - s^{-1})^{n-r}$. This probability factor must be multiplied by the number of ways in which r items may be selected from the total number n. Here we have the analogue of the familiar problem of finding the number of ways in which a toss of n coins will show r heads and $n - r$ tails. This number is $n!/r!(n - r)!$.[16] To obtain this we observe that the total number of ways in which the n items may be permuted equals $n!$. But no change in probability occurs if the r items in the given cell are permuted among themselves and if the remaining items are permuted among one another. Consequently, we divide $n!$ by $r!$ and $(n - r)!$. Finally, the probability of finding any group of r items in the given cell is

$$W = \frac{n!}{r!(n - r)!} \left(\frac{1}{s}\right)^r \left(1 - \frac{1}{s}\right)^{n-r}, \qquad (14.32)$$

which is the relation we had set out to obtain. It should be understood that both r and W apply to a specific cell and that the sum of W over all cells equals unity.

In applications of Eq. (14.32) to fluctuations, ordinarily n and s are extremely large and r is small, so it is convenient to transform the equation to a simpler form. We note that

---

[16] The notation $p!$, read "p factorial," means the product of all the integers from 1 to p inclusive.

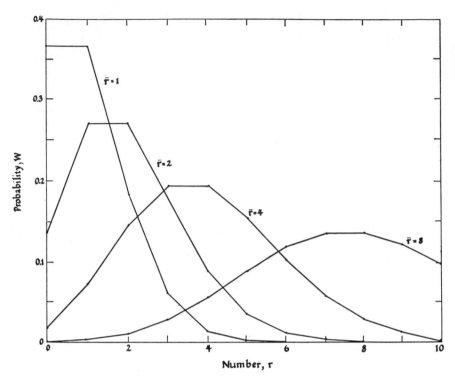

Figure 14.3.   Poisson distributions for small values of $\bar{r}$.

$$n!/(n-r)! = n(n-1) \cdots (n-r+1) \cong n^r$$

and

$$\ln (1 - s^{-1})^{n-r} = (n-r) \ln (1 - s^{-1}) \cong -n/s = -\bar{r}.$$

Thus we write

$$W = (\bar{r})^r e - \bar{r}/r!, \tag{14.33}$$

which is the Poisson distribution law. This function is plotted in Fig. 14.3 for several values of $\bar{r}$. Because the sum of W over all cells equals unity, we find

$$\Sigma_s(\bar{r})^r/r! = e^{\bar{r}}. \tag{14.34}$$

From these equations we can now determine the rms deviation of the occupation number r from its mean value $\bar{r}$ and thus obtain a measure of the fluctuations in the distribution of the n items among the s cells.

The rms deviation is found as follows:

$$\langle (r - \bar{r})^2 \rangle = \Sigma_s(r - \bar{r})^2 W = \overline{r^2} - (\bar{r})^2, \tag{14.35}$$

where

$$\overline{r^2} = \Sigma_s r^2 W = e^{-\bar{r}}\Sigma_s r^2 (\bar{r})^r/r!$$

$$= e^{-\bar{r}}\Sigma_s \left[(\bar{r})^2 \frac{(\bar{r})^{r-2}}{(r-2)!} + \bar{r}\frac{(\bar{r})^{r-1}}{(r-1)!} \right]$$

$$= (\bar{r})^2 + \bar{r}. \tag{14.36}$$

In the last step we apply Eq. (14.34) twice by replacing r in that equation first by $r - 2$ and then by $r - 1$. Finally,

$$\langle (r - \bar{r})^2 \rangle = \bar{r}, \tag{14.37}$$

and therefore the rms fluctuation in the occupation numbers equals $(\bar{r})^{1/2}$.

Although r and $\bar{r}$ are small compared with n and s, they may be large enough that a further simplification of Eq. (14.33) may be carried out. For this purpose we apply Stirling's formula for $r!$ in the form of Eq. (13.7). From Eq. (14.33) we now have

$$\ln W = r \ln \bar{r} - \bar{r} - \ln r!$$

$$= r \ln \bar{r} - \bar{r} - r \ln r + r - \tfrac{1}{2}\ln(2\pi r)$$

$$= -\tfrac{1}{2}\rho^2/\bar{r} - \tfrac{1}{2}\ln(2\pi\bar{r}), \tag{14.38}$$

where ρ equals $r - \bar{r}$ and we have assumed r differs little from $\bar{r}$ so that ρ is small. Thus for the probability factor we find

$$W = (2\pi\bar{r})^{-(1/2)} \exp\left(-\tfrac{1}{2}\rho^2/\bar{r}\right). \tag{14.39}$$

In the neighborhood of $\bar{r}$, values of W decrease rapidly from its maximum at $\bar{r}$. Equation (14.39) is the equation for the well-known normal or gaussian distribution. It has the same form as the maxwellian distribution law.

14.6. *The Shot Effect*

The thermionic current in a vacuum tube generally is assumed to be a steady rate of flow of electrical charge between plate and cathode. Actually, this current cannot be steady, but must fluctuate about an average value, because the electrons of which it is composed bear discrete negative charges and leave the cathode in a random manner. These fluctuations were discovered by Schottky and were called by him the Schrott or small-shot effect, because of their analogy to the random patter of gunshot on a target. They give rise to undesirable noise in the plate circuit of a tube.

For this phenomenon $\bar{r}$ of Eq. (14.37) is identified with the average number of electrons leaving the cathode per unit time, and, for a finite time interval τ, it equals $\bar{i}\tau/e$, in which $\bar{i}$ is the average plate current and e is the charge on an electron. The mean fluctuation in current is

$$\langle (i - \bar{\imath})^2 \rangle = (e/\tau)^2 \langle (r - \bar{r})^2 \rangle = (e/\tau)^2 \bar{r}$$
$$= \bar{\imath} e/\tau;$$

thus

$$\Delta i_{\text{rms}} = (\bar{\imath} e/\tau)^{1/2}. \tag{14.40}$$

Ordinarily these fluctuations are not observed because of the very small value of the charge on the electron. But the electronic charge can be computed by means of this equation from experimental values of the plate-current fluctuations in a vacuum tube. In this way Hull and Williams[17] (1925) obtained a value of 1.586×10^{-19} coulomb for e, which is in good agreement with the accepted value of 1.6019×10^{-19} coulomb.

The space charge in a vacuum tube under ordinary operating conditions masks the shot effect. By a Fourier analysis similar to that in Section 14.4 the mean square current in the frequency range $f - \frac{1}{2}\Delta f$ to $f + \frac{1}{2}\Delta f$ can be shown[18] to be given by the equation

$$\overline{I^2} = 2e\bar{\imath}\Delta f, \tag{14.41}$$

and if space-charge effects are present, a space-charge smoothing factor is inserted on the right side. This factor may be as low as 0.03, according to Bleaney and Bleaney, which indicates that the smoothing effect is rather large.

14.7. Density Fluctuations in a Gas

Imagine a volume of gas to be divided into a large number of equal volume elements V_0. Because of the random motions of the gas molecules we should expect the number of them in one of these elements to fluctuate about an average value. We might equally well select a group of ν molecules and observe that the volume they occupy fluctuates about a mean. From either point of view it is clear that the density of the gas at any single instant is not uniform throughout all the volume elements.

The probability for the number of molecules in a volume element to deviate from the mean by an amount between ρ and $\rho + d\rho$ is written

$$W d\rho = (2\pi\bar{r})^{-(1/2)} \exp\left(-\frac{1}{2}\rho^2/\bar{r}\right) d\rho, \tag{14.42}$$

from which we find

$$\overline{\rho^2} = \int_{-\infty}^{\infty} \rho^2 W d\rho = \bar{r}, \tag{14.43}$$

---

[17] Hull, A. W., and N. H. Williams, *Phys. Rev.*, **25**, 147 (1925).
[18] See Bleaney, B. I., and B. Bleaney, *Electricity and Magnetism*, pp. 476–480 (The University Press, Oxford, 1957).

which is in agreement with Eq. (14.37). If instead we select ν molecules and ask about the fluctuations in their volume, Eqs. (14.1) through (14.6) may be applied, where Z is replaced by volume V, and $\bar{Z}$ by $\bar{V}$. Smoluchowski named the fractional change in volume $\delta = (V - \bar{V})/\bar{V}$ the condensation.

Suppose, however, that the volume elements V_0 are so small that a large number r of them are required to contain the ν molecules. Then this volume V equals rV_0, and its mean value $\bar{V}$ for many such groups of molecules equals $\bar{r}V_0$. All the equations and results in Section 14.5 now apply here. If we let V_0 be the average volume per molecule so that $\bar{r}$ equals ν, then we can rewrite Eq. (14.39) in terms of condensation. Thus

$$W = (2\pi\nu)^{-(1/2)} \exp\left(-\tfrac{1}{2}\nu\delta^2\right), \qquad (14.44)$$

and the differential $d\rho$ becomes $\nu d\delta$, so

$$W'd\delta = (\nu/2\pi)^{1/2} \exp\left(-\tfrac{1}{2}\nu\delta^2\right)d\delta \qquad (14.45)$$

is the probability that the ν molecules have a condensation between δ and $\delta + d\delta$. In the usual way we find the rms condensation equals $\nu^{-(1/2)}$. One cubic millimeter of air at room temperature and standard atmosphere of pressure contains about 2.5×10^{16} molecules, and therefore the rms condensation for it equals approximately 6×10^{-9}. That is, the fluctuation in volume from the average of 1 mm^3 is only six parts in one-thousand-million! For a volume of 1 μ^3, on the other hand, the fluctuation is two parts in ten-thousand or 0.02%.

Because fluctuations in atmospheric density within volumes of the order of a cubic wavelength of light (0.05 to 0.5 μ^3) are several hundredths of a percent, variations in refractive index are appreciable and light is scattered as it passes through the air. Thus Smoluchowski derived the Rayleigh law of scattering, which states that the fraction of incident light scattered from each unit volume of a gas is inversely proportional to the fourth power of the wavelength. Owing to its shorter wavelength blue light is scattered more effectively than red, which accounts for the blue color of the sky.

As the volume of the ν molecules varies, the local pressure also must change. Consequently, the potential energy of the molecules fluctuates. Let $\bar{P}$ represent the mean pressure and $P - \bar{P}$ its deviation from the mean; then

$$\varphi = -\int_{\bar{V}}^{V} (P - \bar{P})dV \qquad (14.46)$$

is the potential energy of the ν molecules relative to its value at pressure $\bar{P}$ and volume $\bar{V}$. For an ideal gas,

$$PV = \bar{P}\bar{V} = \nu kT, \qquad (14.47)$$

from which

$$P - \bar{P} = -\bar{P}(V - \bar{V})/\bar{V}$$
$$= -\bar{P}\delta/(1 + \delta) \doteq -\bar{P}\delta. \tag{14.48}$$

Furthermore, dV equals $\bar{V}d\delta$. The integral in Eq. (14.46) now is evaluated as

$$\varphi = \int_0^\delta \bar{P}\bar{V}\delta d\delta$$
$$= \tfrac{1}{2}\bar{P}\bar{V}\delta^2 = \tfrac{1}{2}\nu kT\delta^2, \tag{14.49}$$

from which we obtain a value for the mean potential energy,

$$\bar{\varphi} = \tfrac{1}{2}\nu kT\overline{\delta^2} = \tfrac{1}{2}kT, \tag{14.50}$$

because $\overline{\delta^2}$ equals ν^{-1}. Although φ is proportional to the number of molecules in the system, its mean value is not. The mean potential energy due to density fluctuations for every volume element throughout the gas equals $\tfrac{1}{2}kT$. This is another illustration of the equipartition principle.

14.8. Density Fluctuations Near the Critical Point

The value of $\tfrac{1}{2}\nu\delta^2$ from Eq. (14.49) may be substituted into Eq. (14.44) to obtain the probability factor W in terms of φ:

$$W = A \exp{(-\varphi/kT)}, \tag{14.51}$$

where we have replaced the coefficient $(2\pi\nu)^{-(1/2)}$ by A. Although this expression has been obtained for a specific system, it is actually applicable to a wide variety of problems. As we shall discover in the next chapter, a form of W appears almost invariably in statistical problems and is called the Boltzmann factor. Let us now apply Eq. (14.51) to the phenomenon of density fluctuations near the critical point of a liquid-vapor system.

In general, pressure P is a function of volume V and may be expanded in a Taylor's series about the mean value $\bar{V}$:

$$P = \bar{P} + (\partial P/\partial V)_{\bar{V}}(V - \bar{V}) + (\partial^2 P/\partial V^2)_{\bar{V}}(V - \bar{V})^2/2!$$
$$+ (\partial^3 P/\partial V^3)_{\bar{V}}(V - \bar{V})^3/3! + \cdots. \tag{14.52}$$

Here we have assumed the temperature is constant. For the ideal gas of Section 14.7 we see that $(\partial P/\partial V)_{\bar{V}}$ equals $-\bar{P}/\bar{V}$, and therefore we obtain $-\bar{P}\delta$ for $P - \bar{P}$, in agreement with Eq. (14.48), provided we neglect all but the first two terms in Eq. (14.52). At the critical point, however, both $(\partial P/\partial V)_{\bar{V}}$ and $(\partial^2 P/\partial V^2)_{\bar{V}}$ vanish and we retain only the cubic term. Now

$$\varphi = -\tfrac{1}{6}\int_{\bar{V}}^V (\partial^3 P/\partial V^3)_{\bar{V}}(V - \bar{V})^3 dV. \tag{14.53}$$

In this equation $\bar{P}$ and $\bar{V}$ equal the critical values of pressure and volume P_c and V_c.

In terms of condensation δ, Eq. (14.53) is written

$$\varphi = -\tfrac{1}{6}(\bar{V})^4(\partial^3 P/\partial V^3)_{\bar{V}} \int_0^\delta \delta^3 d\delta$$

$$= -\tfrac{1}{24}(\bar{V})^4(\partial^3 P/\partial V^3)_{\bar{V}}\delta^4. \qquad (14.54)$$

The potential energy associated with density fluctuations at the critical point is proportional to the fourth power of the condensation. The coefficient of δ^4 can be evaluated explicitly from the state function for the system; here let it be represented by α so that

$$\alpha = -\tfrac{1}{24}(\bar{V})^4(\partial^3 P/\partial V^3)_{\bar{V}}. \qquad (14.55)$$

The probability of the system having a condensation between δ and $\delta + d\delta$ now is

$$W d\delta = A \exp(-\alpha\delta^4/kT_c)d\delta, \qquad (14.56)$$

where T_c is the critical temperature and A may be found in the usual way by setting the integral of this equation over all values of δ equal to unity. The result[19] is

$$A = 0.55163(\alpha/kT_c)^{1/4}. \qquad (14.57)$$

The mean condensation equals zero, and the mean square value is found to be

$$\overline{\delta^2} = 0.3380(kT_c/\alpha)^{1/2}. \qquad (14.58)$$

Whether we introduce the state equation for an ideal gas or for a van der Waals fluid, α comes out to equal a small fraction of νkT, and therefore the rms condensation is inversely proportional to the fourth root of ν. Consequently, rather large fluctuations in density can occur at the critical point, even though ν may have large values. For many substances there are about 10^9 molecules in a critical volume with dimensions of the order of a wavelength of light, so the rms density fluctuation is about 0.5%. The concomitant variations in refractive index account for the opalescence seen at the critical point.

---

[19] For integrals involving $\exp(-x^p)$ apply the relation

$$\int_0^\infty x^{pn-1} \exp(-x^p)dx = p^{-1}\Gamma(n),$$

where $\Gamma(n)$ is the gamma function. By means of the identity

$$\Gamma(n+1) = n\Gamma(n)$$

and tables of values for the gamma function in the range $1 < n < 2$ a numerical value of $\Gamma(n)$ may be found for any positive n. This table may be found in the *Handbook of Chemistry and Physics*.

Bibliography

Band, W., *An Introduction to Quantum Statistics* (Van Nostrand, New York, 1955).

Bleaney, B. I., and B. Bleaney, *Electricity and Magnetism* (Clarendon, Oxford, 1957).

Einstein, A., *Investigations on the Theory of the Brownian Movement* (Methuen, London, 1926).

Kennard, E. H., *Kinetic Theory of Gases* (McGraw-Hill, New York, 1938).

Perrin, J. B., *Atoms* (Constable, London, 1920).

Rice, J., *Introduction to Statistical Mechanics for Students of Physics and Physical Chemistry* (Constable, London, 1930).

Sears, F. W., *An Introduction to Thermodynamics, the Kinetic Theory of Gases, and Statistical Mechanics* (Addison-Wesley, Reading, Mass., 1953).

Slater, J. C., *Introduction to Chemical Physics* (McGraw-Hill, New York, 1939).

van der Ziel, A., *Noise* (Prentice-Hall, New York, 1954).

Problems

1. Assume z_i and z_j can have values $\bar{z} \pm a$, $\bar{z} \pm b$, and $\bar{z} \pm c$. Show that Eq. (14.3) is satisfied, and generalize the result.

2. Prove that the mean square deviation of the momentum of a subsystem in one direction equals $\frac{1}{2}NmkT(\pi - 1)/\pi$. Also prove that its relative value equals $(\pi - 1)/N$.

3. The general form of Eq. (14.7) for energy fluctuations in a gas is

$$\langle (E - U)^2 \rangle = kT^2 C_v,$$

where C_v is the heat capacity of the gas at constant volume.

   (a) Show that this general form reduces to Eq. (14.10) for an ideal gas which satisfies the Maxwell-Boltzmann distribution law.

   (b) For a quantum degenerate Bose-Einstein gas of N molecules the internal energy is given by the equation

$$U = 0.7701 NkT(T/T_0)^{3/2},$$

   in which T_0 represents the transition temperature to the degenerate state and $T \leq T_0$. Show that the relative energy fluctuation $\langle (E - U)^2/U^2 \rangle$ is inversely proportional to $T^{3/2}$ in this range of temperatures.

4. The torque constant of a fine quartz fiber, which serves as the suspension of a sensitive galvanometer in a room at 20°C, is approximately 4×10^{-6} cm-dyne/radian. Determine a value for the deflection of the light spot on the galvanometer scale, at

the standard distance of one meter from the mirror, due to random thermal oscillations.

5. Show in detail how to obtain Eq. (14.24).

6. Suppose the capacitive term in Eq. (14.25) is negligible and i is replaced by $dq/d\tau$; then this equation has the same form as Eq. (14.12). Prove that the mean square charge which crosses a section of conductor in a given time equals $2kT\tau/R$. Furthermore, if the average current $\bar{i}$ in time interval τ is defined to equal q/τ, show that

$$\langle (\bar{i})^2 \rangle = 2kT/R\tau.$$

7. The mean square Johnson current at frequency f is defined by the equation

$$d\bar{i^2} = d\bar{V^2}/Z^2,$$

where Z is the impedance of the circuit and $d\bar{V^2}$ is written in place of $\bar{V^2}$ of Eq. (14.31) when Δf is replaced by df. Carry out the integration to show that $\frac{1}{2}L\bar{i^2}$ equals $\frac{1}{2}kT$.

8. Suppose r is replaced by $r - 1$ or $r - 2$ in Eq. (14.32). Prove that

$$\Sigma_s(\bar{r})^{r-1}/(r-1)! = \Sigma_s(\bar{r})^{r-2}/(r-2)! = e^{\bar{r}}.$$

9. Show that the mean square condensation $\bar{\delta^2}$ for a van der Waals fluid at the critical point equals $0.9013/\nu^{1/2}$, where ν is the number of molecules in an arbitrary volume V_c at the critical point.

CHAPTER 15

Theories of Specific Heat and Dipole Moment

THE elementary methods of earlier chapters have been found inadequate for developing satisfactory theories of specific heat. Even for such simple systems as ideal gases consisting of polyatomic molecules these methods fail to account for the observed phenomena.

We recall that the specific heat capacity at constant volume for a pure substance equals the increase in its specific internal energy per degree rise in temperature while its volume is maintained constant. In any theory of specific heat therefore an equation is first developed for the internal energy per unit mass of the substance. For this purpose usually we postulate a suitable microscopic structure for the system. The many molecules in a monatomic real gas, for instance, are replaced by an equal number of point-mass molecules in the ideal gas. From the kinetic theory of this assemblage we find the molar internal energy to be $\frac{1}{2}fRT$, in which f equals the number of degrees of freedom (three for a monatomic ideal gas) and R is the universal molar gas constant. Although this result is applied to diatomic and other polyatomic molecules, it becomes less and less satisfactory as the molecules become more complex. For diatomic molecules we assume there are two rotational degrees of freedom in addition to the three translational degrees of freedom. But we neglect any linear and torsional vibrations which also can absorb energy. Clearly a more detailed model is required, and more elabo-

224

rate computations must be performed. The result of such a computation for carbon monoxide is given in Section 11.7.

Similarly, for theories of dipole moment the molecules of a real system are replaced by elementary dipoles in the ideal system. But as the molecules become more complex the simple dipole model must be modified.

Finally, for liquids and solids, where atoms and molecules are crowded so close together they can interact with one another, the simple models and theories for noninteracting particles again fail. Here we shall introduce the ideal crystalline solid and apply thermophysical statistics to derive equations for the specific heat capacity at constant volume and for the specific dipole moment.

15.1. The Ideal Crystalline Solid

The ideal crystalline solid contains neither impurities nor distortions, and its lattice is built up of repeating unit cells which contain a few atoms in characteristic sites. The entire structure may be conceived as a gigantic molecule whose internal parts are in thermodynamic equilibrium.

Each atom is associated with a definite site in the lattice and is conceived to vibrate about this point under the action of forces exerted by neighboring atoms. The atoms really are not isolated; however, it is sometimes convenient to suppose that the atoms are independent systems, insofar as the total internal energy of the crystal lattice is concerned, and that equilibrium is established by means of a few free interstitial particles, such as electrons in random thermal motion.

If the displacements of the atoms from their mean positions are not too large, the vibratory motion may be considered simple harmonic. The N_0 atoms in one mole of the crystalline solid therefore are assumed to have $3N_0$ independent normal modes of oscillation each of frequency ν. On the average we associate energy kT with each of these modes, $\frac{1}{2}kT$ for the kinetic energy and $\frac{1}{2}kT$ for the potential energy of oscillation. If now the result we found for an ideal gas can be applied here, the specific internal energy of the ideal crystalline solid should equal $3N_0kT$, and therefore its molar heat capacity at constant volume should be the classical value $3R$.

As early as 1819 Dulong and Petit[1] had established the fact that experimental values of specific heat at constant volume for a large number of substances at moderate temperatures equals approximately $3R$. From this result

---
[1] Dulong, P. L., and A. T. Petit, *Ann. de Chimie et de Physique*, **10**, 305 (1819)

Neumann and Regnault later stated that the molecular heat of a solid chemical compound equals the sum of the atomic heats of the constituent elements. For several substances (such as beryllium, boron, carbon, and silicon), however, measured values of specific heats are significantly less than $3R$ at moderate temperatures but approach $3R$ at high temperatures. On the other hand, the specific heats of sodium and potassium above 250°K are much larger than $3R$, and in no temperature region is the specific heat of these alkali metals constant. Furthermore, specific heats of *all* substances decrease as the temperature is lowered and indeed drop rapidly toward zero at 0°K. Since $c_p - c_v$ equals zero at 0°K, the specific heat capacity at constant pressure also vanishes at this temperature. These discrepancies between observed values of specific heat and the simple theory were unresolvable until the advent of the quantum theory.

15.2. Einstein's Theory of Specific Heat

In the elementary theory of specific heat for gases and crystalline solids we have assumed that classical equipartition of energy holds. Einstein[2] pointed out, however, that the N_0 atoms in the crystal behave like $3N_0$ monochromatic Planckian oscillators of energy

$$u = 3N_0 h\nu/[e^{h\nu/kT} - 1]. \quad (15.1)$$

From this we obtain

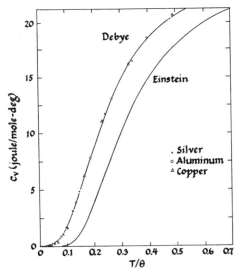

Figure 15.1.   Comparison of experimental values of c_v for aluminum, copper, and silver at low temperatures with curves from the Einstein and Debye theories.

$$c_v = (\partial u/\partial T)_v = 3Rx^2 e^x(e^x - 1)^{-2}, \quad (15.2)$$

where x equals $h\nu/kT$. For large values of T, Eq. (15.2) reduces to $3R$, and at 0°K c_v equals zero, but the variation of c_v with T, especially for low temperatures, does not agree at all with experiment, as is suggested in Fig. 15.1.

---

[2] Einstein, A., *Ann. Physik*, **22**, 800 (1907); **35**, 683 (1911).

Although Einstein recognized that the assumption of monochromatic oscillations is unsatisfactory, it was Debye[3] who introduced a spectrum of frequencies for the Planckian oscillators.

15.3. Debye's Theory of Specific Heat

The internal energy of a three-dimensional crystalline lattice equals its total vibrational energy. This is distributed throughout a spectrum of frequencies from zero to a maximum value consistent with the $3N_0$ degrees of freedom of the lattice. Born and von Kármán[4] developed a theory from this point of view. Almost simultaneously, Debye proposed a simpler theory which is adequate for our purposes. In these theories the principle of equipartition of energy is completely abandoned.

Debye disregards the crystalline and even the atomic structure of the solid and instead considers it to be an isotropic elastic continuum whose spectrum of vibrational frequencies normally range from zero to infinity and thereby imply an infinitude of vibrational modes. In order to make the number of modes of oscillation finite Debye now *assumes* the spectrum extends only from zero to a maximum value v_m, such that the number of vibrations in this range is consistent with the $3N_0$ degrees of freedom of the solid. Although this procedure is not logical or rigorous, it does lead to equations which describe the experimental results rather well.

When an isotropic homogeneous solid is thrown into elastic vibrations two kinds of waves are excited in it: longitudinal waves of speed $\mathcal{S}_l$, and transverse waves of speed $\mathcal{S}_t$. These speeds are directly related to the elastic moduli and mass density of the solid substance. Furthermore, the transverse waves are equivalent to two plane waves polarized at right angles to one another.

In general, the wavelength for either kind of wave equals speed $\mathcal{S}$ divided by frequency v, and therefore the number of wavelengths along a dimension L of the solid equals $Lv/\mathcal{S}$ when a standing wave is set up. This number we identify with the number of normal modes of vibration at frequency v along L. For the entire solid the number of such modes simultaneously in the frequency ranges v_1 to $v_1 + dv_1$, v_2 to $v_2 + dv_2$, v_3 to $v_3 + dv_3$ for the three dimensions L_1, L_2, L_3 is the product $L_1L_2L_3dv_1dv_2dv_3/\mathcal{S}^3$, or $4\pi Vv^2dv/\mathcal{S}^3$ by a transformation of coordinates. Here we have set $L_1L_2L_3$ equal to volume V of the solid.

For longitudinal waves in an isotropic homogeneous solid the number of

---

[3] Debye, P., *Ann. Physik*, **39**, 789 (1912).
[4] Born, M., and T. von Kármán, *Phys. Zeits.*, **13**, 297 (1912).

modes of oscillation between frequencies ν and $\nu + d\nu$ is $4\pi V \nu^2 d\nu / \mathcal{S}_l^3$. Similarly, for transverse waves this number is $8\pi V \nu^2 d\nu / \mathcal{S}_t^3$. If we add these together and integrate from $\nu = 0$ to $\nu = \nu_m$, the result should equal $3N_0$:

$$4\pi V(\mathcal{S}_l^{-3} + 2\mathcal{S}_t^{-3}) \int_0^{\nu_m} \nu^2 d\nu = 3N_0. \tag{15.3}$$

From this computation we find

$$\nu_m^3 = 9N_0/4\pi V(\mathcal{S}_l^{-3} + 2\mathcal{S}_t^{-3}), \tag{15.4}$$

and therefore the total number of modes for both waves in the frequency range ν to $\nu + d\nu$ is $(9N_0/\nu_m^3)\nu^2 d\nu$.

The specific internal energy of the solid now is obtained by integrating the product of the energy of a Planckian oscillator and this total number of modes over the frequency range from zero to ν_m; thus

$$u = (9RT/x_m^3) \int_0^{x_m} \frac{x^3 dx}{e^x - 1}, \tag{15.5}$$

where x_m equals $h\nu_m/kT$. This integral cannot be evaluated in finite terms. Finally, the specific heat of the solid at constant volume is obtained by differentiating u with respect to T:

$$c_v = (9R/x_m^3) \int_0^{x_m} \frac{x^4 e^x dx}{(e^x - 1)^2}$$

$$= (9R/2x_m^3) \int_0^{x_m} \frac{x^4 dx}{\cosh x - 1}. \tag{15.6}$$

Here we have obtained Debye's equation for the specific heat of a solid. Explicit values of c_v have been worked out by numerical methods and are plotted in Fig. 15.1. Clearly, Debye's equation fits the experimental data rather well.

At high temperatures x is very small, so $\cosh x - 1$ can be replaced by $\frac{1}{2}x^2$, and therefore Eq. (15.6) reduces to $3R$ when the integration is performed. On the other hand, at very low temperatures x_m is so large that we set the upper limit of the integral equal to infinity. The resulting definite integral has the value $8\pi^4/15$, and therefore near $0°K$ the Debye specific heat is given by the equation

$$c_v = 12\pi^4 R/5x_m^3. \tag{15.7}$$

It is common practice to call $h\nu_m/k$ the Debye or characteristic temperature Θ, so Eq. (15.7) has the form

$$c_v = 12\pi^4 R T^3/5\Theta^3. \tag{15.8}$$

Observed values of c_v very nearly satisfy the T-cube law for T/Θ less than 0.1, although experimental errors introduce considerable uncertainty in the comparison.

The Debye temperature is a parameter which depends on the atomic constitution and structure of a solid. Its value for a substance may be found from speeds of elastic waves by means of Eq. (15.4) and from specific heat data near 0°K by means of Eq. (15.8), or at higher temperatures by means of Eq. (15.6). Furthermore, the Debye temperature can be determined from thermal expansion data. Values of Θ for a few substances are gathered in Table 15.1.

The values in column I were computed from elastic constant data at room temperature; those in column II from specific heat data in the temperature range $\frac{1}{2}\Theta$ to $\frac{3}{4}\Theta$; those in column III from the T-cube law for temperatures less than 20°K.

TABLE 15.1.   *Debye Temperatures for Several Substances.*

Substance	I	II	III	Substance	I	II	III
Ag	212	220	229	KBr	179	177	—
Al	394	410	375	KCl	227	230	—
Au	158	185	164	KI	132	175	—
C (diamond)	—	1860	2230	LiF	715	650	—
CaF$_2$	499	474	—	NaCl	302	281	—
Cd	189	165	165	S	—	180	174
Cu	342	310	343	W	384	315	270
Hg	69	96	75	Zn	306	240	235

15.4. Remarks on Theories of Specific Heat

If Eq. (15.6) were the correct form for the specific heat at constant volume, we should expect a single value of characteristic temperature Θ to describe the entire curve of $c_v/3R$ against T/Θ. In practice we find that Θ is a slowly varying function of temperature. The inadequacy of Debye's theory is suggested by the great variability among values of Θ for several substances in Table 15.1. Only at very low temperatures would we expect a theory based on an isotropic elastic continuum to give a satisfactory solution, for there the standing waves have low frequencies and long wavelengths of many atomic diameters. As the temperature is raised, more and more energy enters modes of oscillation of higher and higher frequencies, and the atomic structure of the crystal lattice then must be taken into account. Actually, discrepancies between values of c_v from the Debye theory and from experiment occur even at temperatures as low as 20°K.

The theoretical calculation of c_v for real crystals is a difficult matter, but it has been done in some detail for a few substances, such as diamond, silver, potassium chloride, and sodium chloride. Apparent values of Θ may be plotted against T, as shown in Fig. 15.2 for silver and sodium chloride. We see that Θ changes by as much as 10% within the first 25°. This observation is in agreement with experimental measurements of Θ, as suggested by the dashed curves, although the peak for silver near 5°K remains unexplained by the theory.

Conduction electrons contribute to

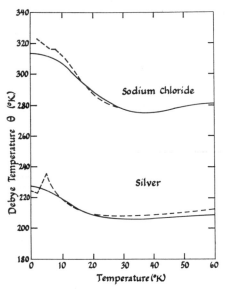

Figure 15.2.   Apparent values of the Debye temperature Θ for silver and sodium chloride below 60°K. Solid curves, theory; dashed curves, smoothed experimental results.

the specific heat of metals. According to classical theory they should behave like an ideal monatomic gas, and therefore they should make a contribution of $\frac{3}{2}R$ per mole of electrons. But nothing like this is observed. In 1928 Sommerfeld applied Fermi-Dirac statistics to show that the electrons contribute only a small added amount which is proportional to temperature. This application of quantum statistics is discussed in Chapter 17.

In spite of its inadequacies, Debye's theory has been remarkably successful in describing the gross variation of specific heat with temperature for a very large number of substances.

15.5. Classical Theory of Dipole Moment

Specific dipole moments, whether paramagnetic or dielectric, increase as the temperature falls toward 0°K. This behavior is contrary to that of specific heat capacities and requires a different but equally cogent explanation. For this purpose we suppose the molecules in a real gas or crystalline solid are replaced by an equal number of essentially independent elementary rigid dipoles, which may be oriented in a preferred direction by an appropriate applied field. Actually, random thermal motions of the dipoles counteract the orienting influence of the field, so the mean dipole moment is much less than its maximum possible value. Qualitatively, the specific dipole moment of a specimen ought to increase with field strength and decrease with temperature.

It should be noted that the only effect of a magnetic field is to cause precession of magnetic dipoles about the field axis. Orientation of these dipoles is brought about by collisions either directly, as in gases, or indirectly through an intermediary, as in crystals. Generally electric dipoles are not rigid. When they are distorted by the applied field an additional term enters the specific dipole moment. For isotropic media this term is directly proportional to the field intensity and completely disappears with it. In the following discussion we shall be concerned only with the first term which arises from the orientation process.

Suppose an elementary permanent dipole of strength μ is at angle θ with respect to direction of field F. Its potential energy then equals $-\mu F \cos \theta$, and the Boltzmann factor for a statistical distribution among angles is $\exp(\mu F \cos \theta / kT)$. The probability of finding a dipole pointed in the direction θ equals the product of the Boltzmann factor and the conical element of solid angle $d\Omega$. As illustrated in Fig. 15.3, $d\Omega$ is given by the ratio

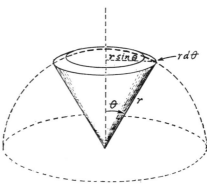

Figure 15.3.   Element of solid angle $d\Omega$.

$$d\Omega = 2\pi r \sin \theta \cdot r d\theta / 4\pi r^2$$

$$= \tfrac{1}{2} \sin \theta d\theta. \tag{15.9}$$

From this the mean value of dipole moment per molecule is found in the usual way:

$$\bar{\mu} = \mu \, \frac{\displaystyle\int_0^\pi \exp(\mu F \cos \theta / kT) \cos \theta \sin \theta d\theta}{\displaystyle\int_0^\pi \exp(\mu F \cos \theta / kT) \sin \theta d\theta}$$

$$= \mu[\coth(\mu F / kT) - (kT / \mu F)]$$

$$= \mu \mathcal{L}(\mu F / kT). \tag{15.10}$$

The symbol $\mathcal{L}(y)$ is used for the Langevin function $(\coth y - 1/y)$, which was named after the man who first developed the classical theory of paramagnetism. The curve of this function is shown in Fig. 15.4.

The molar dipole moment of the foregoing system is

$$M = \bar{\mu} N_0 = \mu N_0 \mathcal{L}(\mu F/kT), \qquad (15.11)$$

where N_0 is the Avogadro number. For strong fields and low temperatures

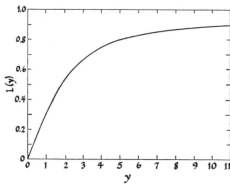

the argument $\mu F/kT$ is very large, so its reciprocal is negligible and coth $(\mu F/kT)$ is nearly unity. The molar dipole moment then simply equals μN_0, for all the dipoles are aligned with the field. In weak fields and at high temperatures

Figure 15.4.   Curve for the Langevin function. As y increases $\mathcal{L}(y)$ approaches unity asymptotically.

the argument is very small, so through the first two terms in its expansion,

$$\coth y \cong 1/y + \tfrac{1}{3}y,$$

and therefore

$$M = N_0\mu^2 F/3kT. \qquad (15.12)$$

This result may be applied to either magnetic or electric dipole moments.

Because the magnetization is very small in all paramagnetic substances we may set F equal to $\mu_0 H$, the product of the permeability of free space and the magnetic field intensity. Also we replace μ with the symbol μ_m for *magnetic* dipole moment. Thus,

$$M_m = N_0\mu_m^2\mu_0 H/3kT, \qquad (15.13)$$

which is the Curie law, as described in Section 3.2. Similarly, for electrification of dielectrics in weak fields, F equals $\epsilon_0 E$, the product of the permittivity of free space and the electric field intensity, and μ is replaced by μ_e, the symbol for *electric* dipole moment. Thus

$$M_e = N_0\mu_e^2\epsilon_0 E/3kT, \qquad (15.14)$$

which is Debye's equation for the dipole moment of N_0 rigid dipoles. Again it must be emphasized that these results apply only if $\mu F/kT$ is very small.

Actually, the foregoing approximation may be quite satisfactory even for rather large applied fields. To show this we evaluate $y(=\mu_m\mu_0 H/kT)$ for oxygen, which is paramagnetic with a molecular dipole moment μ_m of 2.65 × 10^{-23} amp-m². At a temperature T of 300°K and for a magnetic flux $\mu_0 H$ of 2 webers/m², we get

$$2.65 \times 10^{-23} \times 2/1.38 \times 10^{-23} \times 300$$

or 0.0128 for y. This value of y appears sufficiently small to justify the application of the Curie law to oxygen. Even a strong magnetic field is unable to produce significant alignment of the oxygen dipoles, for disorientation by thermal motions is too severe at 300°K.

15.6. Quantum Theory of Dipole Moment

To develop the detailed quantum theory of dipole moment would carry us too far beyond the scope of this book. Nevertheless, we should not leave the subject of dipole theory without a brief glimpse into the newer point of view. Our introduction is best made through the Zeeman effect. In this effect spectral lines separate into components when emission takes place in a magnetic field. Here we have an indication that the molecular dipole is associated with the number and arrangement of electrons in the molecule. Furthermore, the distinct separation of the lines suggests that the molecular dipoles can assume only a few definite orientations relative to the direction of the applied magnetic field. This is a manifestation of space quantization.

The dipole moment of an electron revolving with speed v in a circular orbit of radius r may be readily computed. The period of this motion equals the circumference divided by the speed, $2\pi r/v$, and from this the equivalent current of the electron equals $ev/2\pi r$, namely the mean charge flowing around the orbit per unit time. But as shown in any standard treatise in electricity, a current in a closed loop is equivalent to a magnetic dipole whose moment, in mks units, equals the product of the current into the area of the loop. We thus find the dipole moment of the circulating electron to be $\frac{1}{2}evr$. The angular momentum of this electron, however, is mvr, which is equal to an integral multiple of $h/2\pi$ in quantum theory. Thus we find the dipole moment of the electron in the first Bohr orbit of hydrogen, for which the integer equals unity, is

$$\mu_B = eh/4\pi m. \tag{15.15}$$

In quantum theory μ_B is the fundamental unit of magnetic moment and is called the Bohr magneton. Thus the dipole moment of O_2 equals $2.80\mu_B$ and that of Ni equals $1.79\mu_B$. Furthermore, the magnetic moment of an electron due to its own spin is μ_B.

Space quantization of magnetic moments may be tested directly by observing the deviation of atomic beams as they pass through inhomogeneous magnetic fields. Experiments of this nature were begun by Gerlach and Stern[5] in 1921 and were continued over several years by Stern and his

---

[5] Gerlach, N., and O. Stern, *Zeits. f. Physik*, **8**, 110 (1921).

collaborators. Today the method is widely employed for investigating dipole moments of atoms and molecules. The essential parts of the apparatus are indicated in Fig. 15.5. Atoms diffuse through a hole in a small oven, pass through slits to form a narrow atomic beam, and then traverse a highly nonhomogeneous magnetic field where they may be deflected. If the atoms behaved like little classical magnets, the resulting deflection pattern would be a Gaussian distribution with its maximum at the position of the undeflected beam. Instead it consists of several sharply separated components, as recorded by a suitable detecting device. The entire apparatus is in an evacuated enclosure. Although the apparatus is small and the method is simple, for good results an elaborate technique must be followed in which accurate alignment and careful attention to details are paramount.

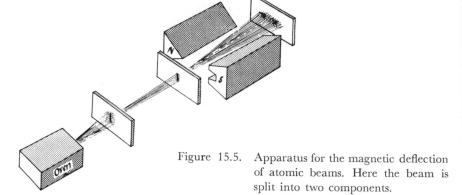

Figure 15.5.   Apparatus for the magnetic deflection of atomic beams. Here the beam is split into two components.

Magnetic dipoles of silver become aligned with the applied magnetic field either in the parallel or the antiparallel orientation, and thus only two resolved beams of silver atoms are formed. From measurements on these beams the molar dipole moment of silver is found to equal 5690 amp-m²/kg mole. This differs by less than 2% from the Bohr unit value of 5587 amp-m²/kg mole. This theoretical dipole moment equals the product of the Bohr magneton and the Avogadro number. In other words, the dipole moment of a silver atom equals μ_B.

By means of quantum mechanical methods Brillouin derived an equation for the molar dipole moment of a paramagnetic gas. He obtained the relation

$$M = \tfrac{1}{2}Ng\mu_B[(2J + 1) \coth \{(2J + 1)g\mu_B\mu_0H/2kT\}$$

$$- \coth \{g\mu_B\mu_0H/2kT\}], \qquad (15.16)$$

in which g and J are quantum constants which differ from atom to atom. For silver $g = 2$ and $J = \tfrac{1}{2}$, so

$$M = N\mu_B[2 \coth (2\mu_B\mu_0 H/kT) - \coth (\mu_B\mu_0 H/kT)],$$

which simplifies to

$$M = N\mu_B \tanh (\mu_B\mu_0 H/kT). \tag{15.17}$$

If $\mu_B\mu_0 H/kT$ is small, we obtain the Curie law,

$$M = N\mu_B^2\mu_0 H/kT, \tag{15.18}$$

in which the coefficient of H/T (the Curie constant) is three times the classical value in Eq. (15.13). It is not surprising to find that a graph of Eq. (15.17) has the same general form as that for the Langevin function, since Eq. (15.16), and therefore Eq. (15.17), can be written as the difference between two Langevin functions:

$$M = \tfrac{1}{2}N g\mu_B[(2J + 1)\mathcal{L}(2J + 1)y - \mathcal{L}(y)], \tag{15.19}$$

where y equals $g\mu_B\mu_0 H/2kT$.

Although the Brillouin equation was derived for a paramagnetic gas, it has been applied to crystals as well, where the elementary magnetic dipoles are so widely separated that little interaction takes place between them.

Bibliography

Bleaney, B. I., and B. Bleaney, *Electricity and Magnetism* (Clarendon, Oxford, 1957).
Böttcher, C. J. F., *Theory of Electric Polarization* (Elsevier, New York, 1952).
Debye, P., *Polar Molecules* (The Chemical Catalog Co., New York, 1929).
Ramsay, N. F., *Molecular Beams* (Clarendon, Oxford, 1956).
Saha, M. N., and B. N. Srivastava, *A Textbook of Heat* (The Indian Press, Allahabad, India, 1931).
Shankland, R. S., *Atomic and Nuclear Physics* (Macmillan, New York, 1955).

Problems

1. Consider a two-dimensional isotropic elastic sheet to have $2N$ degrees of freedom. Apply the method of Debye to develop an equation for the specific heat capacity of this system, and show that near $0°K$ it reduces to a T-square law.

2. Elastic moduli and other data for several elements are given in the following

table. From them compute values for the Debye temperatures of these elements. Longitudinal and transverse speeds of elastic waves in a medium are given by the equations

$$s_l^2 = (B + \tfrac{4}{3}G)/\rho \quad \text{and} \quad s_t^2 = G/\rho,$$

where B is the bulk modulus, G is the shear modulus, and ρ is the mass density of the medium.

TABLE 15.2.   *Physical Properties of Several Elements.*

Element	At. Wt. (gm/mole)	Density (gm/cc)	Bulk Modulus (dyne/cm²)	Shear Modulus (dyne/cm²)
Aluminum	26.98	2.699	7.5×10^{11}	3.28×10^{11}
Cadmium	112.41	8.65	4.6	2.40
Copper	63.54	8.94	13.3	4.13
Gold	197.0	19.32	16.7	2.79
Silver	107.88	10.50	10.1	2.90

---

3. Compute the value for the Bohr magneton μ_B in mks and electromagnetic units.

4. The molar susceptibility of oxygen at 20°C equals 0.00338 cgs electromagnetic units. From these data compute the Curie constant C and from it the effective magnetic dipole moment μ_m for oxygen. Express μ_m in terms of Bohr magnetons. Oxygen is a paramagnetic gas which satisfies the simple form of Curie's law for temperatures greater than 90°K. Carry out a similar computation for neodymium for which the molar susceptibility at 20°C equals 0.00565 cgs electromagnetic units.

5. How is Eq. (15.17) obtained from Eq. (15.16)?

6. A beam of silver atoms splits into two beams as it passes through an inhomogeneous magnetic field. The atoms in one beam have their magnetic moments μ parallel to the applied field B and acquire magnetic energy $-\mu B$; those in the other beam have their magnetic moments antiparallel to B and acquire energy $+\mu B$. Since there are only two possible energy states for a silver atom, its partition sum consists of two terms.

    (a) Prove that this partition sum equals $2 \cosh (\mu B/kT)$, and then solve for the numbers of silver atoms per unit volume in each of the energy states.

    (b) Show that the net magnetization in the direction of B equals $n\mu \tanh (\mu B/kT)$, in which n is the total number of silver atoms per unit volume.

7. Suppose the beam of silver atoms in problem 6 is split by a magnetic field of flux density B equal to 0.1 weber/m² at a temperature of 1000°K. Show that there are 0.013% more atoms in the parallel than in the antiparallel state.

8. Show that Eq. (15.19) reduces to Eq. (15.13) when the arguments of the Langevin functions are very small, provided μ_m is equated to $\mu_B g[J(J+1)]^{1/2}$.

Thermal Radiation

EVERY body, whether visibly luminous or not, is believed to emit and absorb electromagnetic radiation. When this radiation is a direct function of the temperature of the body, it is thermal and the radiated energy is one form of heat. Although radiation arising from chemiluminescence and phosphorescence also is heat, it comes from chemical and optical effects and depends on temperature only indirectly. In this chapter we shall limit our discussion to thermal radiation.

If conduction and convection are prevented from taking place and if neither mechanical nor chemical processes occur either between the system and its near-surround or between one part of the system and another, the system will exchange radiant energy with the near-surround until a steady state of dynamic equilibrium becomes established. In this condition as much heat enters the system by radiation as leaves it by the same process. This is Prevost's "theory of exchanges" (1791). It is really a special case of a more general universal law of heat exchanges in which transfers of heat by conduction and convection occur as well. This general law is discussed and applied in Chapter 20.

When radiant energy is analyzed by means of a spectrograph it is found to be distributed among a continuous range of frequencies. The spectrum extends from the low-frequency electric and radio waves to the extremely high-frequency hard gamma rays (Fig. 16.1). If the radiation to and from a system is to be studied with care, the system should be enclosed by an evacuated chamber to eliminate conduction and convection effects. The walls of the chamber should be made opaque to the radiation. In this way

237

the near-surround is limited solely to the chamber walls. If the system were perfectly transparent or perfectly reflecting, it would remain unaffected by the radiation and would never come to the temperature of the walls. On the other hand, if the system has some degree of nontransparency and non-reflectivity, no matter how slight, eventually it will come to thermal equilibrium with the walls. It then follows that the amount of energy leaving a unit area of both the system and the walls in a unit time is uniform throughout *at each frequency of radiation.*

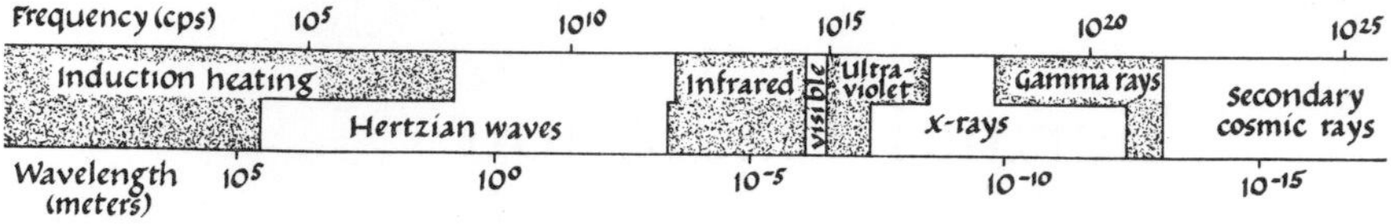

Figure 16.1.   Major divisions of the electromagnetic spectrum.

16.1. Intensity of Radiation

Consider a semi-opaque system of any material in temperature and radiative equilibrium with the walls of an enclosing evacuated chamber. The intensity of radiation everywhere in the chamber is equal to the amount of radiant energy streaming to or from a unit area in a unit time. The intensity of radiation falling on a surface, the irradiancy, may be represented by J_b. That leaving a surface, the radiancy, is represented by R_b, which is made up of two parts. The true radiancy R_s is the intensity of radiation actually emitted by the system, and the reflectancy rJ_b is the amount of the incident energy reflected from a unit area in a unit time where r is the reflectivity of the surface. For radiative equilibrium, however, J_b is equal to R_b, so

$$R_s = R_b - rJ_b = R_b(1 - r) = eR_b. \qquad (16.1)$$

The factor $1 - r$ is the emissivity of the surface and is represented by e. Any system for which the reflectivity is zero must absorb or transmit all the radiation incident on it. A body that absorbs all the incident radiation and neither reflects nor transmits any of it is "dead black" and is called a blackbody. The emissivity of a blackbody therefore equals unity.

Among the best substances with approximately blackbody surfaces are carbon black, platinum black, zinc black, and silicon carbide. A very close approximation to a source of blackbody radiation is a small aperture in the wall of a cavity which is maintained at a uniform temperature. The wall may be of any material. Radiation coming from such an aperture is of the blackbody type because it consists not only of the emitted radiation from the surface directly opposite the aperture but also of multiply reflected radiation from other parts of the wall. Frequently, for analytical purposes, it is convenient to imagine the wall of a blackbody cavity replaced by an ideal reflecting wall that encloses a small blackbody and any other system under investigation.

If the reflectancy of the semi-opaque system is rJ_b, then the amount of energy absorbed by a unit area in a unit time is $(1 - r)J_b$ or aJ_b, where a is the absorptivity of the surface. *The absorptivity of any body is just equal to its emissivity.* This is the essence of the Kirchhoff-Stewart law for radiative systems. Notice that the absorptivity of a blackbody equals unity. A blackbody is not only a 100% emitter but also a 100% absorber of radiant energy.

In the discussion up to this point irradiancy, radiancy, and other quantities have been defined for the total radiation of all frequencies. Let $J_b(\lambda)$ and $J_b(\lambda + \Delta\lambda)$ represent the values of the irradiancy at the wavelengths λ and $\lambda + \Delta\lambda$, respectively. The limit of the ratio of $J_b(\lambda + \Delta\lambda) - J_b(\lambda)$ divided by $\Delta\lambda$ as $\Delta\lambda$ approaches zero is the monochromatic irradiancy J_λ of the system. We define the monochromatic radiancy R_λ in a similar manner. The foregoing discussion for total radiation now may be applied to monochromatic radiation, where r, e, and a become r_λ, e_λ, and a_λ. The Kirchhoff-Stewart law applies to each part of the radiation spectrum.

16.2. The Fourth-power Law of Radiation

In 1879 Stefan[1] suggested that the total radiation from a heated body is proportional to the fourth power of its temperature in degrees Kelvin. He based his conclusion in part on rather meager data reported by Tyndall for a hot platinum wire. Tyndall measured the relative total emission at 1200°C and 525°C and found the ratio to equal 11.7. The ratio 1473/798 raised to the fourth power equals 11.6. As pointed out by Worthing and Halliday[2] this seeming agreement was highly fortuitous, for more recent accurate measurements of the emission from platinum at these temperatures yield a ratio of 18.6. If careful measurements of the total intensity of radiation from a blackbody cavity are made, however, they are found to satisfy the fourth-power law very closely. We must conclude that platinum does not behave like a blackbody at the foregoing temperatures.

In 1884 Boltzmann[3] deduced the fourth-power law by thermodynamic

[1] Stefan, J., *Wien. Ber.*, **79A**, 391 (1879).
[2] Worthing, A. G., and D. Halliday, *Heat*, p. 438 (Wiley, New York, 1948).
[3] Boltzmann, L., *Wied. Ann.*, **26**, 287 (1884).

reasoning. He assumed a relation between radiant energy density and radiation pressure, which had been derived purely theoretically by Maxwell[4] in 1871 (see Section 9.3). Not until 1900–1901 was experimental evidence available to verify Maxwell's relation for radiation pressure, and that was several years after the fourth-power law for blackbody radiation had been put on a firm experimental foundation by Paschen[5] and by Lummer and Pringsheim.[6]

In present notation the fourth-power law for a nonblackbody which emits a continuous spectrum may be written

$$R_s = e\sigma T^4. \tag{16.2}$$

The accepted value of σ, the universal radiation constant, is 5.685×10^{-8} watt/m²-deg to the fourth power, where temperatures are measured on the Kelvin scale. If a system is at the uniform temperature T and the near-surround is at the uniform temperature T_0, then the net intensity of radiation from the system is

$$R = e\sigma T^4 - a\sigma T_0^4.$$

But by the Kirchhoff-Stewart law, a, the absorptivity of the system at temperature T, equals e; therefore

$$R = e\sigma(T^4 - T_0^4). \tag{16.3}$$

16.3. Pyrometry

As mentioned in Section 2.7 optical pyrometers are devices for measuring elevated temperatures, especially outside the range of mercury-in-glass and resistance thermometers. In a common type of total radiation pyrometer the sensitive element is a thermocouple or thermopile. A concave mirror may be mounted within the casing of the instrument to focus the radiation on the element. For precision work at high frequencies, such as in the visible and ultraviolet parts of the spectrum, the pyrometer may be evacuated. A temperature reading obtained with an optical pyrometer is not a true temperature, but rather the temperature of a blackbody whose radiancy equals that of the body being measured. It is the effective or radiation temperature of the body. By dividing the radiation temperature by the fourth root of the total emissivity for the body at the given temperature the true temperature may be found. Often, however, the furnace or other hot system is sufficiently similar to a blackbody cavity that the total emissivity is nearly unity.

[4] Maxwell, J. C., *A Treatise on Electricity and Magnetism*, Vol. II, p. 440 (Clarendon, Oxford, 1892).
[5] Paschen, F., *Wied. Ann.*, **60**, 662 (1897); *Ann. d. Physik*, **4**, 277 (1901).
[6] Lummer, O., and Pringheim, E., *Verh. d. D. Phys. Geo.*, **1**, 213 (1899).

The disappearing-filament optical pyrometer is a spectral radiation instrument in that only a narrow range of frequencies is admitted. One common form contains a filter in the eyepiece, which transmits a narrow band of wavelengths centering around 0.665 μ. The filament of a calibrated low-voltage incandescent lamp within the instrument is viewed against the radiation from the system whose temperature is desired. The current in the lamp is adjusted until the image of the filament merges with the background radiation. The brightness temperature of the system then is found by means of the current reading and the calibration curve or chart for the pyrometer. This temperature is less than the true temperature by a factor which equals the fourth root of the spectral emissivity of the body for the frequency of radiation transmitted by the filter in the pyrometer. The compact form, ruggedness of construction, simplicity of operation, and precision of which it is capable have made the disappearing-filament optical pyrometer not only a useful tool in industry but also an excellent instrument for high-temperature research.

The photoelectric cell and photomultiplier tube with associated circuits are sensitive devices for measuring radiation, especially of low intensity. In the photomultiplier tube the incident light ejects a few photoelectrons from a coated surface. Thereafter the electrons are multiplied in number by several successive stages of secondary emission. Finally, the photoelectric current from this tube may be further amplified to activate a suitable recorder.

16.4. Temperatures of the Sun and Planets

The Sun and every other star pours billions upon billions of joules of radiant energy into space every second. Of the vast amount of energy from the Sun, the Earth intercepts only a minute fraction, and of this not all is absorbed. Brightness measurements for the Sun, the full Moon, and the Moon at times of solar eclipse have shown that about 35% of the intercepted radiation is reflected by the Earth. The remaining 65% is absorbed and reradiated. Of this, 19% is absorbed by the atmosphere and 46% reaches the surface of the earth. Careful and extensive worldwide measurements, largely under the direction of Langley and, later, Abbot of the Smithsonian Institute, have led to a fairly accurate value for the irradiancy of solar energy on the Earth. The average irradiancy at the upper reaches of the atmosphere, where little absorption and reflection has taken place, is called the solar constant and usually is represented by S. It is equal to 1.395 kw/m². The measurements are made with special automatically recording calorimeters that may be left for several weeks in exposed positions at many stations scattered over the Earth's surface. Data from them must be corrected for atmospheric absorption. The solar constant varies somewhat, owing to sunspot activity and other solar disturbances as well as to the periodic changes in the Earth–Sun distance.

Let us now compute the radiancy and temperature of the Sun's surface. We shall assume the Sun is spherical in shape and that it radiates uniformly in all directions. To determine the radiancy the solar constant is multiplied by the square of the ratio of the average Earth–Sun distance and the radius of the Sun. These distances are 149.5 and 0.6953 million kilometers, so the radiancy of the Sun equals 1.395 $(149.5/0.6953)^2$ or 64,500 kw/m². If the Sun radiates like a blackbody, Eq. (16.2) applies. Thus the radiation temperature of the Sun's surface equals approximately 6000°K.

The Moon has no observable atmosphere or water, and its surface is believed to consist largely of dust formed by thermal erosion. Under these conditions relatively little conduction and no convection can occur, and nearly all radiation (93%) is absorbed. A unit area of surface directly exposed to sunlight therefore attains dynamic thermal equilibrium by radiative processes alone. We can assume that the solar constant for the Earth applies equally well on the Moon; hence, if the Moon is assumed to be a blackbody, we find the temperature of its surface may be as high as $(1395/5.6685 \times 10^{-8})^{1/4}$ or 396°K. The measured value is 400°K. Incidentally, since only 46% of the incident solar radiation reaches the surface of the Earth we should expect a blackbody, which is exposed to direct sunlight at the Earth's surface on a clear cloudless day, to reach a maximum temperature of only $(0.46)^{1/4} \times$ 396 or 326°K. Temperatures within 1% of this value have been observed at Azizia in North Western Libya (September 13, 1922) and near Death Valley, California (July 10, 1913).

The fourth-power law may be applied in the same way for determining the temperature of any other planet or satellite in the solar system, provided it is in radiative equilibrium. The Earth and perhaps other planets actually are sources of heat and therefore would have higher *mean* temperatures than those computed. To illustrate this remark, consider the Earth once again, but this time as a whole. It intercepts $\pi r^2 S$ units of radiation, of which 65% are absorbed, where r represents the radius of the Earth. We now assume that this energy is dispersed over the Earth primarily by convective processes in the atmosphere and oceans, so reradiation takes place from the entire surface. For radiative equilibrium we write

$$0.65\pi r^2 S = 4\pi r^2 \sigma T^4,$$

from which T is found to equal 251°K. But the observed mean temperature of the Earth equals 287°K. This difference we suppose arises because the core and mantle of the Earth are at elevated temperatures and, furthermore, because the Earth as a whole really is not a blackbody at a uniform temperature. Nevertheless, this mean value does lie between 251°K and the maximum of 326°K.

16.5. Spectral Energy Distribution for Blackbody Radiation

As so often happens in physics, when a newly invented measuring device is applied in making new or more accurate measurements than those made hitherto, it can be the beginning of a far-reaching sequence of discoveries. In 1880 Langley[7] devised a very sensitive indicator of heat which he named a bolometer. It consisted of two thin grids of blackened platinum foil placed in opposite arms of a Wheatstone bridge. When one grid was exposed to radiation it became warmer and its resistance changed. The other grid was protected from the radiation and served as a compensatory element in the opposite arm of the bridge. With this instrument spectral energy distribution data were obtained. In Fig. 16.2 are constructed a few

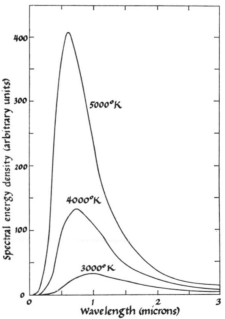

Figure 16.2.   Spectral energy distribution in the radiation from a blackbody at three different temperatures.

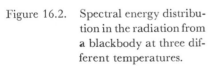

curves to illustrate the principal features displayed by such data. In order to explain these features Wien developed his general displacement and distribution laws as described below and, later, Planck invented the quantum of energy.

[7] Langley, S. P., *Am. J. Sci.*, **21**, 187 (1881); see also Draper, C. H., *Heat*, pp. 234–244 (Blackie, London, 1911).

The two features we observe are an increase in the intensity of emission as the temperature of the blackbody is raised and a simultaneous shift of the maximum toward shorter wavelengths. Langley discovered these features with his newly invented bolometer. The wavelength for maximum emission and the temperature satisfy the simple empirical relation

$$\lambda_m T = \text{universal constant.} \qquad (16.4)$$

The constant may be determined once and for all by careful measurements on radiation from a blackbody cavity in the laboratory. The accepted value for it today is 2897.94 ± 0.09 μ-deg.

By means of Eq. (16.4) temperatures of inaccessible radiant bodies may be found. The measured energy distribution in the solar spectrum after correction for atmospheric absorption and scattering has a maximum at 0.46 μ. If we assume the Sun is a blackbody emitter, its surface temperature would be 2898/0.46 or 6300°K. This value is only 5% higher than that obtained in the foregoing section from total emission data.

16.6. Wien's Displacement and Distribution Laws[8]

Consider an equilibrium distribution of blackbody radiation confined in a spherical enclosure with perfectly reflecting walls. This distribution may be obtained by first placing a small blackbody in the enclosure until equilibrium is established and then removing it without disturbing the distribution. Suppose now the volume is reduced quasistatically such that the energy density increases without any exchange of heat with the near-surround. For this adiabatic process,

$$d'Q = 0 = d(uV) + P dV. \qquad (16.5)$$

The radiation pressure equals $\frac{1}{3}u$, and therefore the equation is written

$$V du + \tfrac{4}{3} u \, dV = 0,$$

which integrates to

$$uV^{4/3} = \text{constant.} \qquad (16.6)$$

Since u is proportional to T^4 (Section 3.2) and V equals $\frac{4}{3}\pi r^3$, it follows that

$$Tr = \text{constant.} \qquad (16.7)$$

Wien next applied Doppler's principle to the radiation in the enclosure. As the radiation strikes the moving walls of the sphere, when the volume of radiation is reduced, it experiences Doppler increases in frequency throughout the spectrum. This effect is most easily seen as simply a decrease in each

---

[8] Wien, W., *Wied. Ann.*, **52**, 132 (1894).

wavelength at the same rate as the decrease in the radius of the sphere. In other words, for any one wavelength $d\lambda/\lambda$ equals dr/r. If we integrate and combine the result with Eq. (16.7), we get

$$\lambda T = \text{constant} \tag{16.8}$$

for every point along a spectral energy distribution curve. This is Wien's displacement law. The empirical relation, Eq. (16.4), is seen to be a special case of it.

Let us now investigate the adiabatic reduction in volume for blackbody radiation in a narrow spectral band of width $\Delta\lambda$ centered on wavelength λ. The energy density in this band may be written as $u_\lambda\Delta\lambda$ and the partial radiation pressure as $\frac{1}{3}u_\lambda\Delta\lambda$, where u_λ is the energy density per unit wavelength interval. Since there is no interaction between spectral bands we can apply Eq. (16.5) to each of them separately; thus we find

$$d(u_\lambda\Delta\lambda V) + \tfrac{1}{3}u_\lambda\Delta\lambda dV = 0. \tag{16.9}$$

Expanding the first term we get

$$u_\lambda V d(\Delta\lambda) + V\Delta\lambda du_\lambda + \tfrac{4}{3}u_\lambda\Delta\lambda dV = 0$$

or

$$d(\Delta\lambda)/\Delta\lambda + du_\lambda/u_\lambda + \tfrac{4}{3}dV/V = 0. \tag{16.10}$$

But $d(\Delta\lambda)/\Delta\lambda$ equals $\Delta(d\lambda)/\Delta\lambda$, and this in turn must be the same as $d\lambda/\lambda$. Furthermore, dV/V equals $3dr/r$ or $3d\lambda/\lambda$. On making the substitutions, Eq. (16.10) becomes simply

$$5d\lambda/\lambda + du_\lambda/u_\lambda = 0, \tag{16.11}$$

from which

$$\lambda^5 u_\lambda = \text{constant}. \tag{16.12}$$

Here we have the second displacement law.

Since Eqs. (16.8) and (16.12) are not independent of one another we conclude that their constants must be related. We now write

$$u_\lambda = \lambda^{-5}f(\lambda T), \tag{16.13}$$

which is Wien's general distribution law. The function $f(\lambda T)$ is found by statistical methods as described in the following sections.

16.7. *Classical Forms of* $f\,(\lambda T)$

According to Rayleigh[9] and Jeans,[10] blackbody radiation in a spherical enclosure exists as standing waves. Just as for a crystalline solid (Section

---

[9] Lord Rayleigh, *Phil. Mag.*, β⁻, 539 (1900).
[10] Jeans, J., *Phil. Mag.*, 1†, 239 (1909).

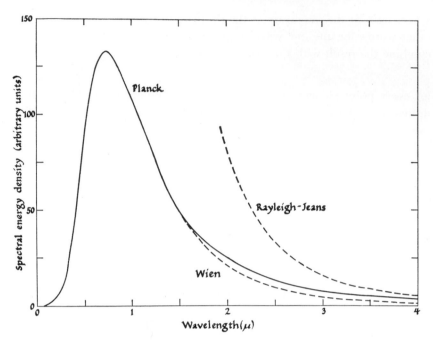

Figure 16.3.   Comparison of the Wien, Rayleigh-Jeans, and Planck spectral energy
distribution laws for blackbody radiation.

15.3), the number of modes of oscillation per unit volume for transverse
waves in the cavity equals $8\pi\nu^2 d\nu/c^3$. Here ν equals c/λ, where c is the speed
of the waves. Each mode is identified with a degree of freedom of energy
kT by the equipartition principle. The monochromatic energy density therefore is

$$u_\lambda = (8\pi/\lambda^4)kT, \tag{16.14}$$

from which we infer that $f(\lambda T)$ is directly proportional to λT. Although this
function is satisfactory in the far infrared region and beyond, it fails badly
at shorter wavelengths, as can be seen in Fig. 16.3.

Wien[11] assumed the blackbody radiation in the spherical enclosure to be
in equilibrium with resonators of molecular dimensions. He further assumed
that the frequency of an emitted wave is proportional to the kinetic energy
of a resonator and that the intensity of radiation at this frequency is proportional to the number of resonators with that energy. If we suppose the energies of the resonators satisfy a maxwellian distribution, then the equation
for monochromatic energy density comes out to be

---

[11] Wien, W., *Ann. Physik*, **58**, 662 (1896).

$$u_\lambda = \varphi(v) \exp\left(-\tfrac{1}{2}mv^2/kT\right)$$
$$= \varphi(\lambda) \exp\left(-c_2/\lambda T\right). \tag{16.15}$$

By comparing Eqs. (16.13) and (16.15) we conclude that $\varphi(\lambda)$ must be proportional to λ^{-5}. Thus we obtain Wien's form of $f(\lambda T)$. In spite of the arbitrary assumptions he made and the questionable procedure for developing it, Wien obtained an equation which describes the short-wavelength region of the distribution curve rather well, as can be seen in Fig. 16.3.

Neither the Rayleigh-Jeans nor the Wien form of distribution function describes the entire distribution curve. In fact, every attempt to obtain a function by classical methods has failed. Only by introducing a radically new idea was Planck able to obtain the correct form.

16.8. *Planck's Law*

Planck,[12] like Wien, assumed the blackbody radiation in an enclosure to be in equilibrium with resonators of molecular dimensions. But Planck abandoned the notion of continuous emission. Instead, he assumed each resonator emitted energy in integral multiples of a unit amount ϵ, which would allow him to apply the Maxwell-Boltzmann statistics. He hoped eventually to obtain an equation for the energy distribution of blackbody radiation by letting ϵ approach zero.

Let $N_0, N_1, N_2, \cdots, N_r, \cdots$ be the number of resonators of energies $0, \epsilon, 2\epsilon, \cdots, r\epsilon, \cdots$. Then the total number of resonators N and their energy E are the sums

$$N = N_0 + N_1 + N_2 + \cdots N_r + \cdots \tag{16.16}$$

and

$$E = \epsilon(N_1 + 2N_2 + \cdots rN_r + \cdots), \tag{16.17}$$

in which, by the Maxwell-Boltzmann distribution law,

$$N_r = N_0 \exp\left(-r\epsilon/kT\right). \tag{16.18}$$

When this value of N_r is inserted in the sums and the additions are performed we get

$$N = N_0[1 - e^{-\epsilon/kT}]^{-1} \tag{16.19}$$

and

$$E = \epsilon N_0 e^{-\epsilon/kT}[1 - e^{-\epsilon/kT}]^{-2}. \tag{16.20}$$

The ratio E/N then equals the mean energy of the resonators,

---

[12] Planck, M., *Ann. Physik*, **4**, 553 (1901).

$$\bar{\epsilon} = \epsilon[e^{\epsilon/k\mathsf{T}} - 1]^{-1}, \tag{16.21}$$

a value very different from $k\mathsf{T}$ as given by the equipartition principle.

Each mode of oscillation for the radiation in the enclosure is identified with a resonator, so the density of resonators is simply $8\pi/\lambda^4$, and therefore the monochromatic energy density [compare with Eq. (16.14)] is

$$u_\lambda = 8\pi\bar{\epsilon}/\lambda^4$$
$$= 8\pi\epsilon\lambda^{-4}[e^{\epsilon/k\mathsf{T}} - 1]^{-1}. \tag{16.22}$$

We see that in order to satisfy Wien's general distribution law ϵ must be proportional to λ^{-1} and cannot vanish. It is here that Planck was inevitably led to postulate the existence of a quantum of energy. Specifically he let ϵ equal hc/λ, in which h is now called Planck's constant. The accepted value for it is $6.6253 \pm 0.0003 \times 10^{-34}$ joule-sec. We now write Planck's distribution law in the form

$$u_\lambda = 8\pi hc\lambda^{-5}/[e^{hc/k\lambda\mathsf{T}} - 1]$$
$$= c_1\lambda^{-5}/[e^{c_2/\lambda\mathsf{T}} - 1]. \tag{16.23}$$

This function also is plotted in Fig. 16.3.

Ordinarily, in applications of Planck's law the second constant c_2 is assigned a standard value, which may be evaluated thus:

$$c_2 = hc/k$$
$$= 6.6253 \times 10^{-34} \times 2.997923 \times 10^8/1.38041 \times 10^{-23}$$
$$= 0.0143886 \pm 0.0000005 \text{ m-deg Kelvin.}$$

The first constant also may be computed; it has the value $(4.9919 \pm 0.0002) \times 10^{-24}$ joule-m. Often, however, a radiating system involves factors which modify this first constant, and therefore the coefficient c_1 is measured for the prevailing conditions of emission. This procedure was suggested in establishing the international scale at high temperatures (Section 2.8).

16.9. Verification of Plank's Law

Planck's law has been thoroughly tested. Rubens and Nichols performed a series of painstaking measurements and finally reported, in 1921, that no discrepancy existed between their experimental observations of energy flux from blackbody cavities and the predicted values from Planck's law for temperatures between 93°K and 1831°K. Measurements by Coblenz, Paschen, Warburg, and others established the validity of Planck's function beyond doubt. In addition, we can derive from it both the fourth-power law and the displacement equation for the maximum point of the spectral energy distribution curve.

The fourth-power law is obtained simply by integrating $u_\lambda d\lambda$ over all wavelengths. Thus

$$u_b = \int_0^\infty u_\lambda d\lambda$$

$$= c_1 \int_0^\infty \frac{\lambda^{-5} d\lambda}{e^{c_2/\lambda T} - 1}$$

$$= (c_1 T^4 / c_2^4) \int_0^\infty \frac{x^3 dx}{e^x - 1}, \tag{16.24}$$

where x equals $c_2/\lambda T$. When the integrand is expanded and the integration is carried out, the definite integral is found to have the value $\pi^4/15$. Since J_b equals $\frac{1}{4} c u_b$ (Section 3.2), it follows that the Stefan-Boltzmann constant σ is given by the equation

$$\sigma = (\tfrac{1}{4} c c_1 / c_2^4)(\pi^4/15)$$

$$= 2\pi^5 k^4 / 15 c^2 h^3. \tag{16.25}$$

When the foregoing values of h, c, and k are substituted we find

$$\sigma = 5.6685 \times 10^{-8} \text{ watt/m}^2\text{-deg}^4.$$

In order to obtain Eq. (16.4) we differentiate u_λ with respect to λ and equate the result to zero. In this way we find that

$$\lambda_m T = c_2/y, \tag{16.26}$$

where y satisfies the transcendental equation

$$y = 5(1 - e^{-y}). \tag{16.27}$$

The solution of this equation is $y = 4.9651$, and therefore

$$\lambda_m T = 0.0143886 \times 10^6/4.9651$$

$$= 2897.9 \ \mu\text{-deg}. \tag{16.28}$$

During the early part of the twentieth century the quantum of energy became a well-established construct in physics as a result of its successful applications in explaining the photoelectric effect, atomic spectra, and a host of other atomic and nuclear phenomena. These successes reflected on Planck's original work, thus helping to confirm his form of the distribution law for radiation. Out of these applications there arose two new kinds of thermophysical statistics, and through them physicists have acquired a better insight into the structure and operations of the physical world. These quantum statistics are described and applied in Chapter 17.

16.10. Maxwell's Sorting Demon

In our study of blackbody radiation within an enclosure we have assumed the space completely devoid of matter or else filled with linear resonators in equilibrium with the radiation. Although these resonators sometimes are identified with gas molecules, generally this is unnecessary for devising the fundamental laws of radiation. In the one exception, where Wien obtained his specific form of the distribution law, the assumptions and arguments employed by him are very questionable. At this time we should like to examine a composite system consisting of both blackbody radiation and an ideal gas.

An ideal gas within an enclosure is in complete thermodynamic equilibrium if the temperature and pressure are uniform throughout and if no chemical processes take place no matter how slowly. From a thermodynamic viewpoint the temperature of half the system cannot rise spontaneously while that of the other half falls. Such an extraordinary process would violate the second law of thermodynamics. Even from a statistical point of view the random agitation of the molecules composing the system insures that the two halves almost never differ in temperature; except for momentary imperceptible fluctuations, the temperature is uniform. But, suggested Maxwell, "if we conceive a being whose faculties are so sharpened that he can follow every molecule in its course, such a being, whose attributes are still as essentially finite as our own, would be able to do what is at present impossible to us." Let us suppose this being can operate a trapdoor over a hole of molecular dimensions in a partition dividing the two halves of an ideal-gas system. Then, according to Maxwell, he could separate the fast-moving molecules from the slow-moving molecules in due time and thereby, without the transfer of work or heat, raise the temperature of half the system and lower that of the other half. He could violate the second law of thermodynamics at will. We should like to conceive Maxwell's sorting demon to represent any living system, and life to contradict the second law of thermodynamics.

There is a fallacy in the foregoing sorting procedure: *neither the demon nor any living system can violate the second law.* Maxwell's argument rests on the assumption that his being "can follow every molecule in its course." If the enclosed system is in thermal equilibrium at the start, the enclosure contains not only a random distribution of molecules but also blackbody radiation. No being could *see* the molecules in order to follow them unless he were endowed with an extraphysical vision. The features of the molecules are completely obliterated in the radiation field of uniform energy density, so the sorting procedure is physically impossible. Maxwell could not have realized this, for he invented his demon many years before the properties of blackbody radiation were discovered. It was Szilard who, in 1929, first pointed out the fallacy. From 1871 to 1929 Maxwell's demon was a singular creature.

To enable the sorting demon to *see* the molecules we may equip him with a flashlight, but the filament of the lamp must operate at a temperature in excess of (or less than!) that for the system as a whole. We suppose each molecule is sufficiently large that it is not diverted from its path a significant amount when it intercepts one or more quanta of radiation from the flash-light.

The radiation from the flashlight is not in equilibrium. Suppose the light is flashed momentarily on a molecule. A small amount of energy is added to the system, and if nothing further is done, the temperature of the system and its entropy increase slightly. Suppose, however, the demon receives a portion of the flashlight radiation after it has been intercepted by a molecule, thus giving him some information about the speed and direction of motion of the molecule. The demon may then open the trapdoor to allow a fast molecule to pass in one direction or a slow molecule to pass in the opposite direction. After a while the temperature on one side of the partition is greater than that on the other. The entropy of the system is less than it would have been if the demon had not intervened.

16.11. Negative Entropy and Information

We should like to demonstrate in a quantitative manner that the entropy of the system is increased, although the demon has helped to prevent it from reaching its maximum possible value through the information gathered by means of the nonequilibrium radiation from the flashlight. The cycle proposed by Brillouin is

negative entropy $\longrightarrow$ *information* $\longrightarrow$ *negative entropy.*

We shall show how this cycle applies to man and scientific observation.

In the preceding section the implication is made that the overall change of entropy for the local universe, even in the presence of an information source, always is greater than zero. We observe that the system under investigation consists of an ideal gas at temperature T_0 within a divided enclosure, a flashlight with a filament heated to temperature T, and the Maxwell demon who can operate a trapdoor over a small hole in the partition dividing the enclosure. The hot filament yields quanta of energy greater than kT_0 so its radiation can be distinguished from that of the background in the enclosure.

Suppose the light is flashed momentarily by the demon. The battery-lamp system radiates energy E, and its entropy decreases by E/T. If the demon does not intervene, the energy is absorbed by the gas at temperature T_0, and the entropy of the gas therefore increases by the amount E/T_0. On the other hand, if a quantum of energy $h\nu$ is scattered by a molecule into the eye of the demon, he obtains information regarding the molecule which enables him to make a decision about opening the trapdoor. The entropy of this radiation $h\nu/T_0$ is more than k, as noted in the foregoing paragraph, and may be set equal to kb, where b is greater than unity. The demon continues the separation process until there is an excess of high speed molecules on one side of the trapdoor (say A) and an excess of low speed molecules on the other side (say B).

Suppose the temperature in A then equals $T_0 + \frac{1}{2}\Delta T$ and the temperature in B equals $T_0 - \frac{1}{2}\Delta T$. Now the demon allows a fast-moving molecule in A of kinetic energy $\frac{3}{2}kT_0(1 + \epsilon_A)$ to enter B and a slow-moving molecule in B of kinetic energy $\frac{3}{2}kT_0(1 - \epsilon_B)$ to enter A. At least two light quanta are required by the demon to produce this separation, and therefore the entropy of the local universe is increased by ΔS_d, where

$$\Delta S_d \geq 2kb. \qquad (16.29)$$

The exchange of molecules results in an energy transfer Q from A to B which equals $\frac{3}{2}kT_0(\epsilon_A + \epsilon_B)$. This corresponds to a decrease of entropy,

$$\Delta S_i = Q\left[\frac{1}{T_0 + \frac{1}{2}\Delta T} - \frac{1}{T_0 - \frac{1}{2}\Delta T}\right]$$

$$= -Q\frac{\Delta T}{T_0^2}. \qquad (16.30)$$

Now ϵ_A and ϵ_B usually are very small, and likewise ΔT is much smaller than T_0, so ΔS_i equals $-\frac{3}{2}ka$, where a is less than unity. The total change of entropy for the local universe then is the sum of ΔS_d and ΔS_i:

$$\Delta S = \Delta S_d + \Delta S_i = k(2b - \frac{3}{2}a). \qquad (16.31)$$

This sum is greater than zero because b is greater than unity and a is less than unity, and therefore the second law of thermodynamics is satisfied.

It should be noted that negative entropy from the flashlight yields information which in turn enables the demon to introduce negative entropy ΔS_i into the gas system. Brillouin's cycle is satisfied.

16.12. Laboratory Observations

The scientist in his laboratory is no better off than the demon. Every observation is made at the expense of batteries, compressed springs, light sources, and other systems capable of supplying negative entropy. What is the smallest amount of negative entropy needed to read an ammeter or to make some other similar observation?

The needle of the meter executes oscillatory brownian motions with an average total energy kT, where T represents room temperature. Let us now assume that an additional energy δkT, where δ is a small number, is needed to obtain a correct reading. This energy is dissipated in friction of the bearings and viscous damping within the meter while the needle returns to zero. The increase of entropy associated with making the reading therefore equals δkT divided by T or simply the Boltzmann constant multiplied by δ. This number apparently represents the lowest limit of negative entropy required to make the reading. On the other hand, radiation of energy $h\nu$ greater than kT is required in order to distinguish the light signal from the background blackbody radiation. The negative entropy then must be greater than $h\nu/T$ or δk, whichever is the larger. Here is a limitation on observation of a thermophysical origin.

As man extracts information from his apparatus he decreases negative entropy. By utilizing this information in appropriate ways he may convert a large portion of it to negative entropy again in the form of more complex and ordered systems. Throughout the entire process, however, it must be remembered that the total entropy of the local universe is increased.

From the foregoing discussion we conclude that negative entropy is a measure of information. Brillouin invented the word *negentropy* for it. The negentropy of a system equals its information value. A system with some degree of negentropy is not in thermodynamic equilibrium. As time goes on, the information value of the system decreases, and concomitantly the entropy increases by an equal amount to a final steady value.

Perhaps living systems are the most complex and therefore the most difficult to study from the thermophysical point of view. Schrödinger[13] has pointed out, however, that the essential characteristic of a living system is its ability to maintain a high degree of negative entropy in the form of organization and structure by decreasing the order of its near-surround. Life lives on negative entropy!

---

[13] Schrödinger, E., *What is Life?* (The University Press, Cambridge, 1944).

Bibliography

Brillouin, L., *Science and Information Theory* (Academic, New York, 1956).
Cork, J. M., *Heat* (Wiley, New York, 1942).
Fritz, S., "Solar Energy on Clear and Cloudy Days," *The Scientific Monthly,* **84** (1957).
Saha, M. N., and B. N. Srivastava, *A Textbook of Heat* (The Indian Press, Allahabad, India, 1931).
Worthing, A. G., and D. Halliday, *Heat* (Wiley, New York, 1948).

Problems

1. In the accompanying table are shown values for the percent of incident sunlight reflected into space by the atmosphere, clouds, and surface of the Earth. This incident radiation consists of 9% ultraviolet, 41% visible, and 50% infrared. What fraction of the incident sunlight is absorbed by the Earth's atmosphere and surface under a clear cloudless sky? What are the mean values of the Earth's reflectivity (albedo) for ultraviolet, visible, infrared, and total radiation?

Reflection of Sunlight into Space (percent)*			
	Ultraviolet	Visible	Infrared
Atmosphere	2.6	5.2	1.3
Clouds	2.6	11.3	10.2
Surface	0.1	1.1	1.1

* Adapted from "Solar Energy on Clear and Cloudy Days," Fritz, S., *The Scientific Monthly,* **84**, pp. 55–65, 1957.

2. Tektites are found scattered over wide areas on the earth's surface. They are glassy fragments which appear to have been through a molten stage. How close to the Sun would a body need to pass in order to become molten? (Some glasses become molten between 600°C and 800°C; magnesium aluminum silicates melt near 1600°C.)

3. Compute a value for the temperature of Saturn and compare it with the observed value of −150°C. Do the same thing for Mars, for which the observed values are in the range −60°C to +75°C.

4. (a) If thermal energy is transferred between a body at temperature T and its near-surround at temperature T_s solely by radiation, show that

$$dQ/d\tau = 4Ae\sigma T_s^3(T_s - T),$$

provided $T_s - T \ll T_s$, where A is the surface area of the body and e is its emissivity.

(b) A hot body at the initial temperature T_o cools only by radiation over a short range of temperature. Show that at time τ

$$T - T_s = (T_o - T_s) \exp(-b\tau),$$

in which b equals $4Ae\sigma T_s^3/C_p$ and C_p is the heat capacity of the body at constant pressure.

5. A very hot body cools solely by exchange of radiant energy with its near-surround. Derive a general equation for the temperature of the body at any time τ.

6. Carry through the steps in the derivation of Eq. (16.28).

7. (a) Derive the equation

$$T^{-1} = T_a^{-1} + (\lambda/c_2) \ln e_\lambda$$

for the temperature of a breybody whose apparent or brightnooo temppru- ture is T_a and whose spectral emissivity at wavelength λ is e_λ. (For this derivation it is convenient to apply Wien's equation for monochromatic energy density rather than Planck's law; very little error is introduced.)

(b) Compute a value for the melting-point temperature of silver from these data: The brightness temperature of polished silver is $1047.5°K$ at its melting point, and its spectral emissivity is 0.044 at a wavelength of $0.665\ \mu$.

8. A blackbody, such as a house roof, near the Earth's surface absorbs solar radiation, which has the spectral energy distribution of a body at $6000°K$, and reradiates it at $287°K$, the mean temperature of the Earth's surface. The blackbody serves as a transformer of radiant energy with 100% efficiency from a high-temperature distribution to a low-temperature distribution. Determine the rate of entropy production from solar radiation by this process per unit area of absorbing surface.

CHAPTER **17**

Quantum Statistics

PLANCK introduced the quantum of energy in order to bring about agreement between his equation for the spectral energy distribution of black-body radiation and the Wien general distribution law. He had assumed the radiation is in dynamic equilibrium with an assembly of dipole radiators, which are identified with atoms in a gas, and then he had applied Maxwell-Boltzmann statistics to the system (Section 16.8). Insofar as this procedure calls on a particular model with specific properties and physical processes, it may be likened to the application of kinetic theory to derive the equation of state for an ideal gas. For both the radiation system and the ideal gas, semi-empirical equations are obtained by comparisons with thermodynamic equations. It is not surprising therefore to discover that we may derive the Planck distribution law without recourse to the foregoing model by means of a new statistics, just as the state equation for an ideal gas can be derived without reference to specific properties and processes of a molecular aggregate by means of classical statistics.

In the Maxwell-Boltzmann statistics the microsystems are distinguished from one another. Consequently, this kind of statistics should not apply to a group of identical microsystems of molecular size. As we recall, wrong results are obtained for the contribution of electrons to the specific heat of a metal. Furthermore, the velocity distribution of photoelectrons, as predicted from an application of Maxwell-Boltzmann statistics, does not agree with experimental observations. Because electrons are minute and indistinguishable these results are not unexpected, but even atoms and molecules under certain conditions, as well as other elementary material particles, can-
256

not be described by classical statistics. In a sense, Maxwell-Boltzmann statistics is a limiting form of quantum statistics.

17.1. The Uncertainty Principle

In our studies we have taken for granted that the position and velocity of every molecule in a system can be measured in principle with any desired accuracy. Furthermore, we have supposed that the act of measurement has no effect on the molecule. Quantum physics has changed all this. We know now that there is not only an experimental but also a theoretical limit to the accuracy of such measurements. Consider a simple example. If we want to determine the position of an electron, or even a molecule, we would need to illuminate it with some radiation. The position therefore cannot be measured to an accuracy Δq of less than one wavelength λ of the radiation (assumed monochromatic). But a quantum of this radiation equals $h\nu$ and has momentum $h\nu/c$ or h/λ, where h is Planck's constant. Part or all of this momentum is transferred to the molecule as a result of the interaction, and therefore the observed momentum of the molecule is uncertain by an amount Δp of the order h/λ. The product $\Delta p \cdot \Delta q$ thus is of the order h. By a more rigorous treatment we find this result applies to the position and momentum along each coordinate and indeed to each degree of freedom. Because this is a lower limit we write for each degree of freedom

$$\Delta p \cdot \Delta q \geq h. \qquad (17.1)$$

In other words, it is impossible, even in a highly idealized experiment, to measure simultaneously both a coordinate q and its conjugate momentum p for a molecule with such an accuracy that the product of the uncertainties in p and q is less than h. Equation (17.1) is a statement of Heisenberg's uncertainty principle.[1]

Because of the implications of this principle we must review what we mean by the state of a statistical system. We recall that for the purposes of classical statistics, values for the momenta and coordinates of the particles in the system were specified with arbitrary exactness. Now we know this cannot be done. Instead we imagine momentum-coordinate or phase-space subdivided into a very large number of cells of volume h^f, where f represents the number of degrees of freedom per particle, and then we determine the distribution of particles among these cells. Although this method of defining the state of

---

[1] Heisenberg, W., *Zeits. f. Physik*, **43**, 172 (1927); *The Principles of the Quantum Theory* (University of Chicago Press, Chicago, 1930).

a system is less precise than the classical one, it is consistent with the uncertainty principle.

The size of a cell in phase space is so small that even an element of volume $dxdydzdp_xdp_ydp_z$ contains a very large number of them. In general, this number is very much larger than the number of elementary particles to be distributed among the cells. Consequently, the distribution function must be found by counting complexions in a different way from that for the Maxwell-Boltzmann statistics. Two forms of quantum statistics have been developed. In one, the Bose-Einstein, we suppose a single cell can contain an arbitrary number of identical particles, whereas in the other, the Fermi-Dirac, each cell contains no more than one particle at a time.

17.2. Bose-Einstein Statistics

The distribution law from Bose-Einstein statistics is obtained by making three fundamental assumptions: (1) phase space is subdivided into cells of volume h^f; (2) all particles are identical; and (3) any number of these particles may occupy a single cell. Phase space first is divided into equal volume elements $\Delta \upsilon$ of sufficient size to contain a great number of cells $G = \Delta \upsilon / h^f$. But $\Delta \upsilon$ is small enough that all the particles in it have very nearly the same value of energy. Consider a volume element which contains n_i particles each of energy U_i. We seek the most probable distribution of the n_i particles among the G cells in this volume element. First we compute the number of distinct complexions for these n_i particles, and then we perform a maximizing procedure much as we did in our study of the Maxwell-Boltzmann statistics. Here, however, an interchange of particles produces no new complexion, for the particles are indistinguishable.

Since the n_i particles may be distributed among the G cells at random, it is convenient to visualize the process in the following way. The cells are imagined strung along a line, and the particles are interspersed between them completely at random. One such distribution may look like this:

$$c\,p\,p\,c\,c\,c\,c\,p\,c\,c\,c\,c\,c\,p\,c\,p\,c\,c\,p\,p\,c\,c\,c\,c\,c\,c\,c\,c\,c\,p\,c\,c\,\cdots$$

We now place each group of particles in the cell immediately to its left. Many many cells will contain no particles. On the other hand, particles should not fall to the left of the sequence if every particle is to occupy a cell. Consequently, all but one cell and all the particles may be arranged in any order we please. The number of permutations of $G - 1$ cells plus n_i particles equals $(n_i + G - 1)!$. But interchanges of cells and also of particles do not produce new complexions, and therefore we must divide out permutations among the $G - 1$ cells and among the n_i particles. The number of distinct complexions resulting from this counting is $(n_i + G - 1)!/n_i!(G - 1)!$, which we define to be the thermophysical probability W_i for the ith element of volume. Finally, the probability W for the entire system is given by the product

$$W = \Pi_i W_i = \Pi_i[(n_i + G - 1)!/n_i!(G - 1)!]. \qquad (17.2)$$

As before, we find the distribution which makes $\ln W$ a maximum subject to the conditions that the total number of particles n and the total energy U of the system are constant. G is so large that unity is negligible, and therefore $\ln W$ may be written in the form

$$\ln W = \Sigma_i[\ln (n + G)! - \ln n_i! - \ln G!]$$
$$= \Sigma_i[n_i \ln (1 + G/n_i) + G \ln (1 + n_i/G)], \qquad (17.3)$$

where we have applied Stirling's approximation. For the most probable distribution, $\delta \ln W = 0$. Because n and U are constant for the system, both δn and δU also equal zero. By means of Lagrange's method of undetermined multipliers therefore,

$$\delta \ln W + \alpha \delta n + \beta \delta U = 0,$$

from which

$$\Sigma_i \delta n_i[\ln (1 + G/n_i) + \alpha + \beta U_i] = 0. \qquad (17.4)$$

In order to satisfy this equation for all variations in the occupation numbers (see Section 13.2) we have

$$\ln (1 + G/n_i) + \alpha + \beta U_i = 0,$$

and therefore

$$n_i = \frac{G}{e^{-(\alpha + \beta U_i)} - 1}. \qquad (17.5)$$

This is the Bose-Einstein distribution law for degenerate gases. It applies to all aggregates of atoms and molecules composed of an even number of elementary material particles.

Values of the parameters α and β in Eq. (17.5) are determined in principle from the conditions that n and U are constant. Because -1 appears in the denominator the evaluation of α is not as simple as it is in classical statistics. Fortunately for our purpose this computation will be unnecessary. On the other hand, β may be found by recalling that $(\partial S/\partial U)_V = T^{-1}$, where $S = k \ln W$. When the volume is held constant no work is done, and therefore all U_i are constant. Hence from Eqs. (17.3) and (17.5) we get

$$dS = k\Sigma_i \ln (1 + G/n_i)dn_i$$
$$= -k\Sigma_i(\alpha + \beta U_i)dn_i$$
$$= -k\beta\Sigma_i U_i dn_i = -k\beta dU, \qquad (17.6)$$

since for this computation n is constant even though U is not. We see that Eq. (17.6) satisfies the thermodynamic relation, provided β equals $-1/kT$.

For a system in which n is not constant we can set α in Eq. (17.5) equal to zero. The average energy per cell for such a system then is

$$U = n_i U_i/G = U_i/(e^{U_i/kT} - 1). \tag{17.7}$$

This is the equation which Planck found for the energy density of blackbody radiation, provided photons are considered to be the particles which are distributed among cells of energies $U_i = h\nu_i$ (see Eq. 16.21). That is, Bose-Einstein statistics applies to radiation systems.

17.3. Condensation of an Ideal Bose-Einstein Gas

We transform Eq. (17.5) into differential form by replacing the element of volume in phase space with its equivalent value for volume V,

$$\Delta \mathcal{U} = Gh^3 \longrightarrow V dp_x dp_y dp_z, \tag{17.8}$$

and by substituting dn for n_i. In addition, for convenience we shall replace U_i by ϵ. The element of volume in momentum space $dp_x dp_y dp_z$ is equivalent to $p^2 dp d\Omega$, which may be integrated immediately over the solid angle to get $4\pi p^2 dp$, where p equals $(2m\epsilon)^{1/2}$. Finally, we rewrite Eq. (17.5) in the form

$$dn = \frac{2\pi V(2m/h^2)^{3/2} \epsilon^{1/2} d\epsilon}{e^{-(\alpha+\beta\epsilon)} - 1}. \tag{17.9}$$

But

$$[e^{-(\alpha+\beta\epsilon)} - 1]^{-1} = \sum_{j=1}^{\infty} e^{j(\alpha+\beta\epsilon)}, \tag{17.10}$$

so

$$dn = 2\pi V(2m/h^2)^{3/2} \sum_{j=1}^{\infty} e^{j(\alpha+\beta\epsilon)} \epsilon^{1/2} d\epsilon. \tag{17.11}$$

To integrate the expression over the entire energy spectrum we make the substitution $z = -j\beta\epsilon = j\epsilon/kT$ and recall that

$$\int_0^{\infty} z^{1/2} e^{-z} dz = \tfrac{1}{2}\sqrt{\pi}.$$

The result is

$$N = (2\pi m kT/h^2)^{3/2} V \sum_{j=1}^{\infty} j^{-(3/2)} e^{j\alpha}. \tag{17.12}$$

This is the relation between N and α by which α might be evaluated, but the inversion is too difficult to perform. Instead we shall consider the two extremes of special interest to us at very high and at very low temperatures.

At very high temperatures, for a constant ratio N/V the exponent must be rather large and negative in order for Eq. (17.12) to be satisfied. The series is dominated then by its first term ($j = 1$); thus we find

$$\alpha \simeq \ln \ (2\pi mkT/h^2)^{3/2}(V/N) \qquad (17.13)$$

at high temperatures in agreement with the results for a classical ideal gas. This may be seen by combining Eqs. (13.14) and (13.30) with c replaced by h^{-3}.

As the temperature is decreased from its high value for a fixed N/V exponent $-\alpha$ must approach zero. The same effect can be accomplished by keeping T fixed and increasing the number concentration N/V. In either procedure a special solution is obtained when α vanishes. The remaining series $\Sigma_{j=1}^{\infty} j^{-(3/2)}$ then is the Riemann zeta-function[2] for argument $\frac{3}{2}$ which equals 2.612. We now have for the special solution

$$N/V = 2.612(2\pi mkT_c/h^2)^{3/2}. \qquad (17.14)$$

Suppose we next reduce the temperature slightly below the critical value T_c so α would be required to take on a small *positive* value in order to maintain a constant ratio N/V. The series should then be only slightly greater than 2.612; instead it diverges immediately to an infinite value. In fact, no value of α exists which can produce a sum for the series between 2.612 and infinity.

The difficulty we encounter here arises as a result of the approximations we made in replacing Eq. (17.5) by the differential form in Eq. (17.11). Specifically, we note in Eq. (17.5) that the lowest energy state at $\epsilon = U_i = 0$ gives $n_0 = G/(e^{-\alpha} - 1)$, and clearly α cannot be equated to zero since n_0 must be finite. On the other hand, as T approaches T_c from above, α does approach zero, and indeed it may be set equal to zero for all but the lowest state. Very nearly then,

$$N = n_0 + 2.612V(2\pi mkT/h^2), \qquad (17.15)$$

in which n_0 equals the occupation number of the lowest state and the second term represents the total number of molecules in the higher states when $0° < T < T_c$. We interpret T_c to be the critical temperature where molecules begin to drop into the lowest energy state. Whereas all the molecules are above the lowest state at T_c, they all occupy this state at 0°K.

The process we have described here is analogous to the vapor-liquid transformation in coordinate space, and therefore it is described as condensation

---

[2] Values for the Riemann zeta-function may be found in Jahnke, E., and F. Emde, *Tables of Functions*, p. 273 (Dover, New York, 1943).

in momentum space. The critical temperature T_c is the Einstein condensation temperature. London[3] (1938) suggested that the λ-transition of liquid helium might be a manifestation of this condensation process. The phenomenon is discussed in Section 19.4 where T_c is evaluated for helium. Compare the value we obtain of 3.13°K with the measured λ-point for helium of 2.17°K.

17.4. Fermi-Dirac Statistics

The Fermi-Dirac distribution law arises from an application of the Pauli exclusion principle to the statistics of a system of elementary material particles. This principle is a statement of an inherent limitation on the availability of states; specifically, it says no two particles in a system may occupy a given quantum state simultaneously. Since the quantum state of a particle is described by certain quantum numbers, the principle is restated in the form, no two particles in a system may have the same set of quantum numbers. It is unnecessary to review quantum mechanics at this point in order to understand the following discussion, but it should be clear that the Fermi-Dirac statistics has a very direct connection with this fundamental principle of Pauli's. Here we make three assumptions: (1) phase space is subdivided into cells of volume h^f; (2) all particles in a given population are identical; and (3) either one particle or none may occupy a single cell. The first two assumptions are exactly the same as those made in developing the Bose-Einstein distribution law. The third is different, for it embodies the exclusion principle.

It is convenient to divide the elementary material particles of a system into two *equal* populations with spin quantum numbers of $\frac{1}{2}$ and $-\frac{1}{2}$ and then to apply statistical methods to each population separately. Consequently, we shall assume a cell of phase space may contain as many as two particles with opposite spin. This means the average population of a cell ordinarily is less than two, and, moreover, the total energy of the system cannot be reduced to zero at 0°K.

As before, phase space is divided into equal volume elements $\Delta\mathcal{V}$ which contain G cells apiece, and then the most probable distribution of n_i identical particles among them is computed by standard statistical methods. Again an interchange of particles produces no new complexion, nor does an interchange of empty cells. Primarily we are concerned with n_i occupied and $G - n_i$ unoccupied cells. How many different combinations of these occupied and unoccupied cells can exist in a volume element? This number we inter-

---

[3] London, F., *Nature, London*, **141**, 643 (1938).

pret to be the probability W_i which is associated with the ith volume element. Clearly it equals $G!/n_i!(G - n_i)!$. The logarithm of the probability W for the entire system therefore has the form

$$\ln W = \Sigma_i[\ln G! - \ln n_i! - \ln (G - n_i)!]$$
$$= \Sigma_i[n_i \ln (G/n_i - 1) - G \ln (1 - n_i/G)], \qquad (17.16)$$

where we have introduced Stirling's approximation. From here on the argument follows exactly that for Maxwell-Boltzmann and Bose-Einstein statistics. We shall not repeat it but shall quote the final result for the Fermi-Dirac distribution law. It is

$$n_i = G/[e^{-(\alpha + \beta U_i)} + 1], \qquad (17.17)$$

in which parameters α and β are determined from the conditions that n and U are constant.

Here too β equals $-1/kT$, and α is difficult to compute. We replace α by U_m/kT and then rewrite Eq. (17.17):

$$n_i = G/[e^{U_i - U_m)/kT} + 1]. \qquad (17.18)$$

The calculation for the value of U_m is rather long and complicated, but it has been carried out by Sommerfeld for $U_m \gg kT$ in his application of Eq. (17.18) to electrons in metals. He obtained

$$U_m \doteq U_{mo}[1 - (\pi^2/12)(kT/U_{mo})^2 + (\pi^4/720)(kT/U_{mo})^4 + \cdots], \qquad (17.19)$$

in which U_{mo} is the value of energy U_m at $0°K$. When $T = 0°K$ the number of particles per cell, n_i/G, equals unity for $U_i < U_{mo}$ and equals zero for $U_i > U_{mo}$. Thus we find two electrons with opposite spins in each cell of energy less than U_{mo} and none in cells of greater energy. In other words, if we identify an energy level in a metal at $0°K$ with a cell, we find electrons completely fill all energy levels below the Fermi level at U_{mo} with a density of two electrons per level.

An explicit value of U_{mo} now may be computed, since the entire phase volume extending from zero energy to U_{mo} is filled with the N electrons of the system. We suppose the number of degrees of freedom f per electron in the metal is three, so the cell volume equals h^3. Then N equals $2\mathcal{V}/h^3$. Phase volume $\mathcal{V}$ is the product of the coordinate volume of the metal and the momentum volume of the N electrons. This momentum volume is simply the volume of a sphere of radius $(2mU_{mo})^{1/2}$, provided all the energy is kinetic. Hence

$$\mathcal{V} = \tfrac{4}{3}\pi(2mU_{mo})^{3/2}V = Nh^3/2, \qquad (17.20)$$

from which we get

$$U_{mo} = (h^2/8m)(3N/\pi V)^{2/3}. \qquad (17.21)$$

The Planck constant is $h = 6.625 \times 10^{-34}$ joule-sec, and the mass of an electron is $m = 9.108 \times 10^{-31}$ kg. The number of active or free electrons per unit volume N/V is *assumed* to be approximately equal to the number of atoms in a unit volume of the metal. Thus for sodium there are 2.54×10^{28} free electrons per cubic meter. From these data the Fermi energy of sodium equals 3.15 electron-volts. Although there is no good reason for the assumption that the number of free electrons equals the number of atoms, it seems plausible for the alkali metals which are monovalent. For other metals of higher valence we might expect a larger number per atom, but more advanced studies suggest that the extra electrons in these metals really are not very free, and even the assumption of one active electron per atom may be too much. In general, the Fermi energy of most metals probably is less than 10 electron-volts.

17.5. The Electronic Specific Heat of a Metal

Values of n_i/G from Eq. (17.18) are plotted in Fig. 17.1(a) for $T = 0°K$ and for two higher temperatures. Here we see that at temperatures above 0°K electrons are raised from levels below the Fermi level into levels above it. This means that the average number of electrons per energy level in this region is less than two. Furthermore, the thermal energy of an electron usually is a very small fraction of its total energy, so even at room temperature the curve for n_i/G is not changed much from its 0°K form.

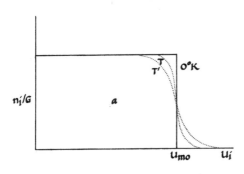

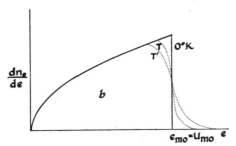

Figure 17.1. Fermi-Dirac distribution of electrons in a metal near 0°K: (a) electron concentration in a cell; (b) energy distribution of the electrons.

This slight effect suggests that the specific heat of electrons in the metal is very small.

In order to find an equation for the electronic specific heats we shall com-

pute the internal energy of one mole of electrons and then apply the thermodynamic equation $c_v = (\partial u/\partial T)_v$. To do this we transform Eq. (17.18) into
differential form exactly in the same manner as was done for Eq. (17.5) in
Section 17.3. Here, however, we also replace U_m by ϵ_m and we introduce a
factor 2 to account for electrons of both spins in a single cell of phase space.
The result is

$$dn = \frac{4\pi v(2m/h^2)^{3/2}\epsilon^{1/2}d\epsilon}{e^{(\epsilon-\epsilon_m)/kT}+1}. \qquad (17.22)$$

At $T = 0°K$ this equation reduces to zero if $\epsilon > \epsilon_m$; but only the exponential
term in the denominator vanishes if $\epsilon < \epsilon_m$. Hence we get for the distribution
of electrons in a metal at $0°K$,

$$dn_o = 4\pi v(2m/h^2)^{3/2}\epsilon^{1/2}d\epsilon = \tfrac{3}{2}N_o U_{mo}^{-(3/2)}\epsilon^{1/2}d\epsilon, \qquad (17.23)$$

where N_o is Avogadro's number. The curve of $dn_o/d\epsilon$ which is plotted against
ϵ in Fig. 17.1(b) shows an abrupt step-discontinuity at ϵ_{mo}. For higher temperatures the sharp corners are rounded, as suggested by the two dotted
curves in the same figure, and ϵ_m $(= U_m)$ changes slightly in value as indicated in Eq. (17.19).

The total number of electrons in the system may be determined by integrating Eq. (17.22) over all available energies. Similarly, the total internal
energy of these electrons equals the integral of ϵdn over the same range of
energies. At $0°K$ these computations are especially simple, for then Eq.
(17.23) applies and the integration extends from $\epsilon = 0$ to $\epsilon = \epsilon_{mo} = U_{mo}$.
From the integration of dn_o we get N_o, and from the integration of ϵdn_o we
get $\tfrac{3}{5}N_o U_{mo}$. The average energy of an electron in a metal at $0°K$ equals
three-fifths of the Fermi energy. In sodium it is about 1.9 electron-volts. For
the molecules of an ideal monatomic gas to have this average energy they
would need to be at $15,000°K$. Thus we find the electrons in a metal have a
tremendous zero-point energy.

At temperatures greater than $0°K$

$$u = \int_0^\infty \epsilon dn = 4\pi v(2m/h^2)^{3/2} \int_0^\infty \frac{\epsilon^{3/2}d\epsilon}{e^{(\epsilon-\epsilon_m)/kT}+1}$$

$$= \tfrac{3}{2}N_0 kT(k/U_{mo})^{3/2} \int_0^\infty \frac{x^{3/2}dx}{e^{(x-x_m)}+1}, \qquad (17.24)$$

where x is the dimensionless parameter ϵ/kT, x_m equals ϵ_m/kT, and v has been
eliminated by means of Eq. (17.21). The integral on the right has not been
solved by elementary methods. Because of the large zero-point energy, however, we might expect that for temperatures within a few hundred degrees
of $0°K$ values of u would not differ too much from $\tfrac{3}{5}N_0 U_{mo}$. To two successive
approximations we find

$$u = \tfrac{3}{5}N_0 U_{mo}[1 + (5\pi^2/12)(kT/U_{mo})^2 - (\pi^4/16)(kT/U_{mo})^4 + \cdots]. \quad (17.25)$$

The series converges very rapidly since kT is very much smaller than U_{mo}. The derivation of Eq. (17.25) may be found in more advanced books, such as *Quantum Statistics* by Band.

For our purpose we shall neglect the third and higher terms of the foregoing series. The electronic specific heat may now be found. It is

$$c_{el} = (\partial u/\partial T)_v = \tfrac{1}{2}\pi^2 R(kT/U_{mo}), \quad (17.26)$$

in which we have substituted the universal gas constant R for $N_0 k$. Finally, we introduce the value of U_{mo} from Eq. (17.21) into Eq. (17.26) to obtain

$$c_{el} = \pi^2 R(2mk/h^2)(\pi/3\rho_{el})^{2/3}T. \quad (17.27)$$

The electronic specific heat is proportional to the Kelvin temperature. Here m is the mass of an electron, k is the Boltzmann constant, h is the Planck constant, and ρ_{el} is the density of free electrons in the metal. This equation has been amply verified at low temperatures, as will be discussed in Chapter 19.

As we learned earlier, classical theory predicts a large contribution by free electrons to the specific heat of a metal, namely $\tfrac{3}{2}R$, which is independent of temperature. Here we find the contribution is small in magnitude and increases with temperature. For sodium we find

$$c_{el} = \tfrac{1}{2}\pi^2 R(kT/U_{mo})$$
$$= \tfrac{1}{2}\pi^2(1.38 \times 10^{-23}/3.15 \times 1.60 \times 10^{-19})RT$$
$$= 0.000135RT.$$

Even at 300°K this is only 2.7% of the classical value.

17.6. Probability in Classical and Quantum Statistics

From Maxwell-Boltzmann statistics we find the logarithm of the probability function may be written in the form[4]

$$\ln W_{\text{M-B}} = \ln n! + \Sigma_i n_i[\ln (G_i/n_i) + 1] \quad (17.28)$$

by rearranging Eq. (13.8). From Eqs. (17.3) and (17.16) we can write comparable relations for the Bose-Einstein and Fermi-Dirac statistics:

$$\ln W_{\text{B-E}} = \Sigma_i[n_i \ln (1 + G_i/n_i) + G_i \ln (1 + n_i/G_i)] \quad (17.29)$$

and

$$\ln W_{\text{F-D}} = \Sigma_i[n_i \ln (G_i/n_i - 1) - G_i \ln (1 - n_i/G_i)]. \quad (17.30)$$

---

[4] See footnote 3, p. 197.

In these equations we have inserted G_i in place of G, since here we shall assume the volume elements in phase space generally need not be of equal size. If $n_i \ll G_i$ for all volume elements $\Delta \mathcal{V}$, then in the limit as n_i/G_i approaches zero:

$$\ln W_{\text{F-D}} = \ln W_{\text{B-E}} = \ln (W_{\text{M-B}}/n!) = \Sigma_i n_i \ln (G_i/n_i). \qquad (17.31)$$

This common limit of all three statistics is the logarithm of the probability for classical statistics as we developed it in Chapter 13.

Let us compare the number of states occupied by a system of N identical particles according to each of the three forms of statistics. If all N particles are in different cells, then the system occupies only one state in either Bose-Einstein or Fermi-Dirac statistics, but $N!$ states in Maxwell-Boltzmann statistics, because the $N!$ permutations of particles among the cells are counted as different states. If some cells contain several particles, there exists only one state for the Bose-Einstein statistics and somewhat less than $N!$ states for the Maxwell-Boltzmann statistics, because a permutation of particles in a single cell does not produce different states. This situation never can arise for Fermi-Dirac particles. Finally, if all N particles of the system are in a single cell, then there is only one state in either Maxwell-Boltzmann or Bose-Einstein statistics and, of course, none in Fermi-Dirac statistics.

The Maxwell-Boltzmann statistics had been corrected by dividing the probability $W_{\text{M-B}}$ by $n!$ long before the arguments for making it were justified by quantum mechanics. The number of states as found by the corrected Maxwell-Boltzmann counting lies between the numbers found by Einstein-Bose and Fermi-Dirac counting. It is an intermediate limit to quantum statistics.

Bibliography

Band, W., *Quantum Statistics* (Van Nostrand, New York, 1955).

Chisholm, J. S. R., and A. H. de Borde, *An Introduction to Statistical Mechanics* (Pergamon, New York, 1958).

Fowler, R. H., *Statistical Mechanics* (The University Press, Cambridge, 1929).

ter Haar, D., *Elements of Statistical Mechanics* (Rinehart, New York, 1954).

Hill, T. L., *Statistical Mechanics* (McGraw-Hill, New York, 1956).

Landau, L. D., and E. M. Lifshitz, *Statistical Physics* (Addison-Wesley, Reading, Mass., 1958).

Mayer, J. E., and M. G. Mayer, *Statistical Mechanics* (Wiley, New York, 1940).

Rice, J., *Introduction to Statistical Mechanics for Students of Physics and Physical Chemistry* (Constable, London, 1930).

Schroedinger, E., *Statistical Thermodynamics* (The University Press, Cambridge, 1952).

Sears, F. W., *Thermodynamics, the Kinetic Theory of Gases, and Statistical Mechanics* (Addison-Wesley, Reading, Mass., 1953).

Tolman, R. C., *The Principles of Statistical Mechanics* (Clarendon, Oxford, 1938).

Wilson, A. H., *Thermodynamics and Statistical Mechanics* (The University Press, Cambridge, 1957).

Problems

1. Show that in Eq. (17.17) β equals $-1/kT$.

2. Compute values for the Fermi energy of silver and copper.

3. Determine a value for U_m of sodium at 300°K.

4. Show that for tungsten at 2900°K U_m differs from U_{mo} ($=9.0$ electron volts) by less than one-tenth of one percent.

5. If $P = 2U/3V$ for an electron gas as well as for a molecular gas, find the pressure of the electron gas within silver at 0°K.

6. Derive the function $(4\pi v m^2 kT/h^3) \ln \{\exp [(U_m - U_x)/kT] + 1\}$ for the Fermi-Dirac distribution in the x-component of velocity, where U_x is the energy associated with this component. [*Hint:* Write Eq. (17.15) in terms of velocity components instead of the total energy ϵ, and then integrate it over all possible values of the y- and z-components of velocity (from $-\infty$ to $+\infty$), by transforming the product of these two integrals from cartesian to polar coordinates in a plane.]

7. Show that the one-dimensional distribution function in problem 6 reduces to $(4\pi v m^2/h^3)(U_m - U_x)$ at 0°K.

8. Find the number of electrons per second passing in one direction through a unit cross-section within a metal at 0°K.

9. Determine a value for the coefficient of RT in Eq. (17.26) for tungsten, assuming two free electrons per tungsten atom.

CHAPTER 18

Very Low Temperatures

ALTHOUGH the problem of obtaining temperatures close to 0°K and measuring them with precision is an intriguing one, it has not been nearly as exciting as the problems raised in the study of substances at these very low temperatures. Such temperatures may be reached by several different thermophysical processes and combinations of them. By suitable operational techniques a temperature scale is established, and then the low temperature reservoirs become useful for a wide variety of thermophysical experiments.

18.1. Production of Low Temperatures

The five thermophysical processes which have been utilized in producing very low temperatures are adiabatic expansion of a gas as it does external work, expansion of a gas through a throttling valve, rapid evaporation of a liquid, adiabatic demagnetization of a paramagnetic salt, and adiabatic demagnetization of polarized nuclei.

Adiabatic Expansion. Whenever a gas is allowed to do external work under adiabatic conditions, its internal energy decreases, according to the first law of thermodynamics, and therefore its temperature falls. Suppose a gas of volume V_i at pressure P_i performs a reversible adiabatic expansion against a piston until it occupies a greater volume V_f at a lower pressure P_f. If the equations for an ideal gas may be applied, then

269

$$T_f = T_i(P_f/P_i)^{1-\gamma^{-1}}, \tag{18.1}$$

in which γ is the ratio of the heat capacities of the gas at constant pressure and constant volume. Because P_f is less than P_i and γ is greater than unity, the final temperature T_f is less than the initial temperature T_i. The drop in temperature $T_f - T_i$ may be large at high temperatures, but the rate of fall usually decreases, so this method becomes rather impractical at low temperatures. Furthermore, at the reduced temperatures mechanical devices in the system become difficult to operate. Nevertheless, several common gases have been liquefied by means of adiabatic expansion. Notable are Claude's gas-liquefying machines and the modifications of them which were invented by Heylandt and Kapitza. These are described in treatises on low-temperature physics.[1]

Throttling Process. In this process a gas is cooled by forcing it through one or more small openings, as through a throttling valve or a porous wall, provided the initial temperature of the gas is below its inversion value (see Section 8.3). Under ideal conditions the Helmholtz function of the gas is unchanged by the expansion, so the coefficient of temperature change is given by Eq. (8.18). Only if this coefficient is positive will the temperature fall as the gas expands through the throttling valve. For this reason hydrogen cannot be liquefied unless its initial temperature is well below 200°K (in practice, 65–90°K). Similarly, helium ordinarily is cooled to approximately 15°K before the throttling process is applied successfully.

In an actual liquefier the pressure drop is finite, often large, so Eq. (8.18) is applied in the integrated form,

$$\Delta T = \int_{P_i}^{P_f} c_p^{-1}[T(\partial v/\partial T)_p - v]dP. \tag{18.2}$$

Because of the complexness of the state equation for real gases the integral is difficult to evaluate. Nevertheless, it can be solved by numerical methods if by no other. When air at 325°K undergoes a throttling process from 200 to 1 atmosphere of pressure, its temperature drops through 29°K. The drop can be much greater for the same pressure change if the initial temperature is less. This condition is suggested by the isenthalpic curves for nitrogen in Fig. 8.8. The throttling process therefore is unlike adiabatic expansion in that it becomes more, rather than less, efficient as the initial temperature of the gas falls. Although this process involves no moving parts, the small openings in a throttling valve can become easily plugged by the freezing of contaminants.

---

[1] For example, Squire, C. F., *Low Temperature Physics* (McGraw-Hill, New York, 1953).

In modern liquefiers both the adiabatic expansion and throttling processes are employed. The Collins helium-liquefying system is a compact commercial unit of this kind. The helium gas is first pre-cooled with liquid nitrogen and then subjected to an adiabatic expansion process to reduce its temperature below 15°K. Finally, it is liquefied by means of a throttling process. A schematic diagram of the Collins system is shown in Fig. 18.1.

Rapid Evaporation. In order to lower the temperature of liquid helium it may be evaporated rapidly under reduced pressure. By this means temperatures as low as 0.71°K have been reached (0.3°K for He³). A further de-

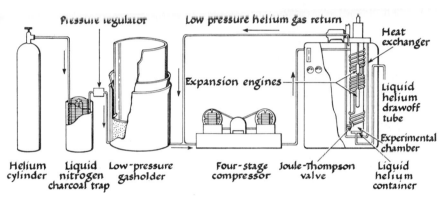

Figure 18.1. The Collins cryostat for liquefying helium.

crease is possible only by recourse to other methods. Even so, the helium cannot be solidified at reduced pressures, for it does not form a stable solid under its own vapor pressure.

Adiabatic Demagnetization of Polarized Atoms. In order to carry out this process a paramagnetic salt is mounted inside a chamber which is completely immersed in a liquid helium bath. Helium gas serves as the heat exchanging fluid between the salt and the chamber walls. The salt crystal is subjected to a strong magnetic field in order to align its atomic dipoles while it comes to thermal equilibrium with evaporating liquid helium. Then the helium gas is pumped out, and the entire apparatus is quickly swung out of the magnetic field. As the highly ordered atomic dipoles rapidly become randomly disoriented under adibatic conditions the temperature of the paramagnetic salt falls. This is a manifestation of the magnetocaloric effect. The equation for the thermodynamic coefficient of this effect is (see problem 18.3)

$$(\partial T/\partial H)_s = -(T/C_H)(\partial M/\partial T)_H. \tag{18.3}$$

Here C_H, the heat capacity of the salt at constant magnetic field intensity, may be replaced by C_p without serious error. Because the magnetization M of a paramagnetic substance in a constant magnetic field always decreases as temperature is increased, the coefficient $(\partial M/\partial T)_H$ is intrinsically negative, and therefore $(\partial T/\partial H)_s$ is a positive number. This means that the temperature of the salt must fall if the magnetic field is decreased under adiabatic conditions.

Giauque and MacDougall[2] first made observations of the magnetocaloric effect in gadolinium sulfate in 1933. With an initial field intensity of 8000 oersteds and an initial temperature of 1.5°K they obtained a final temperature of approximately 0.2°K. In order to reduce the final temperature to lower values the interactions between the magnetic moments of the salt ions themselves and between them and the crystal lattice should be as small as possible. A temperature of 0.0014°K has been reported for a mixture of chromium alum and aluminum alum by de Klerk, Steenland, and Gorter.

Adiabatic Demagnetization of Polarized Nuclei. The notion that very low temperatures may be reached by adiabatic demagnetization of polarized nuclei was suggested in 1933 by Gorter of Leiden and independently by Simon and Kurti of Oxford.[3] To a first approximation the final temperature T_f attained through this method is given by the equation

$$T_f = T_i(H_{\text{eff}}/H_i), \tag{18.4}$$

where T_i and H_i are the initial temperature and applied magnetic field intensity and H_{eff} is a final effective magnetic field intensity resulting from the residual dipole field. For a given separation of the dipoles this residual field is about a thousand times smaller for polarized nuclei than for polarized atoms; therefore nuclear demagnetization should yield temperatures with orders of magnitude lower than those from the demagnetization of a paramagnetic salt. The principal difficulty arises because very large values of H_i/T_i are needed to orient the nuclear dipoles, which have small magnetic moments. A method finally was devised by Robinson, Simon, Spohr, and Kurti, and the experiment was carried out in 1956.

In this method the nuclear stage is coupled with an electronic stage, namely a paramagnetic salt which can be cooled to 0.01°K by adiabatic demagnetization. The two stages are well separated but joined by means of a heat-conducting link. The cryostat is illustrated in Fig. 18.2. The electronic

[2] Giauque, W. F., and D. P. MacDougall, *Phys. Rev.*, **43**, 768 (1933).
[3] Kurti, N., *Physics Today*, **11**, 19 (1958).

stage is surrounded by successive coaxial thermal shields; the outermost is a
bath of liquid hydrogen at approximately 20°K. Inside this is liquid helium
at 4°K; then rapidly evaporating liquid helium at 1°K; and finally adiabatically demagnetized manga-
nous ammonium sulfate with
imbedded copper wires in liquid
helium. The electronic stage consists of chromic potassium alum
with 1500 enameled copper wires
of 0.1 mm diameter imbedded in
it. The bundle of wires serves both
as the thermal link and, at its
lower end, as the nuclear stage.
Suitable coils around the nuclear
stage provide means for determining the nuclear magnetic susceptibility and thereby the magnetic temperature of the specimen.

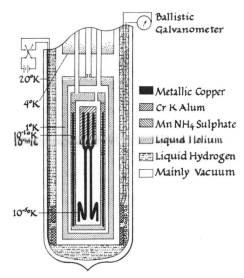

Figure 18.2.   The Kurti cryostat for nuclear cooling.

   The procedure is carried out
in four steps as diagrammed in
Fig. 18.3. Initially both the electronic and nuclear stages are at
1°K, and the electronic stage is magnetized isothermally (a). Then this stage
goes through an adiabatic demagnetization process (b) during which the
temperature of both stages is reduced to approximately 0.01°K. In the third
step (c) the nuclear stage is magnetized isothermally while the heat of nuclear
magnetization is absorbed by the electronic stage. Finally, in the fourth step
(d) the nuclear stage is demagnetized. Ideally the heat-conducting link
should be broken before this step, but in the experiments of Robinson,
Simon, Spohr, and Kurti the change in temperature of the copper specimen is measured as a function of time after the fourth step is completed.
More than a minute is required for the specimen to warm up to 0.01°K.
The lowest temperature actually measured by these experimenters is nearly
0.00002°K (magnetic), but if the curves are extrapolated back to zero time,
the temperature of the specimen immediately after demagnetization probably
was about 0.000016°K (magnetic). The corresponding values of thermodynamic temperature are even less. Kurti reports that Eq. (18.4) is satisfied
for these data if H_{eff} equals 27 oersteds, a value almost seven times that
estimated from theory. He suggests that electric quadrupole coupling may
be responsible for this large discrepancy.

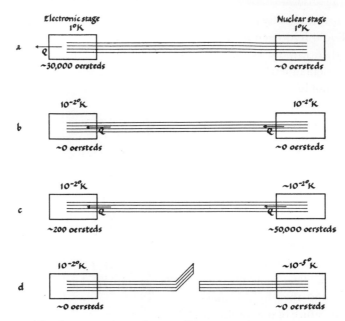

Figure 18.3.   The four steps in nuclear cooling.

18.2. *Thermometry at Low Temperatures*

The International Temperature Scale is defined in terms of certain fixed
points and suitable interpolating thermometers (Section 2.8). This scale
extends upward from the oxygen point and agrees within experimental
errors with the Kelvin thermodynamic scale. Below the oxygen point, however, it is undefined, although many laboratories have established more or
less satisfactory private scales down to nearly 0°K. In order to extend the
International Temperature Scale it is first necessary to obtain accurate
values of thermodynamic temperatures for a number of fixed points in the
low-temperature region. These fixed points then become standards for calibrating the interpolating thermometers. Not only must these thermometers
be stable, reproducible, easy to manipulate, and reliable in every way, but
also they should have associated with them relatively simple equations for
converting readings on them into thermodynamic temperatures.

Because the ideal gas and thermodynamic scales of temperature are identical, the thermodynamic value of any fixed point between 15°K and the
oxygen point may be measured by means of hydrogen and helium gas

thermometers as described in Chapter 2. Unfortunately, few fixed points exist in this range. Although certain thermocouple and resistance thermometers may be operated at these temperatures, there are no satisfactory interpolating equations for them.[4] It has been the practice therefore simply to calibrate specially constructed copper-constantan thermocouples and strain-free platinum resistance thermometers directly against the gas thermometers at several points. Scales which have been established in this way agree with one another within 0.1°K, and the 1954 scale of Pennsylvania State University is estimated to agree with the thermodynamic one within ±0.005°K.

The vapor pressure over liquid hydrogen (Fig. 18.4) is a useful thermometric property; in a sense it is a continuous series of fixed points between 14° and 20°K. Similarly, the vapor pressure over solid hydrogen serves in the range 10–14°K, and the vapor pressure over liquid helium in the range 1–4°K. The accuracy of these thermometers depends greatly on the excellence of the equations relating vapor-pressure values to thermodynamic temperatures.

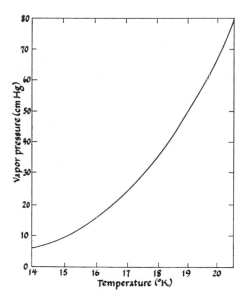

Figure 18.4.   Vapor pressure curve for hydrogen.

The gas and vapor-pressure thermometers are not satisfactory as practical laboratory standards or as simple interpolating instruments for extending the International Temperature Scale. Thermocouples and resistance thermometers, on the other hand, become less and less sensitive as the temperature decreases toward 0°K. For these reasons a search has been made for other devices which may be suitable at very low temperatures. The most promising are semi-conductors and related systems. The resistance of a semi-conductor increases more and more rapidly with decreasing temperature (as illustrated by germanium in Fig. 18.5), a behavior contrary to that of a

---

[4] Nernst published a formula for the copper-constantan thermocouple over the range 15°K to 100°K:

$$e = 31.32 \ln (1 + T/90) + 10^{-7} T^4 \text{ microvolts.}$$

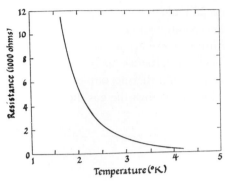

Figure 18.5. Calibration curve for a germanium resistance thermometer. [Adapted from S. A. Friedberg, *Temperature, Its Measurement and Control in Science and Industry, Vol.* 2, H. C. Wolfe, ed., Reinhold, New York, 1955.]

standard resistance thermometer. Although a semi-conductor has relatively high sensitivity and nonmagnetic characteristics, it is rather unsatisfactory as a thermometer because its readings are not always reproducible. Furthermore, no simple relation between these readings and temperature is known. These difficulties, however, are not insurmountable.

18.3. The Thermodynamic Scale Below 1°K

The paramagnetic salt thermometer has become the standard device for measuring thermodynamic temperatures below 1°K. The salt first is brought to thermal equilibrium in state a at zero magnetic field intensity and at thermodynamic temperature T somewhat greater than 1°K as measured on a helium-vapor thermometer (see Fig. 18.6). Then it is subjected to a quasistatic isothermal magnetization by a slowly increasing field intensity from 0 to H. As the salt changes from state a to state b it acquires specific dipole moment m and evolves measured heat q per unit mass. The change in specific entropy Δs for this process thus equals q/T. The salt now undergoes a quasistatic adiabatic demagnetization process from state b to state c, as indicated by the heavy line in Fig. 18.6. A quasistatic adiabatic process is always isentropic, and therefore the change in specific entropy between states a and c also equals q/T.

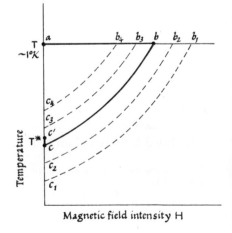

Figure 18.6. Adiabatic demagnetization of a paramagnetic salt below 1°K.

The salt in state c has a *magnetic temperature* T^* given by the Curie law

$$T^* = C/\chi, \qquad (18.5)$$

in which C is the Curie constant and χ is the susceptibility m/H. The value of H here is less than the applied field because of the opposing induced polarization. This induced polarization can be evaluated explicitly for compact solid spheres and ellipsoids, and for this reason specimens are made in these shapes.

Generally the corresponding magnetic and thermodynamic temperatures differ markedly from one another near 0°K. In order to find the thermodynamic temperature T' which is equivalent to T^* a small amount of heat $\Delta'q$ is supplied to the salt specimen to change it from state c to state c' at zero magnetic-field intensity. The entire volume of the specimen must be heated rather quickly and uniformly to insure thermal equilibrium. This has been done by induction heating, by alternating magnetic fields, or by γ-ray absorption. The resulting change in T^* is measured, and then, very nearly,

$$(\Delta'q/\Delta T^*)_0 = (d'q/dT^*)_0 = c_0^* \qquad (18.6)$$

at zero magnetic field intensity. For quasistatic processes $d'q$ equals $T'ds$, and therefore we can write

$$T' = (d'q/dT^*)_0/(ds/dT^*)_0$$
$$= c_0^*/(ds/dT^*)_0. \qquad (18.7)$$

We conclude that the thermodynamic temperature T' which is equivalent to T^* may be found by dividing the magnetic specific heat capacity c_0^* at T^* by the slope of the s-T^* curve at zero magnetic-field intensity.

The s-T^* curve is obtained by plotting values of Δs against corresponding values of T^* for a series of processes ab_1c_1, ab_2c_2, ab_3c_3, and so on, as illustrated in Fig. 18.7. Because all these processes start

Figure 18.7. Specific entropy of chromium potassium alum near 0°K for evaluating $(\partial s/\partial T^*)$ at $H = 0$. [Adapted from M. W. Zemansky, *Heat and Thermodynamics*, McGraw-Hill, New York, 1957.]

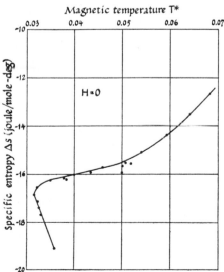

with the specimen in the same initial state a the curve so obtained is the one desired, and its slope at the particular value of magnetic temperature T^* corresponding to c_0^* is introduced into Eq. (18.7) to evaluate T'.

The foregoing procedure is rather involved, but it does make possible a correlation of magnetic and thermodynamic temperatures in the range 0–1°K. In Table 18.1 is reproduced a table of such correlations obtained by Bleaney[5] for a chromium potassium alum thermometer. Presumably a similar correlation may be found for a nuclear paramagnetic thermometer over the microdegree range.

TABLE 18.1.   *Temperature Data for a Chromium Potassium Alum Thermometer.* *

T (°K)	T^*	T (°K)	T^*	T (°K)	T^*
1.000	1.000	0.280	0.291	0.120	0.138
0.600	0.604	0.240	0.252	0.100	0.121
0.480	0.485	0.200	0.215	0.080	0.103
0.400	0.406	0.180	0.195	0.060	0.086
0.360	0.368	0.160	0.174	0.050	0.079
0.320	0.330	0.140	0.156	0.045	0.075

* From B. Bleaney, "Thermal properties of potassium chromic alum between 0.05 and 1°K," *Proc. Roy. Soc., London,* **204**, 216 (1950).

18.4. Negative Temperatures

Purcell and Pound first produced and detected negative temperatures on the Kelvin scale in 1950. In order to understand the significance of these temperatures and how they arise we must review some of the fundamental definitions and procedures in thermodynamics and statistical mechanics. For this purpose we reproduce in part the discussion by Ramsey in volume 103 of the 1956 *Physical Review*.

The essential characteristics of a system for it to support negative Kelvin temperatures, in addition to thermodynamic equilibrium, are an upper limit to the energy of its allowed states and thermal isolation from all other systems. In practice, this second condition means that the time for elements of the system to reach thermal equilibrium must be shorter than the time during which an appreciable amount of energy is exchanged with the near-

---

[5] Bleaney, B., *Proc. Roy. Soc., London,* **204,** 216 (1950).

surround. These conditions have been realized in nuclear spin systems of certain crystals for which spin-lattice relaxation times are several minutes at room temperature whereas spin-spin relaxation times are only fractions of a second.

In thermodynamics a negative temperature implies that the slope of the entropy *versus* internal energy curve becomes negative, for, in general, the first law of thermodynamics may be written

$$dU = TdS + YdX, \tag{18.8}$$

from which

$$T = (\partial U/\partial S)_X = (\partial S/\partial U)_X^{-1},$$

where X is the generalized displacement and Y is the generalized force. Ordinarily there is no explicit statement in thermodynamics that S must increase monotonically with U to always yield a positive value for T, and indeed it is unnecessary for the derivation of many thermodynamic equations.

Suppose there exists a system whose elements can occupy only two energy states L and H. When *all* the elements are in the low-energy state L the system has its lowest possible energy and is highly ordered. Likewise, when *all* the elements are in the high-energy state H the system has its highest possible energy and again it is highly ordered. For both situations we may assign a value of zero to the entropy of the system. But if the system has an intermediate energy, some of the elements are in state H and the others are in state L; the system as a whole has less order and therefore a positive value of entropy. Between the lowest and highest energy states of the system the entropy must pass through a maximum value and then decrease as illustrated in Fig. 18.8. To the left of the maxi-

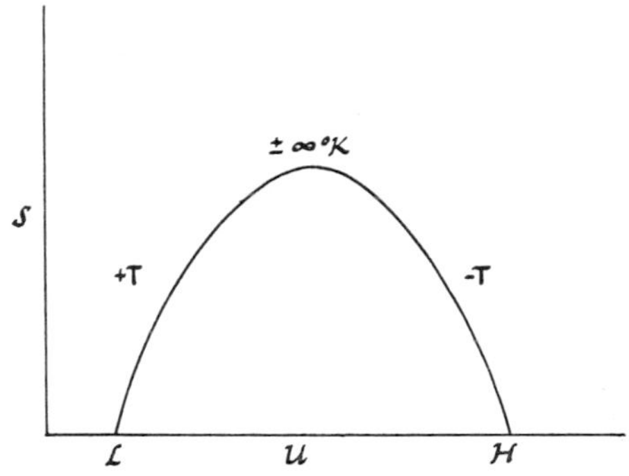

Figure 18.8.   S-U diagram of a system whose nuclei occupy two energy states L and H.

mum the slope is positive and falls to zero as the total energy increases; hence the temperature of the system also is positive but approaches an infinite value. To the right of the maximum the slope is negative and therefore the temperature of the system also is negative, but it becomes less and less so as the total energy continues to increase.

It is clear that as the internal energy decreases and cooling takes place from a negative to a positive temperature, the foregoing system passes through ∞°K rather than 0°K. That is, negative Kelvin temperatures are not *less* than 0°K, but rather they are *greater* than ∞°K. Thus 10,000°K, say, is intermediate between +300°K and −300°K. This curious result arises simply because of our conventional way of defining temperature. Let us write the Kelvin temperatures in a sequence such that those to the right are higher than those to the left; that is, heat can flow from a system A at temperature T' in this sequence to another system B at any temperature to the left of T':

$$+0°K, \cdots, +300°K, \cdots, +\infty°K, -\infty°K, \cdots, -300°K, \cdots, -0°K.$$

If we define a new temperature scale whose numerics equal $-T^{-1}$, this sequence becomes

$$-\infty°, \cdots, -0.0033°, \cdots, -0°, +0°, \cdots, +0.0033°, \cdots, +\infty°$$

on the new scale. Here the algebraic order of numbers agrees with our ordering of systems from cold to hot, and $-\infty°$ appears truly unattainable. But let us remind ourselves again that scales of temperature are not absolute.

In his extension of thermodynamics and statistical mechanics to negative temperatures Ramsey retained the usual definitions of work and heat. This was done essentially to preserve the conventional statement of the first law of thermodynamics for both positive and negative temperatures. But then it does make necessary a restatement of one form of the second law. If the signs of both work and heat were changed in going into the negative temperature region, the statement of the second law would remain unchanged and the first law would need revision. In Ramsey's treatment only the Kelvin-Planck statement of the second law of thermodynamics (see Section 6.1) is revised:

B′. *Kelvin-Planck-Ramsey Statement*: No process exists whereby the only effect is either to convert heat from a single thermal reservoir at a positive temperature completely into work on a system, or to transform work on a system completely into heat and to deliver it to a single thermal reservoir at a negative temperature.

The first and second laws of thermodynamics can now be as easily applied at negative temperatures as at positive ones; however, it must be understood that the difficulty of heating a hot system at negative temperatures is analogous to the difficulty in cooling a cold system at positive temperatures, as is implied in the Kelvin-Planck-Ramsey statement of the second law.

The various statements of the third law of thermodynamics also remain virtually unaltered, provided it is understood that zero degrees Kelvin means zero of both positive and negative temperatures. Thus the unattainability statement would be: It is impossible by any procedure, no matter how idealized, in a finite number of operations to reduce the positive temperature of any system to $+0°K$ or to raise the negative temperature of any system to $-0°K$. The temperatures $+0°K$ and $-0°K$ correspond to completely different physical states, for a system at $+0°K$ is in its lowest possible energy state where it can give up no more energy, and a system at $-0°K$ is in its highest energy state where it can absorb no more energy.

In statistical mechanics no assumption is made regarding an upper limit for the energy levels of the elements in a system. For this reason the usual theorems and methods of statistical mechanics apply equally well to systems at negative as at positive temperatures. For negative temperatures, however, the Boltzmann factor increases exponentially with increasing energy, so high-energy states are occupied more than low-energy ones, which is the reverse of the situation with positive temperatures. Consequently, without a limitation on its energy states and with only a finite amount of internal energy an ordinary system cannot support a negative temperature. For this reason systems with negative temperatures occur only rarely.

Bibliography

Atkins, K. R., *Liquid Helium* (The University Press, Cambridge, 1959).

Daunt, J. G., "Liquid Helium—3," *Science*, **131**, 579–585 (1960).

Dillinger, J. R. (ed.), *Low Temperature Physics and Chemistry* (University of Wisconsin Press, Madison, 1958).

Flügge, S. (ed.), *Handbuch der Physik. Band XIV and XV. Kältephysik* (Springer-Verlag, Berlin, 1956).

Garrett, C. G. B., *Magnetic Cooling* (Harvard University Press, Cambridge, 1954).

Gorter, C. J. (ed.), *Progress in Low Temperature Physics* (North-Holland Publishing Co., Amsterdam, Vol. I, 1955; Vol. II, 1957).

Kurti, N., "Nuclear Orientation and Nuclear Cooling," *Physics Today*, **11**, 19–25 (1958).

von Laue, M., *Theory of Superconductivity* (Academic, New York, 1952).

Ramsey, N. F., "Thermodynamics and Statistical Mechanics at Negative Absolute Temperatures," *Physical Review*, **103**, 20–28 (1956).

Shoenberg, D., *Superconductivity* (The University Press, Cambridge, 1952).

Squire, C. F., *Low Temperature Physics* (McGraw-Hill, New York, 1953).

Symposium, *Low Temperature Physics* (U.S. National Bureau of Standards, Circular 519, 1952).

White, G. K., *Experimental Techniques in Low-temperature Physics* (The University Press, Oxford, 1959).

Wolfe, H. C. (ed.), *Temperature, Its Measurement and Control in Science and Industry*, Vol. II (Reinhold, New York, 1955).

Zemansky, M., *Heat and Thermodynamics* (McGraw-Hill, New York, 1957).

Problems

1. (a) Show that the relative change in temperature of a gas when it does external work during an adiabatic expansion equals $1 - (V_i/V_f)^{\gamma-1}$.

 (b) The pressure in nitrogen gas of initial temperature t is reduced 50% as it does work during an adiabatic expansion. If it is liquefied by this process, what is the highest value t can have?

2. Helium vapor is pumped rapidly away from a thermally insulated vessel which contains liquid helium to reduce its temperature from 1.4°K to 0.7°K. The specific heat capacity of liquid helium in this range equals $0.104T^{6.2}$ joule/gm-deg, and its heat of vaporization equals $57.9 + 26.0T - 3.6T^2$ joules/gm-mole. What fraction of the initial amount of liquid helium must evaporate isentropically during the pumping process?

3. The enthalpy for a paramagnetic salt equals $U - HM$, and its heat capacity at constant magnetic field intensity C_H is defined to be $T(\partial S/\partial T)_H$. Prove that the magnetocaloric coefficient equals $-(T/C_H)(\partial M/\partial T)_H$.

4. A gadolinium sulfate crystal at 1.5°K is magnetized isothermally from zero field to 8000 oersteds (original data of Giauque and MacDougall). If its Curie constant equals 7.88 cm³-deg/gm-ion, what is its heat of magnetization per gram-ion? (For this computation assume gadolinium sulfate is an ideal paramagnetic substance for which the internal energy is a function of temperature only.)

5. The gadolinium sulfate crystal of problem 4 suddenly experiences an adiabatic demagnetization to zero field. If its specific heat capacity at constant dipole moment c_M equals $2.66/T^2$ joules/deg gm-ion, compute a value for the lowest magnetic temperature reached by the crystal. In general, both experimental and theoretical evidence suggests that over a wide range of temperatures the specific heat capacity at constant dipole moment for a paramagnetic salt is inversely proportional to the square of its temperature.

6. A crystal of cerium magnesium nitrate has an unusual property. Parallel to its axis the magnetic susceptibility is practically zero, whereas at right angles to it the susceptibility has reasonable values which satisfy the Curie equation. Simply by rotating the crystal from the parallel to the perpendicular position with respect to

the applied field its temperature drops several orders of magnitude. What is the final value of magnetic temperature for a crystal of cerium magnesium nitrate whose initial temperature is 1°K if it is rotated from the parallel to the perpendicular position in a field of 7000 oersteds? [The Curie constant for this salt is 0.318 cm³-deg/gm-ion, and its specific heat capacity at constant dipole moment is $(6.24 \times 10^{-5})/T^2$ joule/deg gm-ion.]

CHAPTER 19

Superfluidity and Superconductivity

INVESTIGATIONS at very low temperatures are not carried out simply for the sake of reaching lower and lower temperatures. The primary aim is to study the physical properties of substances at temperatures near 0°K. Helium, the last gaseous element to be liquefied, is an excellent subject, for it possesses the unique property of superfluidity. On the other hand, several other elements and many compounds are superconductors at these low temperatures.

Onnes[1] first produced liquid helium in 1908. It is colorless, transparent, very volatile, and mobile with a normal boiling point of 4.22°K. Onnes immediately attempted to solidify it by cooling through rapid evaporation, but was unsuccessful. Nearly twenty years later Keesom[2] obtained solid helium by application of pressure as he lowered the temperature of the liquid. The solid is a homogeneous transparent body which is visually indistinguishable from the liquid because the refractive indices of the two phases, and their densities too, have nearly the same values.

The fact that helium actually has two liquid forms is suggested in Onnes' 1911 data by the appearance of a rather sharp cusp in the density curve at 2.17°K (Fig. 19.1), but this interpretation was not clearly made until the brilliant work of Keesom and his coworkers in 1928 and subsequent years.

[1] Kammerlingh Onnes, H., *Proc. Acad. Sci. Amst.*, **11**, 168 (1908).

[2] Keesom, W. H., *Comptes Rendus*, **183**, 26, 189 (1926); *K. Akad. Amster., Proc.*, **29**, (9) 1136 (1926).

With his new tool Onnes set out to investigate physical properties of other substances at liquid-helium temperatures. He discovered that the electrical resistance of a metal levels off at an essentially constant low value instead of dropping to zero as the temperature approaches 0°K. Even though thermal vibrations in the crystal lattice of the metal become negligible, usually there exist impurities and imperfections which distort the lattice and obstruct the passage of electrons. Mercury, however, behaves differently. Much to his surprise Onnes observed its electrical resistance to fall sharply

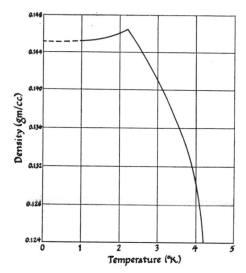

Figure 19.1.   Density of natural liquid helium.

from a residual value of several tenths of an ohm to zero ohms near 4°K (Fig. 19.2). More refined experiments on very pure mercury indicate that the transition takes place within a temperature interval of 0.01°K and that the resistance drops by a factor of 10^{-11} or more. This remarkable behavior could not have been foreseen in terms of classical theory, nor does it find easy explanation in terms of quantum physics. Indeed, there is strong evidence that the phenomenon is not so much a manifestation of infinite conductivity as it is an extreme case of diamagnetism.

19.1. Helium I and Helium II

Several different physical properties of liquid helium have peculiar anomalies at 2.17°K. The heat of vaporization not only is extraordinarily low (approximately 23 joules/gm), but also has a slight minimum at this temperature; and the dielectric constant, like the density, has a cusp at 2.17°K. The specific heat capacity, on the other hand, rises to a sharp peak at 2.17°K, as can be seen in Fig. 19.3. This curve looks very much like that for the specific heat capacity of a ferromagnetic substance near its Curie point where ferromagnetism disappears, or like that for the specific heat capacity of an alloy such as β-brass where long-range order disappears. Because these are second-order phase transitions, it seems reasonable to

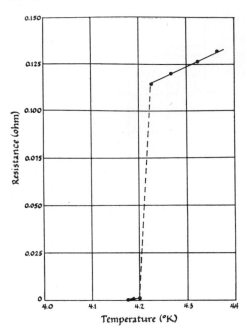

Figure 19.2. Superconductivity in mercury as first observed by H. Kamerlingh Onnes.

suppose that liquid helium also exhibits a similar phase transition, perhaps from a less-ordered to a more-ordered liquid, as it cools. This hypothesis is supported by the fact that no discontinuity in the heat of vaporization is observed at 2.17°K. Following an early suggestion of Keesom and Wolfke,[3] the two forms of liquid helium were named helium I and helium II, and, because the curve in Fig. 19.3 somewhat resembles a written Greek letter λ, the transition temperature is called the λ-point.

By taking cooling curves Keesom and Clusius[4] observed that the λ-point moved to lower temperatures at progressively higher pressures. It follows a nearly straight line from 2.17°K at 0.0508 atm

to 1.77°K at 30 atm, as shown in Fig. 19.4. At the lower point the liquid is in equilibrium with helium vapor, and at the upper point it is in equilibrium with the solid. But because the two liquid phases are not separated by a boundary, these endpoints of the λ-line do not represent triple points in the ordinary sense. Even so, frequently they are referred to as the lower and upper "triple points" of helium.

The phase diagram in Fig. 19.4 contains two other curious features. Although the equilibrium solidification curve rises continuously to well

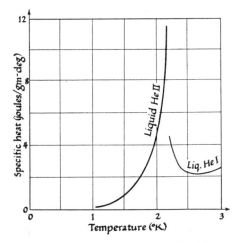

Figure 19.3. Specific heat of liquid helium near the λ-point.

[3] Keesom, W. H., and M. Wolfke, *Comptes Rendus*, **185**, 1465 (1927).
[4] Keesom, W. H., and K. Clusius, *K. Akad. Amster., Proc.*, **34** (5), 605 (1931).

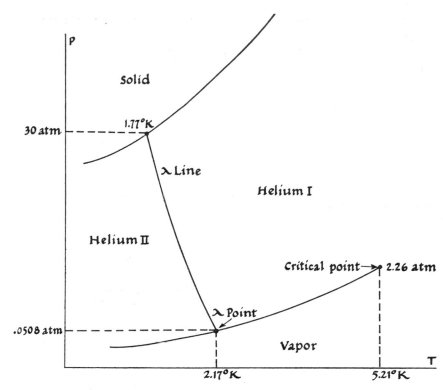

Figure 19.4.   Schematic phase diagram for He⁴. If it were drawn to scale, the
λ-point would be very close to the temperature axis. There are at
least two, perhaps three, solid phases: α, β, and γ. A transition from
the hexagonal close-packed α-phase to the face-centered cubic β-phase
occurs near 15°K and 1250 atm. The γ-phase, possibly with a body-
centered cubic lattice, is reported to exist between 1.45°K and 1.78°K
in a narrow range of pressures bordering on the melting curve (Vignos,
J. H. and H. A. Fairbanks, *Phys. Rev. Letters* 6, 265, 1961).

over 60°K and 10,000 atm, the critical point for helium is at the low point
of 5.21°K and 2.26 atm. Furthermore, the solidification curve bends rather
rapidly just below the upper "triple point" to a constant pressure of 25 atm.
Apparently helium remains a liquid below 25 atm right down to 0°K.
Swenson[5] suggests that this situation arises because the specific internal
energy of the liquid is less than that of the solid below 1.7°K.

The foregoing observations do not apply to the light isotope $_2He^3$, which
has a concentration of only about one part in a million in natural helium.
Fortunately, large quantities of this isotope may be produced in nearly pure

⁵ Swenson, C. A., *Phys. Rev.*, **79**, 626 (1950); **86**, 870 (1952).

form by the radioactive decay of tritium made from lithium through the pair of reactions

$$_3Li^6 + _0n^1 \longrightarrow {}_1H^3 + {}_2He^4$$

and

$$_1H^3 \longrightarrow {}_2He^3 + e^-.$$

The tritium with a half life of 12.5 years is separated from heavy helium $_2He^4$ by means of a hot palladium filter and then is allowed to decay to $_2He^3$.

The P-T diagram for $_2He^3$ is shown in Fig. 19.5. Here there is only one

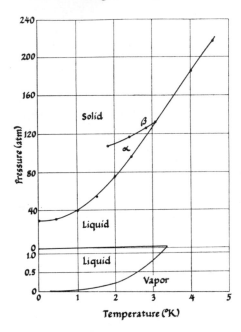

Figure 19.5. Phase diagram for He³. The transition curve from the body-centered cubic α-phase to the hexagonal close-packed β-phase of solid He³ is shown. But the transition curve from the β-phase to the face-centered cubic γ-phase extends far off to the right from the triple point at 17.78°K and 1608 atm through the point at 17.88°K and 1716 atm. (See Franck, J. P., *Phys. Rev. Letters* 7, 435, 1961.)

liquid phase, but there are three solid phases. Furthermore, at pressures below 29.3 atm $_2He^3$ also remains a liquid down to 0°K. Some of the thermophysical constants for the two isotopes are compared in Table 19.1. Because

TABLE 19.1. *Thermophysical Constants of the Helium Isotopes.*

Property	He³	He⁴
Specific heat capacity at 1°K (joules/mole-deg)	4.30	1.75
Normal boiling point (°K)	3.195	4.216
Solidification pressure at 0°K (atm)	29.3	25
Critical temperature (°K)	3.33	5.21
Critical pressure (atm)	1.15	2.26
Critical density (gm/cc)	0.0412	0.0675

masses of the atoms of the two helium isotopes are markedly different we should expect some of the constants to differ greatly from one another. But, in addition, there are more fundamental properties of these atoms which distinguish them. The nucleus of the $_2$He^4 atom contains two protons and two neutrons and therefore has no resultant angular momentum or magnetic moment. Also, the neutral atom in its ground state has no electric or magnetic dipole moment and only a very small polarizability. The $_2$He^3 atom, on the other hand, contains an odd number of fundamental particles and therefore has a resultant angular momentum and magnetic moment. Whereas $_2$He^4 obeys Bose-Einstein statistics, $_2$He^3 obeys Fermi-Dirac statistics. Apparently, at very low temperatures quantum effects come into play in liquid helium, and these structural and statistical differences between the isotopes exert a profound influence on their properties.

19.2. Superfluidity

Helium II exhibits some of its most remarkable properties under flow conditions. If an empty test tube is partially immersed in a reservoir of helium II, as illustrated in Fig. 19.6(a), it gradually fills until the surface levels inside and outside are equal. If it is then raised as in (b), flow occurs

Figure 19.6.   A simple experiment to demonstrate a superfluid property of liquid helium.

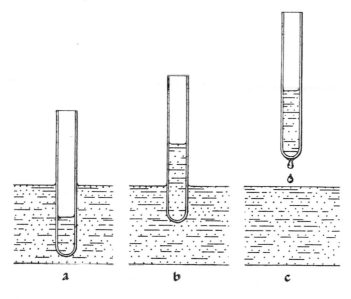

a   b   c

in the opposite direction until the levels again are equal. Even if the test tube is lifted entirely out of the reservoir, as in (c), the liquid in it slowly disappears as drops form on the outside and drip off the bottom. A film of helium II, roughly 300 μ thick, creeps up and over the rim of the test tube by a mechanism, that is yet not completely understood. The film transfer rate equals the volume of helium transported per second across unit length of periphery. It is nearly independent of the wall material, the smoothness of the wall, and the difference in height of the two liquid-helium surfaces. In fact, it is more or less constant over the entire vessel wall. Apparently, helium II is rapidly accelerated for a few millimeters up the wall and then some agent comes into play that limits the film transfer rate to a critical constant value. This critical rate does show a strong temperature dependence (Fig. 19.7). Unfortunately, it is changed to much larger values by solid-air or ice contaminants on the wall, and, furthermore, a small

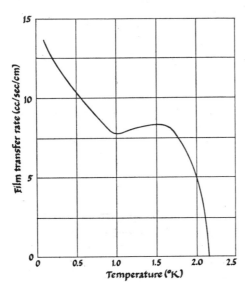

Figure 19.7.   Temperature dependence of film transfer rate in superfluid liquid helium.

vertical gradient of temperature introduces the possibility of thermo-osmosis. Because of these disturbing effects experimental data on the helium-film problem must be carefully evaluated.

If a small heating coil is inserted into the test tube of Fig. 19.6(a), helium II is observed to continue flowing into the tube, even after the inside and outside surfaces reach the same level, until the inner surface is higher than the outer one by several millimeters. This is a manifestation of thermo-osmosis. A related effect was discovered by Allen and Jones in 1938.[6] They set out to investigate the viscosity of liquid helium by measuring rates of flow through the interstices of tightly packed emery powder in a U-tube (Fig. 19.8) completely immersed in helium II. Much to their amazement a jet of helium liquid squirted out of the open end of the tube to heights of several centimeters whenever the emery powder was illuminated. This fountain effect demonstrates the transformation of thermal energy (radiation)

[6] Allen, J. F., and H. Jones, *Nature, London*, **141**, 243 (1938).

into translational kinetic energy. It becomes more pronounced as either the temperature or the size of the emery particles is decreased. Heights up to 30 cm have been measured.

The inverse of the fountain effect was predicted by Tisza[7] and observed by Daunt and Mendelssohn[8] when they forced helium II through narrow channels and small holes. A fall in temperature occurred, just as for gases below their inversion points in the Joule-Thomson porous-plug experiment.

As Jones and Allen found, it is difficult to separate purely viscous effects from thermo-osmosis. The coefficient of viscosity of a liquid usually is obtained from measurements either on rates of flow of the liquid through capillary tubes and narrow channels or on the damp-

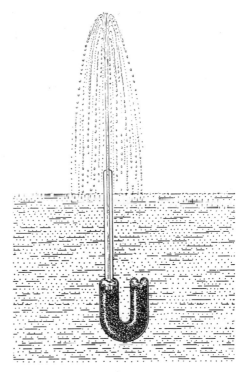

Figure 19.8.   Apparatus for demonstrating the fountain effect.

ing of oscillating disks and cylinders which are immersed in the liquid. Whereas the low-pressure viscosity of all normal liquids increases as the temperature is lowered, that of helium I decreases as for a gas (Fig. 19.9). Furthermore, its value is extremely small, for it does not exceed 50 micropoise even near the boiling point. But, as the pressure is increased, the viscosity also increases and becomes more liquid-like. When the temperature drops below the λ-point the reduction in viscosity is even more remarkable. As measured by the capillary method it falls rapidly to less than 10^{-5} micropoise. With its almost negligible viscosity, helium II appears to be nearly an ideal fluid. On the other hand, if the viscous drag is measured by the oscillating disk method, helium II behaves more nearly like a normal liquid with a viscosity of the order of 10 micropoise. This extraordinary difference in the viscosity of helium II, as measured by the two standard methods, presents a perplexing problem to the physicist. An

[7] Tisza, L., *Nature, London,* **141,** 913 (1938).
[8] Daunt, J. G., and K. Mendelssohn, *Nature, London,* **143,** 719 (1939).

explanation for it, however, is provided by the Tisza-Landau two-fluid theory.

19.3. Super Heat Conduction

As the temperature of liquid helium is lowered, the violent bubbling which normally occurs suddenly ceases on passing through the λ-point. Although

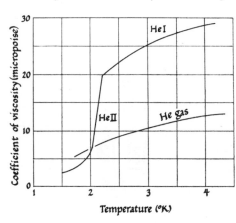

this effect had been observed for a long time its interpretation did not become clear until after the discovery that helium II experiences an enormous increase in heat conduction. The thermal conductivity of helium I is similar to that of a gas both in magnitude and in temperature variation, but immediately below the λ-point a drastic change takes place. The heat current density rises rapidly to very large values, reaching a peak at 1.92°K, and then falls gradually toward zero. The thermal conductivity at the peak has

Figure 19.9. Comparison of the viscosity in liquid helium and in helium gas.

the extraordinarily high value of 3390 watts/cm-deg, which makes helium II by far the best heat conductor known and not at all like a gas. Incidentally, the peak is shifted toward lower temperatures at high pressures.

The anomalous heat flow in helium II is not due to a normal heat conduction, such as occurs for helium I; instead it appears to involve "internal convection," an actual transport of matter compensated by a return flow. This process is not to be confused with common convection, for neither variations in density nor variations in gravitational field are responsible for the flow.

19.4. The Two-fluid Model of Helium II

For theoretical purposes a liquid may be treated as a very imperfect gas in which intermolecular forces are strong or as a loose solid in which binding forces are too weak to hold atoms near lattice points. London pointed out that helium II, with its low density, comes closer to a gas than to an ordinary liquid. At the same time, the specific heat anomaly at the λ-point suggests that helium II has a high degree of order, similar to that for the low-temperature phase of other second-order phase transitions. London[9] surmised from these observations that the transition in liquid helium may be the Einstein quantum condensation process which takes place not in ordinary coordinate space like the familiar condensations but in momentum space where the condensed molecules acquire zero-point energy and momentum. Einstein[10] had shown that, as the temperature of an ideal gas obeying Bose statistics is lowered, a critical temperature T_c is reached below which more and more molecules pass directly into the lowest energy state with momentum zero and therefore with no contribution to the pressure (see Section 17.3).

For the ideal gas satisfying the Bose-Einstein statistics the total number of molecules in nonzero energy states is given by the integral

$$N = \int_0^\infty (2\pi V/h^3)(2m)^{3/2}(Be^{\epsilon/kT} - 1)^{-1}\epsilon^{1/2}d\epsilon, \qquad (19.1)$$

where $B \geq 1$. The maximum value of this integral is found by setting B equal to unity; thus we obtain a value for the number N_n of normal molecules:

$$N_n = 2.612Vh^{-3}(2\pi mkT)^{3/2}. \qquad (19.2)$$

If the total number of molecules N is greater than N_n, only N_n of them can be in nonzero energy states. Clearly, molecules begin to pass over to the zero-point energy condition at the critical temperature T_c given by setting N equal to N_n:

$$T_c = (h^2/2\pi mk)(N/2.612V)^{2/3}. \qquad (19.3)$$

The ratio N/V can be found from measured densities. In this way a theoretical value of T_c for helium is computed to be 3.13°K, which has the same order of magnitude as the observed λ-point of 2.17°K. In Eq. (19.3) we see that T_c should increase with increasing density; but this is contrary to the fact that the λ-line with its negative slope (Fig. 19.4) implies that T_c should decrease. These discrepancies arise undoubtedly because we have neglected the strong intermolecular forces.

In spite of the foregoing difficulties the London theory did suggest a phenomenological treatment of liquid helium which has proved eminently useful to experimentalists. Tisza[11] imagined helium II to contain two completely intermingled fluids, one of normal atoms with normal viscosity and

[9] London, F., *Nature, London,* **141,** 643 (1938); *Phys. Rev.,* **54,** 947 (1938); *J. Phys. Chem.,* **43,** 49 (1939).

[10] Einstein, A., *Preuss. Akad. Wiss., Berlin,* **3,** 18 (1925).

[11] Tisza, L., *Comptes, Rendus,* **207,** 1035, 1186 (1938).

the other of superfluid atoms with zero-point energy and entropy and no viscosity. If ρ is the density of helium II, ρ_n the density of the normal fluid, and ρ_s the density of the superfluid, then

$$\rho = \rho_n + \rho_s. \qquad (19.4)$$

At the λ-point all the atoms are normal, and ρ_n/ρ equals unity; at 0°K all the atoms are superfluid, and ρ_n/ρ equals zero. It must be clear that normal and superfluid atoms actually are indistinguishable and that the two-fluid model is only a convenient fiction for representing the real system.

Tisza[12] now pointed out that the normal part of helium II retards the motion of an oscillating disk immersed in it, whereas the superfluid part flows rapidly through fine capillaries without frictional effects. Thus in a qualitative way he was able to explain the large discrepancy between values of viscosity obtained by the two methods. Similarly, an interpretation can be made for the thermomechanical effects. Since temperature determines the relative concentration of normal and superfluid atoms in helium II, any change in relative concentration is registered as a cooling or a heating of the fluid. According to Tisza, therefore, the anomaly in specific heat capacity at the λ-point arises because heat is required to excite helium atoms from the superfluid to the normal state. Also, if two vessels containing helium II are connected by a capillary and one of the vessels is heated, helium flows from the cold to the warm vessel because of a change in the relative concentration of superfluid to normal atoms. In the heated vessel the concentration of superfluid atoms is decreased, and, consequently, unimpeded flow of superfluid takes place from the cold to the warm vessel. If the capillary is sufficiently fine, the counterflow of normal fluid is extremely slow because of its viscosity, and therefore helium II accumulates in the warm vessel. Tisza then predicted that the inverse of this effect should occur. Helium II forced through a fine capillary should be richer in superfluid atoms and therefore should experience a drop in temperature. Subsequently this effect was observed by Daunt and Mendelssohn, as discussed in Section 19.2.

Super heat flow in helium II may be explained in terms of the Tisza two-fluid model. For simplicity consider the two vessels containing helium II to be connected by a large tube, rather than by a capillary, so that the normal component can flow through it too without undue friction. When one vessel is heated the normal fraction of helium II in it increases at the expense of the superfluid fraction, and, consequently, superfluid flows from the cold into the warm vessel. Now, however, a counterflow of normal fluid from the warm to the cold vessel occurs carrying the energy required to excite

[12] Tisza, L., *J. Phys. Radium*, **1**, 165, 350 (1940); *Phys. Rev.*, **72**, 838 (1947).

the helium atoms in it from the superfluid to the normal state. In other words, an extraordinary internal convection process takes place which has no counterpart in ordinary fluids. Superfluid moves toward the warm vessel carrying no energy, while an equal amount of normal fluid moves toward the cold vessel carrying large amounts of energy. Furthermore, this mechanism of heat transport may be the cause of the observed dependence of the thermal conductivity of helium II on the temperature gradient.

19.5. *Heat Transfer in Helium II*

Suppose two vessels A and B, each equipped with a piston and containing helium II, are connected by a fine capillary (Fig. 19.10). Let the pressure

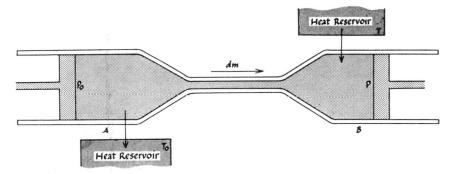

Figure 19.10. Reversible transfer of superfluid mass dm through a capillary tube.

and temperature for each of the vessels be maintained at constant values by suitable reservoirs. Both pistons are moved slowly to the right such that pressures P_0 in A and P in B are unchanged during the process. Therefore some of the helium must pass through the capillary. We assume only superfluid atoms are transferred and that they carry neither energy nor entropy with them. On the other hand, vessel A must lose energy to the reservoir at temperature T_0, and vessel B must gain energy from the reservoir at temperature T in order to maintain isothermal conditions on each side of the capillary. Let an infinitesimal mass of helium dm be transferred from A to B. Then the net heat exchange between the two reservoirs equals $(Ts - T_0 s_0)dm$, where s_0 and s are the specific entropies in A and B; the net work done on the system equals $-(Pv - P_0 v_0)dm$, where v_0 and v are the respective specific volumes; and the net change in internal energy equals $(u - u_0)dm$, where u_0 and u are the specific internal energies. Now by application of the first law of thermodynamics we find that the specific Gibbs function is constant during the process.

For any infinitesimal reversible process on a closed system the change in specific Gibbs function is given by the equation

$$dg = -sdT + vdP. \tag{19.5}$$

Consequently, for the foregoing process

$$(\partial P/\partial T)_g = s/v, \tag{19.6}$$

and therefore the heat transferred from one reservoir to the other per unit mass equals q^*, where

$$q^* = Ts = vT(\partial P/\partial T)_g. \tag{19.7}$$

Values of $v(\partial P/\partial T)_g$ as determined from the thermomechanical effects (fountain effect and its inverse) are compared with the entropy curve from

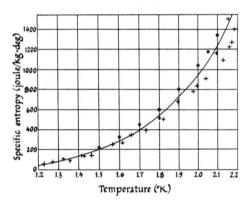

Figure 19.11. Specific entropy of helium II. The solid curve represents values of specific entropy from measurements by Kramers, Wasscher, and Gorter. Points are experimental values of $v(\partial P/\partial T)_g$ from data by Meyer and Mellinck (crosses) and by Kapitza (open circles). [Adapted from M. W. Zemansky, *Heat and Thermodynamics*, McGraw-Hill, New York, 1957.]

specific heat data in Fig. 19.11. The specific entropy is found from the specific heat capacities by means of the equation

$$s = \int_0^T c_p dT/T. \tag{19.8}$$

These results extend only to 1.2°K. Bots and Gorter,[13] however, have verified Eq. (19.7) down to approximately 0.1°K to an accuracy of about 5%. In spite of the excellent agreement here, we cannot conclude that the two-fluid model is valid, because this thermodynamic derivation really is more or less independent of the precise model employed for the argument. As we shall see, the same result is obtained by means of irreversible thermodynamics (Chapter 20).

---

[13] Bots, G. J. C., and C. J. Gorter, *Physica*, **22,** 503 (1956).

Let us now suppose a single vessel contains helium II in which a small heating coil is immersed. If the temperature in the helium around the coil is suddenly increased, the relative concentration of normal atoms will become larger. Tisza[12] postulated that this disturbance would be propagated away from the heater as a thermal wave at a rather low speed. This wave motion would have some resemblance to acoustic waves, but instead of variations in the relative mass density of helium II there would occur variations in the relative density of normal fluid and superfluid and therefore variations in temperature. The significant parameter for the dissipation of heat is the speed of thermal waves rather than ordinary thermal conductivity. This phenomenon has become known as "second sound."

In order to derive an equation for the speed of second sound consider a column of helium II of indefinite length but of cross-sectional area A and at temperature T. Let a reservoir of temperature $T + \Delta T$ supply heat at one end of the column (Fig. 19.12), and suppose the thermal energy is trans-

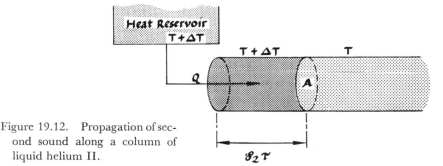

Figure 19.12. Propagation of second sound along a column of liquid helium II.

mitted at speed $\mathcal{S}_2$. After a time τ a length of column $\mathcal{S}_2\tau$ will have been warmed slightly to temperature $T + \Delta T$, and the helium atoms in it will have acquired a net kinetic energy K, so

$$Q = H + K, \qquad (19.9)$$

where Q is the amount of heat supplied by the reservoir and H is that part of it which is necessary to increase the temperature of the helium by the small amount ΔT. If the process is reversible, then the total change in entropy of the local universe vanishes; thus

$$-Q/(T + \Delta T) + H/T - K/T = 0. \qquad (19.10)$$

Here we assume that the production of kinetic energy from the thermal energy decreases the entropy of the system. Combining Eqs. (19.9) and (19.10) we get

$$\Delta T/T = 2K/H. \qquad (19.11)$$

Clearly the kinetic energy per unit volume (K.E./vol) of helium II is

$\frac{1}{2}\rho_n v_n^2 + \frac{1}{2}\rho_s v_s^2$, where ρ_n and ρ_s are the densities of normal fluid and super-fluid and v_n and v_s are the speeds of the two-fluid components. But there is no net flow of either mass or momentum, so

$$\rho = \rho_n + \rho_s = \text{constant}, \qquad (19.12)$$

$$\rho_n v_n + \rho_s v_s = 0, \qquad (19.13)$$

and finally

$$\text{K.E./vol} = \frac{1}{2}\rho_n v_n^2(\rho/\rho_s). \qquad (19.14)$$

The heat required per unit volume of helium II to raise its temperature ΔT is $\rho c \Delta T$, where c is the specific heat capacity for liquid helium exposed to its saturate vapor pressure at temperature T. We can now obtain a value for K/H simply by dividing Eq. (19.14) by $\rho c \Delta T$. If this is now substituted into Eq. (19.11), we find

$$v_n = (\rho_s c T/\rho_n)^{1/2}(\Delta T/T), \qquad (19.15)$$

which is the speed of the normal component of helium II.

We now note that the volume of helium whose temperature has been raised to $T + \Delta T$ is $\mathcal{S}_2 \tau A$, and therefore

$$H = \mathcal{S}_2 \tau A \rho c \Delta T. \qquad (19.16)$$

The entropy increase of the system due to H may then be written

$$\Delta S = H/T = \mathcal{S}_2 \tau A \rho c(\Delta T/T). \qquad (19.17)$$

According to the two-fluid model this entropy is carried by normal atoms only; consequently, we also find that

$$\Delta S = \rho_n s_n v_n \tau A, \qquad (19.18)$$

where s_n represents the specific entropy of normal fluid only. Because the superfluid has zero-point entropy, however, $\rho_n s_n$ equals ρs, where s is the specific entropy and ρ is the density of helium II. We now combine Eqs. (19.15), (19.17), and (19.18) to obtain an equation for $\mathcal{S}_2$:

$$\mathcal{S}_2 = (s v_n/c)(\Delta T/T)^{-1}$$
$$= [(s^2 T/c)(\rho_s/\rho_n)]^{1/2}. \qquad (19.19)$$

Since the specific entropy s, specific heat capacity c, and relative concentration of superfluid ρ_s/ρ_n are all complex functions of temperature, the speed of second sound $\mathcal{S}_2$ also depends on temperature in a complex way.

The complexity of the relation between second-sound speed and temperature is illustrated in Fig. 19.13. In 1944 Peshkov[14] first detected and measured second-sound speeds from the λ-point down to 1.4°K. Later, other investigations extended the range to nearly 0°K. The curve rises to a maximum near 1.7°K and then falls slightly. Below 1.0°K, however, it rises

[14] Peshkov, V. P., J. Phys., Moscow, **8**, 131, 381 (1944); **10**, 389 (1946).

rapidly once more to very high values and perhaps approaches the speed of ordinary sound at 237 m/sec near 0°K. A few

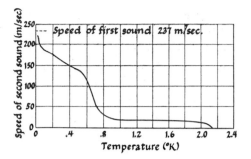

Figure 19.13. Temperature dependence of the speed of second sound in helium II.

values of S_2, computed by means of Eq. (19.19), are entered in the fifth column of Table 19.2. The data for c and s are from measurements by Kramers, Wasscher, and Gorter,[15] and the ratios ρ_s/ρ_n were determined from the data of Andronikashvili.[16] The measured values of S_2 in the last column were read from a graph of the experimental results by Peshkov,[14] and Lane, Fairbank, and Fairbank.[17]

TABLE 19.2. *Values of Second Sound Speed at Several Temperatures.*

T (°K)	c (sat.) (joule gm^{-1} deg^{-1})	s (joule gm^{-1} deg^{-1})	ρ_s/ρ_n	S_2 (comp.) (m/sec)	S_2 (meas.) (m/sec)
1.4	0.780	0.132	10.4	18	20
1.6	1.572	0.284	4.3	19	20
1.8	2.80	0.535	1.9	19	20
2.0	4.95	0.929	0.6	15	17
2.1	6.92	1.215	0.25	11	12
2.17	14.3	1.57	0.0	0	0

19.6. Phonons and Rotons

Attempts to improve the London theory by taking into account intermolecular forces have not been entirely successful. In 1941 Landau[18] proposed a different theory. In it the problem of molecular interactions is avoided by treating helium II as a quasicontinuum with two bands of energy states separated by a finite gap. One of these bands includes all the modes of vibration corresponding to sound waves which can be excited in

[15] Kramers, H. C., J. D. Wasscher, and C. J. Gorter, *Physica*, **18**, 329 (1952).
[16] Andronikashvili, E. L., *J. Phys.*, *Moscow*, **10**, 201 (1946).
[17] Lane, C. T., H. A. Fairbank, and W. M. Fairbank, *Phys. Rev.*, **71**, 600 (1947).
[18] Landau, L. D., *J. Phys.*, *Moscow*, **5**, 71 (1941); **11**, 91 (1947).

the system as a whole. These modes are analogous to standing waves in a solid; in some respects this treatment of helium II resembles the quantum theories for the specific heat of solids. Here, as there, we may associate with each mode of frequency ν_a an energy $(n + \frac{1}{2})h\nu_a$, where n is an integer. (We cannot neglect the zero-point energy $\frac{1}{2}h\nu_a$ for systems at very low temperatures.) Just as we can replace an electromagnetic mode of energy $(n + \frac{1}{2})h\nu_e$ in a blackbody radiation system by n *photons*, so we replace the acoustical mode of energy $(n + \frac{1}{2})h\nu_a$ in our liquid system by n *phonons*. The phonon may be described as an "elementary thermal excitation."

To complete the picture Landau suggested that liquids differ from solids in that they can support vortex motion, and therefore the second band of

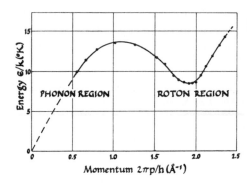

Figure 19.14. Energy spectrum for thermal excitations in liquid He⁴ at 1.1°K from neutron scattering experiments by Yarnell, Arnold, Bendt, and Kerr. [Adapted from J. G. Daunt, "Liquid Helium-3," *Science*, **131**, p. 579, 1960.]

energy states consists of a spectrum of rotational excitation energies. Again we can conceive of a mode of vortex motion of energy $(n + \frac{1}{2})h\nu_v$ which can be replaced by n "elementary vortex excitations" called *rotons*. The roton band is assumed to be at a higher level than the phonon band by an energy gap of approximately 12.4×10^{-23} joule (Khalatnikov's value[19]) or 8.9°K when divided by the Boltzmann constant. This placing of the ground level for the roton spectrum well above the phonon spectrum was done simply to enable Landau to explain superfluidity. A diagram for the elementary excitation energies ϵ is given in Fig. 19.14. Values of ϵ/k in degrees Kelvin are shown as a function of excitation momentum divided by $h/2\pi$ in reciprocal Ångstrom units. Direct evidence for the existence of rotons has been obtained from neutron-scattering experiments[20] performed by Palevsky and his coworkers (1957), by Henshaw (1958), and by Yarnell and his coworkers (1959).

In Landau's theory the rotons travel through the fluid, experience collisions, transport energy and momentum, and otherwise partake of the

---

[19] Khalatnikov, I. M., *J. Exp. Theor. Phys. USSR*, **23**, 8, 21, 169 (1952).
[20] See Daunt, J. G., *Science*, **131**, 579 (1960).

functions ascribed earlier to the uncondensed helium atoms. The phonons, on the other hand, confer on helium its superfluid properties. There is no interaction between roton and phonon motions in the liquid and consequently no friction. According to this theory, below 0.6°K only phonons exist in helium II. Between 0.6° and 1°K the rotons begin to take over, and by 1.6°K they almost completely dominate the situation. By and large we find this theory can give a reasonable explanation of many phenomena observed in helium II below 1.6°K, but it appears inadequate at higher temperatures. In fact, it is unable to give a satisfactory description of the λ-point transition. This is a serious shortcoming.

The successes of both the London and the Landau theories and the Tisza two-fluid model suggest that a complete theory should have in it many of the characteristics of these formulations. Essentially it should contain aspects of the single-atom structure at the higher temperatures and transform to the cooperative situation at lower temperatures where small groups of associated atoms may be the active components of the liquid. Applications of quantum mechanics to the liquid-helium problem along this line have been made by Feynman, de Boer, Cohen and others, but we shall not review them here. Reference should be made to articles by Feynman (1955) and de Boer (1957) in *Progress in Low Temperature Physics*, volumes I and II, and to the current literature.

19.7. *Superconductors*

The extraordinarily large increase in electrical conductivity of mercury below 4°K is not as unique a property as superfluidity in helium II, for more than 20 elements and a very large number of alloys and compounds, some containing nonmetallic elements, become superconducting at low temperatures. All pure elements which are known to exhibit superconductivity are gathered in Table 19.3. Curiously, only mercury crystallizes in the rhombohedral system. Nine of the elements with normal melting points less than 675°C are classed as "soft," and fourteen with normal melting points greater than 825°C are classed as "hard." Daunt makes this distinction in terms of the ratio of the electronic specific heat capacity of an element to the theoretical value computed by means of the Sommerfeld theory for the corresponding free electron system (see Section 17.4).

Table 19.3 lists not only the molecular weights M and the normal melting points NMP of the elements, but also their transition temperatures T_0 from the normal to the superconducting states at zero magnetic field, the minimum

TABLE 19.3.   *Properties of Superconducting Elements.*

Element	Symbol	Crystal System*	NMP (°C)	M (kg)	T_0 (°K)	H_0 (oersteds)	γ (joules/mole-deg²)
			SOFT				
Aluminum	Al	C	660	27	1.171	106	13.6×10^{-4}
Cadmium	Cd	H	320.9	112	0.6	28.8	7.1
Gallium	Ga	O	29.8	69.7	1.103	50.3	5.0
Indium	In	T	156.4	115	3.404	269.2	17.6
Lead	Pb	C	327.4	207	7.22	807	33
Mercury	Hg	R	−38.9	201	4.167	412.6	22
Thallium	Tl	H	302	204	2.392	170.7	31
Tin†	Sn	T	231.9	119	3.729	304.5	18
Zinc	Zn	H	419.5	65.4	0.93	52.5	5.9
			HARD				
Hafnium‡	Hf	H	1700	179	0.37	—	28
Lanthanum	La	H	826	139	4.8	—	—
		C	826	139	5.84	1600	100
Niobium	Nb	C	2500	92.9	8.8	2600	75
Osmium	Os	H	2700	190	0.58	82	27
Rhenium	Re	H	3170	186	1.70	188	25
Rhodium	Rh	C	1966	103	0.9	—	46
Ruthenium	Ru	H	2450	102	0.49	66	24
Tantalum	Ta	C	2996	181	4.27	975	57
Technitium	Te	H	—	99	11.2	—	—
Thorium	Th	C	1845	232	1.37	162	46
Titanium	Ti	H	1800	47.9	0.39	100	35
Uranium	U	O	1150	238	1.1	—	109
Vanadium	V	C	1710	51	5.0	1340	92
Zirconium	Zr	H	1857	91.2	0.55	46.6	16

* C, cubic; H, hexagonal; O, orthorhombic; R, rhombohedral; T, tetragonal.

† White tin. The gray modification, which has a crystal structure of the diamond type (C), does not become a superconductor.

‡ There is some doubt about the superconductivity of hafnium. See Hein, R. A., *Phys. Rev.*, **102**, 1511 (1956).

values of magnetic field intensity H_0 required to obliterate superconduction at 0°K, and the coefficient γ of the electronic specific heat term. We shall have more to say about magnetic effects and electronic specific heats later. It is interesting to note that certain empirical relations exist between H_0 and T_0 for the superconducting elements. In Fig. 19.15 is shown a Lewis log-log plot of H_0 against T_0. The points for the soft superconductors fall close to a straight line which represents the equation

$$H_0 = 68.3T_0^{1.245},$$

and the points for the hard superconductors which crystallize in the cubic system lie near a smooth curve. Here aluminum appears to belong to the hard superconductors rather than to the soft ones. Points for the other hard superconductors are rather scattered at low values of both H_0 and T_0. Evidently metals which crystallize in the cubic and tetragonal structures generally have higher values of transition temperature than the others. Mercury, however, occupies an anomalous position. The curve for hard superconductors crystallizing in the cubic system becomes a straight line with a slope of 325 oersteds/deg Kelvin and an intercept of $0.9°K$ for zero field when H_0 is plotted directly against T_0, as shown in Fig. 19.16.

The distribution of the superconducting elements in the periodic table is shown in Fig. 19.17. No element in either Groups I or VI is a superconductor, nor are any of the ferromagnetic and antiferromagnetic elements. Lanthanum, which can exist in two crystal structures each with its own value of T_0, is the only rare-earth element exhibiting superconductivity; on the other hand, both thorium and uranium of the actinium series are superconductors. Bismuth, which is not a superconductor at low pressures, becomes one at pressures between 20,000 and 40,000 atm with a relatively high transition temperature of approximately $7°K$. Very likely bismuth is transformed from a rhombohedral into a cubic crystal structure at low temperatures and high pressures (see Fig. 10.8). Thin films of bismuth about $0.01\ \mu$ thick also become superconducting with a transition temperature of approximately $6°K$.

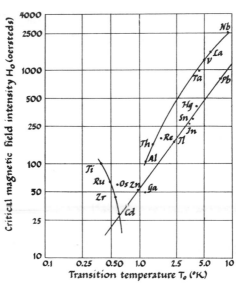

Figure 19.15.   Lewis log H_0-log T_0 plot of the superconducting elements.

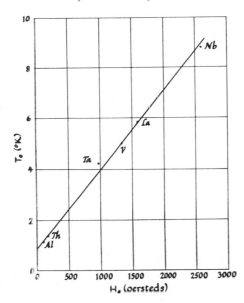

Figure 19.16. T_0-H_0 curve for hard superconductors which crystallize in the cubic system. From it we see that H_0 for rhodium should equal a few oersteds.

Ia	IIa	IIIa	IVa	Va	VIa	VIIa	VIII			Ib	IIb	IIIb	IVb	Vb	VIb	VIIb	O
1 H																	2 He
3 Li	4 Be											5 B	6 C	7 N	8 O	9 F	10 Ne
11 Na	12 Mg											13 Al 1.171°	14 Si	15 P	16 S	17 Cl	18 Ar
19 K	20 Ca	21 Sc	22 Ti 0.39°	23 V 5.0°	24 Cr	25 Mn	26 Fe	27 Co	28 Ni	29 Cu	30 Zn 0.93°	31 Ga 1.103°	32 Ge	33 As	34 Se	35 Br	36 Kr
37 Rb	38 Sr	39 Y	40 Zr 0.55°	41 Nb 8.8°	42 Mo	43 Tc 11.2°	44 Ru 0.49°	45 Rh 0.9°	46 Pd	47 Ag	48 Cd 0.6°	49 In 3.404°	50 Sn 3.729°	51 Sb	52 Te	53 I	54 Xe
55 Cs	56 Ba	Lanthanum Series	72 Hf 0.37°	73 Ta 4.27°	74 W	75 Re 1.70°	76 Os 0.58°	77 Ir	78 Pt	79 Au	80 Hg 4.16°	81 Tl 2.392°	82 Pb 7.22°	83 Bi ~7°	84 Po	85 At	86 Rn
87 Fr	88 Ra	Actinium Series															

High pressure

Lanthanum Series	57 La 4.8°59°	58 Ce	59 Pr	60 Nd	61 Pm	62 Sm	63 Eu	64 Gd	65 Tb	66 Dy	67 Ho	68 Er	69 Tm	70 Yb	71 Lu
Actinium Series	89 Ac	90 Th 1.37°	91 Pa	92 U 1.1°	93 Np	94 Pu	95 Am	96 Cm	97 Bk	98 Cf	99 E	100 Fm	101 Mv	102 No	103 Lw

Figure 19.17. Distribution of superconducting elements in the periodic table.

All isotopes of a superconducting element are superconductors with slightly differing values of transition temperatures. Numerous measurements on mercury, tin, thallium, and lead suggest that T_0 is inversely proportional to a fractional power of the isotopic mass M, or

$$T_0 M^\alpha = \text{constant}, \qquad (19.20)$$

where α very nearly equals 0.5 for mercury, tin, and thallium but has a high value of 0.73 for lead. This isotope effect is of great significance because it shows rather conclusively that superconductivity arises from strong interactions between electrons and lattice vibrations.

Many compounds and mixtures of the elements can become superconducting. A few of them with especially high transition temperatures are listed in Table 19.4. It has been found that a high value of T_0 usually is associated with an *average* of three, five, or seven valence electrons per atom of the system and with a rather bulky crystal structure. Even two elements, such as cobalt and silicon, which separately are unfitted for superconductivity, may be combined to form a superconductor by satisfying these conditions.

Matthais has reviewed the problem in *Progress in Low Temperature Physics*, volume II (1957). According to him 18°K may be an upper limit for T_0.

TABLE 19.4. *Some Superconducting Alloys and Compounds.*

Compound	T_0 (°K)	Compound	T_0 (°K)	Alloy or Mixture	T_0 (°K)
BaBi	6	NbC	10.3	85% Ti, 15% Rh	4.0
MoC	9.8	NbN	15	90% Ti, 10% Ru	3.5
MoGa	9.5	Nb₃Au	11.6	85% Zr, 15% Co	4.0
MoN	12	Nb₃Sn	18	94% Zr, 6% Os	5.8
Mo₂N	5	V₃Ga	16.8	85% Zr, 15% Rh	9.8
Mo₃P	7	V₃Si	17	33% NbC, 66% MoC	12.5
MoRu	10.6	ZrN	9.4	85% NbN, 15% NbC	>17

If bulkiness is an important factor for the occurrence of superconductivity, it should be possible to alter superconductors by subjecting them to tensions and compressions. Sizos and Onnes observed that the transition temperature of tin is lowered by pressure and increased by tension. In general, stresses within a crystal produce marked changes in its superconducting property, and for this reason measurements must be made on carefully annealed specimens. For the soft superconductors tin, indium, and mercury dT_0/dP has a value of the order -4×10^{-5} deg/atm, and for the hard superconductor tantalum it equals -0.29×10^{-5} deg/atm. Both values are negative, but that for tantalum is an order of magnitude less. We find that T_0 decreases nearly linearly with pressure over a range of 10,000 atm. Apparently pressure tends to destroy superconductivity in these elements.

19.8. *Magnetic Properties of Superconductors*

Three years after he discovered superconductivity Onnes observed that a strong magnetic field can restore a superconducting metal to its normal state. The sharpness with which this transformation takes place depends on the shape and orientation of the superconductor as well as on any impurities and strains in it. The best results are obtained on a very pure strain-free specimen in the form of a long, thin (but not too thin) cylinder or wire placed longitudinally in a uniform magnetic field. As the field is increased under isothermal conditions, the metal remains superconducting until a threshold field H_c is reached where its normal resistance is abruptly restored.

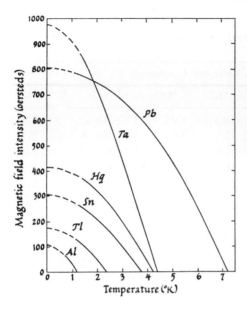

Figure 19.18.   Threshold field curves for several superconducting elements.

This field is a function of temperature only. It increases from zero at the critical temperature T_0 to a maximum H_0 at $0°K$, which is found by extrapolation of the experimental curve, as illustrated in Fig. 19.18. Values of H_0 for many of the superconducting elements are given in Table 19.3. Every threshold field curve is found to have a negative slope which increases in magnitude from zero at $0°K$ to a finite value at T_0. It may be represented by a function of the reduced temperature $t\ (=T/T_0)$ in the form

$$H_c = H_0(1 + at^2 + bt^3 + ct^4 + \cdots). \qquad (19.21)$$

Shoenberg's values of $a, b, c, \ldots$ for a few of the superconductors are given in Table 19.5. For extrapolating experimental curves to $0°K$ in order to find H_0 and for theoretical discussions often it is convenient to replace Eq. (19.21) by the simple quadratic form

$$H_c = H_0(1 - t^2). \qquad (19.22)$$

According to Shoenberg this equation applies to data on aluminum, cadmium, gallium, osmium, ruthenium, and zinc.

TABLE 19.5.   *Values of* a, b, c, $\cdots$ *in Eq.* (19.21).

Metal	a	b	c	d	e	f	g
Indium	−0.626	−0.971	+0.621	−0.024	0	0	0
Lead	−0.91	0	−0.09	0	0	0	0
Mercury	−0.821	−0.374	+0.195	0	0	0	0
Thallium	−1.026	−0.0152	+0.0412	0	0	0	0
Thorium	−1.105	+0.105	0	0	0	0	0
Tin	−1.0720	0	−0.0944	0	+0.3324	0	−0.1660

The experimental results for a superconducting specimen with some other shape or orientation than a long, thin cylinder parallel to a magnetic field generally are more complicated. The field is distorted such that it is no longer uniform over the entire specimen, and consequently there can exist a mixture of normal and superconducting regions, giving rise to the so-called intermediate state. The transformation is not sharp, but extends over a range of values of applied magnetic field. Finally, the magnetic field of the measuring current itself can cause the appearance of an intermediate state in the specimen, and, moreover, at temperatures below T_0 this current cannot exceed a critical value without destroying the superconductive property completely.

If a superconductor were simply a conductor with zero resistance, we should expect its interior to be completely insensitive to any electromagnetic influence from the outside. Consequently, when such a superconductor is placed in a static magnetic field the interior should be field free, as though it had zero permeability. This condition is depicted in Fig. 19.19(a). On the other hand, when the specimen is first placed in the magnetic field at a temperature above the transition value T_c and then cooled down below T_c, the field lines should continue to pass through the superconductor as shown in Fig. 19.19(b). Above T_c the field inside is the same as that outside because the magnetic permeability of a metal in its normal state is very nearly equal to unity. Below T_c no change in flux through the specimen should occur simply because of an abrupt drop in resistance from a very small value to zero. By reducing or removing the applied field, however, a superconducting current should be induced. Meissner and Ochsenfeld[21] put this inference to an experimental test. By means of a small coil they measured the field near a single crystal of tin, in the form of a long cylinder, which was placed transverse to the direction of a uniform applied field. As the temperature was lowered through T_c, the field outside the crystal suddenly changed to conform to a state of zero magnetic induction inside it, as shown in Fig. 19.19(c). The magnetic flux seemed to be expelled from the interior of the crystal at the transition temperature.

The absence of magnetic induction inside a substance in its superconductive phase is a fundamental property of all superconductors.[22] It is named the Meissner effect.

The only way we can explain the absence of magnetic induction inside a superconductor in the presence of a static external applied field is to suppose a suitable distribution of superconducting shielding currents comes into existence on its surface. These are not induced currents, for they do not

[21] Meissner, W., and L. Ochsenfeld, *Naturwiss.*, **21**, 787 (1933).

[22] Actually, experimental and theoretical evidence indicate that the magnetic field penetrates the surface of a superconductor to a distance of the order of 0.01 μ.

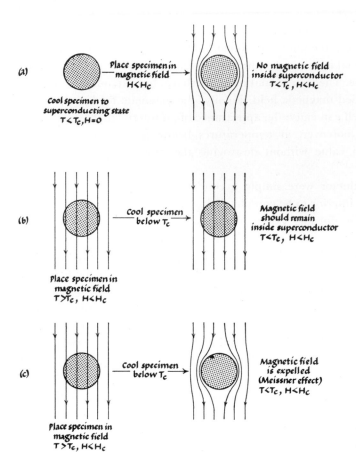

Figure 19.19.   (a) A superconductor is a good dielectric when placed in a magnetic field. (b) Expected behavior when the specimen is first placed in a weak magnetic field and then cooled to the superconducting state. (c) Observed Meissner effect; the magnetic field is expelled when the specimen is cooled below T_c.

depend on changes in flux; instead, they are uniquely determined by the shape of the specimen and by the distribution of the external magnetic field. When the applied field is removed these superconducting currents cease in singly connected specimens, such as spheres and cylinders, but they persist in multiply connected specimens, such as rings and shorted coils. Consider a ring of lead wire in its normal state subjected to a uniform transverse magnetic field. When the ring is cooled below the transition temperature for lead, the magnetic flux is expelled from the interior of the lead but continues to thread the ring. Consequently, if now the field is reduced suddenly, a current must be induced on the surface of the ring. This current is superposed on the shielding current, giving rise to a total persistent current which maintains zero magnetic induction inside the lead. Such persistent currents can exist for months.

We can now conclude that infinite conductivity is a necessary but not a sufficient condition for the existence of the Meissner effect. Within a superconductor the magnetic flux density B equals zero. We recall thàt

$$B = \mu_0 H + m = \mu_0(1 + \chi)H, \tag{19.23}$$

in which μ_0 is the permeability of free space, H is the magnetic field intensity, m is the dipole moment per unit volume, and χ is the susceptibility of the superconducting specimen. For such a perfect conductor therefore, $\chi = -1$. (In the electromagnetic system $\chi = -1/4\pi$.) In other words, a superconductor has the susceptibility of a perfect diamagnetic material. Here we have the explanation for the statement that superconductivity is not so much a manifestation of infinite conductivity as it is an extreme case of diamagnetism.

Since it is relatively easy to measure the critical field for the disappearance of magnetic induction and since this field is identical with the threshold field for the restoration of resistance, the Meissner effect is commonly applied today for determining threshold field curves of superconductors.

19.9. *Thermodynamics of Superconducting Systems*

The Meissner effect demonstrates that the transition from the normal to the superconductive phase is completely reversible. Consequently, a massive superconductor is a thermodynamic system whose equilibrium states are described by its magnetic moment and the intensity of the applied magnetic field, as well as by other common thermodynamic variables. The threshold field curve is a phase diagram for it, which divides the H-T plane into two regions (Fig. 19.20). Below the curve the system can exist only in the superconductive phase and above it only in the normal phase. The curve itself represents a continuous series of states where the normal and superconductive phases coexist in equilibrium.

The specific Gibbs function for a magnetic system may be written in the form

$$g = u - Ts + Pv - Hm, \tag{19.24}$$

in which u, s, v, and m represent specific values of internal energy, entropy, volume, and magnetic moment. Here we shall assume that m has the same direction as H and is uniform throughout the system. For a large body in which m may not be uniform, such as a superconductor in an intermediate state, we suppose Eq. (19.24) applies to each small region in it over which it can be considered uniform.

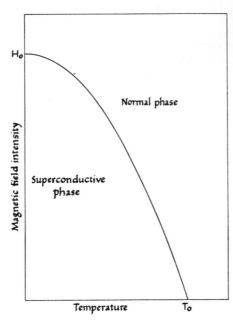

For an infinitesimal reversible process we obtain

$$dg = vdP - sdT - mdH, \quad (19.25)$$

since by the first law of thermo-dynamics

$$du = Tds - Pdv + Hdm. \quad (19.26)$$

Now we see that dg equals zero for a phase change at constant pressure, temperature, and magnetic field intensity. We conclude therefore that for each state along a threshold field curve of a super-conductor the specific Gibbs function for the normal and the super-conductive phases are equal.

Figure 19.20. H_c-T_c phase diagram of a superconductor.

Let the subscripts n and s designate the normal and superconductive phases. For this analysis we hold the pressure constant. Then for infinitesimal transformations along a threshold field curve where dg_n equals dg_s we find

$$(s_n - s_s)dT = -(m_n - m_s)dH_c. \quad (19.27)$$

But in the normal phase the magnetization is negligible, so m_n equals zero, and in the superconductive phase B vanishes, so m_s is given by the equation

$$m_s = \mathfrak{m}_s v = -\mu_0 v H_c. \quad (19.28)$$

We now solve for the discontinuous change in specific entropy for the transition from the superconductive to the normal phase:

$$s_n - s_s = -\mu_0 v H_c(dH_c/dT). \quad (19.29)$$

Here s_n equals s_s both at the zero-field transition point where dH_c/dT has a finite value and at $0°K$ where dH_c/dT equals zero. Furthermore, at all points in between s_n is greater than s_s because dH_c/dT has only negative values, and therefore we can conclude that more order exists in the superconductive than in the normal phase, as was to be expected.

The heat of transformation may be derived from Eq. (19.29):

$$l = T(s_n - s_s)$$
$$= -\mu_0 v T H_c (dH_c/dT). \tag{19.30}$$

Here l equals zero for zero applied field, and from this we infer that the transition at $H_c = 0$ is truly one of second order. The difference in specific heats likewise may be obtained from Eq. (19.29) by means of the relation $c = T(ds/dT)$:

$$c_s - c_n = \mu_0 v T [H_c d^2 H_c/dT^2 + (dH_c/dT)^2]. \tag{19.31}$$

From this equation we get Rutgers' formula for the discontinuity in specific heats at zero field:

$$\Delta c_{T_0} = \mu_0 v T_0 (dH_c/dT)_{T_0}^2. \tag{19.32}$$

Values of Δc_{T_0} computed by means of Eq. (19.32) are compared with observed values in Table 19.6. Discrepancies between them may be due to the presence of impurities and mechanical strain. The temperature variation of Δc is found by substituting the value of H_c from Eq. (19.21) into Eq. (19.31). When this is done for tin the agreement between computed and experimental results is reasonably good.

TABLE 19.6.   *Discontinuity in Specific Heat Capacity Δc.*

Metal	M (gm/mole)	T_0 (°K)	ρ (gm/cc)	$(dH_c/dT)_{T_0}$ (oersteds/deg)	Δc_{T_0} (comp.) (joule/mole-deg)	Δc_{T_0} (obs.) (joule/mole-deg)
Al	27.0	1.171	2.69	163	0.0025	0.0019
In	114.8	3.404	7.43	156	0.0102	0.0096
Pb	207.2	7.22	11.48	226	0.053	0.053
Sn	118.7	3.729	7.30	147	0.0104	0.0100
Ta	180.9	4.27	17.1	334	0.042	0.034, 0.038
Tl	204.4	2.392	11.7	126	0.0053	0.0062
Th	232.1	1.37	12.0	190	0.0076	—

Ordinarily, the specific heat of a metal at low temperatures is made up of two terms: an electronic term which is directly proportional to the temperature (Section 17.4), and a lattice term which is proportional to the cube of the temperature (Section 15.3). The equation for the specific heat in joules per mole-degree is

$$c_n = \gamma T + 464.4(T/\Theta)^3, \tag{19.33}$$

in which γ is the electronic constant and Θ is the Debye temperature of the metal. If c_n/T is plotted against T^2, a straight line should be obtained whose intercept on the ordinate axis equals γ and from whose slope a value of Θ

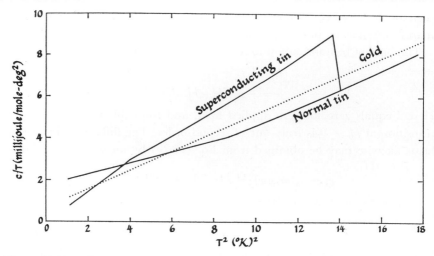

Figure 19.21.   Comparison of the specific heat of normal and superconducting tin with that of gold at liquid helium temperatures.

may be calculated. Measurements of c_n for a superconductor can be made even at temperatures below T_0 by applying an external magnetic field. In this way Keesom and Van Laer[23] and Corak and Satterthwaite[24] were able to measure the specific heat of tin in its normal and in its superconductive phase down to nearly 1°K. Their results are compared with those for gold in Fig. 19.21. Here we see that Eq. (19.33) is satisfied rather well for gold and also for tin at temperatures less than 2.8°K. The specific heat of tin shows the characteristic increase for the superconductive phase at the transition temperature and then falls more rapidly than the specific heat of the normal phase, with a crossover at slightly less than 2°K. Similar results have been obtained for aluminum, lanthanum, niobium, tantalum, and vanadium.

19.10. Theories of Superconductivity

Many properties of superconductors and of helium II are strikingly similar. The zero-field transition from the normal to the superconductive phase in metals, like the transition from helium I to helium II, is of the second order with no latent heat but with a discontinuous jump in specific heat. Pressure lowers the transition temperature in both instances. The superconducting electrons and the superfluid helium atoms move freely over surfaces in thin

[23] Keesom, W. H., and P. H. van Laer, *Physica*, **4**, 487 (1937).
[24] Corak, W. S., and C. B. Satterthwaite, *Phys. Rev.*, **102**, 662 (1956).

layers or films at rates which depend only on temperature and are limited. Apparently they carry no entropy.

The differences between superconductors and helium II are no less striking. Whereas a magnetic field can destroy the superconductive state of a metal, no known field can destroy the superfluid state of helium. Similarly, there is no counterpart of the Meissner effect in superfluidity. On the other hand, second sound in helium II is unlike any phenomenon in superconductive metals. Then, too, electrons are charged particles of small mass which obey Fermi-Dirac statistics, whereas the atoms in helium II are uncharged particles of comparatively large mass which obey Bose-Einstein statistics. For these reasons any analogies between superconductivity and superfluidity must be drawn with caution.

Because of the foregoing similarities and the successes of Tisza's theory for helium II, two-fluid theories of superconductivity have been developed. Two general assumptions are made: (1) electrons exist either in an ordered superconductive condensed phase or in a less-ordered normal excited phase, and (2) all entropy effects are associated with electrons in the normal phase. The number of electrons in the normal phase depends markedly on temperature and on an ordering parameter. The first and best known two-fluid model for superconductivity was proposed by Gorter and Casimir[25] in 1934. Although it predicts the T^3 law for the variation of specific heats, generally it does not give a satisfactory description of the phenomenon. Several modifications, including those with energy gaps, have introduced no significant improvements.

London and London[26] published a complete and consistent electrodynamic theory of superconductivity which has been very successful in correlating and predicting experimental results. One notable success was the prediction prior to observation of a depth of approximately 0.01 μ for the penetration of an applied magnetic field. Otherwise the theory has not received good quantitative confirmation, nor have modifications of it been any more successful.

Fröhlich[27] and Bardeen[28] independently have worked on theories of superconductivity involving interactions between electrons and lattice vibrations. As the temperature of a metal is reduced a state is reached where suddenly instead of lattice vibrations offering resistance they aid the passage of electrons by carrying the electron wave along. According to these theories, a

[25] Gorter, C. J., and H. Casimir, *Physica*, **1**, 306 (1934).
[26] London, H., and F. London, *Proc. Roy. Soc.*, **149**, 71 (1935); *Physica*, **2**, 341 (1935).
[27] Fröhlich, H., *Phys. Rev.*, **79**, 845 (1950); *Proc. Phys. Soc.*, **64**, 129 (1951).
[28] Bardeen, J., *Phys. Rev.*, **79**, 167 (1950); **80**, 567 (1950); **81**, 829 (1951); **82**, 978 (1951).

metal which is a poor electrical conductor at high temperature makes a good superconductor, whereas excellent normal conductors do not become super-conductors at all. It is found that correlations between electrons of opposite spin through interactions with the lattice produce superconductivity.

At high temperatures electrons are scattered by collisions with vibrating lattice points, or lattice waves, and this scattering gives rise to the tempera-ture-dependent part of the resistivity. The lattice waves constitute a phonon field. As the temperature decreases toward 0°K the lattice vibrations dis-appear, and the phonon part of the resistance goes to zero. Any residual resistance therefore arises from scattering of electrons by impurities and lattice imperfections. However, it is still possible for an electron to excite a lattice wave *virtually*. This virtual lattice wave, or phonon, can interact with another electron to produce effectively an electron-electron interaction. This mechanism allows correlations between electrons of opposite spin to take place and thus makes possible the appearance of the superconductive state. Now we can see that a normal metal with high resistance should be a good superconductor because both phenomena require strong interactions between electrons and phonons; on the contrary, good conductors at elevated tem-peratures should make poor superconductors. This theory has been developed by Bardeen, Cooper, and Schrieffer[29] and is summarized by Cooper in the February 1960 issue of the *American Journal of Physics*.

For further discussions of superfluidity and superconductivity consult the bibliography at the end of Chapter 18.

Problems

1. Combine Eqs. (19.2) and (19.3) to show that the ratio of superfluid atoms to the total number by London's theory is

$$N_s/N = 1 - (T/T_c)^{3/2},$$

and compare this with observed results.

2. (a) s_2 is essentially constant at approximately 20 m/sec from 1.0°K to 1.8°K. How does ρ_n/ρ vary with T in this range?

   (b) Between 0.05°K and 0.55°K $s_2 = 200 - 125T$ in meters per second; $c = 0.0235T^3$ and $s = 0.0078T^3$, each in joule per gram-degree. Obtain a

[29] Bardeen, J., L. N. Cooper, and J. R. Schrieffer, *Phys. Rev.*, **108**, 1175 (1957).

relation for ρ_n/ρ as a function of T over this range of temperatures, and plot a curve.

3. Integrate Eq. (19.31) to get

$$H_0 = [(2/\mu_0 v) \int_0^{T_c} (c_s - c_n)dT]^{1/2},$$

and evaluate H_0 for tin from data given in Fig. 19.21.

4. Show that $(\partial T_c/\partial P)_{H_e} = T(v_n - v_s)/l$ for a superconductor, where T is the temperature, P is the pressure, v_n and v_s are the specific volumes for the normal and superconductive phases, and l is the heat of transformation.

5. (a) By means of Eq. (19.22) prove that

$$c_n - c_s = \gamma'(t - 3t^3),$$

in which $\gamma' = 2\mu_0 v_0 H_0^2/T_0$.

(b) If

$$c_n = \gamma T + 464.4(T/\Theta)^3,$$

and c_s is proportional to the cube of the temperature, show that $\gamma' = \gamma T_0$.

6. If

$$c_n = \gamma T + 464.4(T/\Theta)^3,$$

and

$$c_s = Ae^{-bT_0/T} + 464.4(T/\Theta)^3,$$

find the equation of the threshold field curve for a superconductive specimen.

CHAPTER 20

Irreversible Flow Processes

THE transfer of mass, charge, thermal energy, or any other thermophysical entity in a more or less continuous manner from one region to another constitutes a flow process. We are already familiar with the flow of liquids in hydrodynamics and the flow of charges in electricity. In addition, we have studied the transport of momentum, kinetic energy, and molecules across boundaries in gases (Chapter 12) and the transfer of radiant energy from a high-temperature source to other bodies across a void (Chapter 16). These too are flow processes. The concept of flow also may be applied to the propagation of entropy, temperature, and magnetization. In each instance the thermophysical quantity is treated as though it were a "thing" which can be transferred from region to region. Often it is conceived to behave like an incompressible ideal fluid, but this analogy should not be carried too far.

Generally, flow processes are irreversible, and therefore they are outside the purview of classical thermodynamics. Applications of statistical mechanics, on the other hand, often are very tedious if not practically impossible. Consequently, other methods have been developed for studying nonequilibrium flow situations by means of macroscopic variables and techniques. In one, equations of continuity are combined with experimental laws of conduction to obtain differential equations for fluid flow. In another, thermodynamics is extended and modified for applications to systems in steady states. We shall describe these two methods in the following sections.

20.1. Thermal Conduction

In thermal conduction heat passes through a material medium without large-scale movements of mass from region to region. Its rate of flow through and normal to a small area in the medium is proportional to that area and to the temperature gradient across it. Fourier's name has been associated with this law ever since the publication of his analytical results in 1822.[1] Ohm's law (1826) for electrical conduction in wires, Poiseuille's law (1846) for the flow of fluids in capillary tubes, and Fick's law (1855) for the diffusion of substances through membranes were patterned after it. In symbols, Fourier's law for one-dimensional heat conduction is written

$$\partial Q/\partial \tau = -\sigma_t A(\partial t/\partial x), \qquad (20.1)$$

in which A represents the area normal to the flow, and $\partial t/\partial x$ is the temperature gradient along it. The proportionality constant σ_t is the thermal conductivity of the medium. Sometimes it is convenient to divide Eq. (20.1) through by A, and then the thermal current density $\partial Q/A\partial \tau$ is represented by j_{tx}. Note that the electrical analogue of $\partial t/\partial x$ is the electrical potential gradient.

Equation (20.1) is useful as it stands for solving one-dimensional heat conduction problems in which the thermal current is constant. For more complicated situations t may be a function of y and z as well as x and τ. Then Eq. (20.1) and two others like it for the y and z directions are combined with the equation of continuity in the form

$$\nabla \cdot \vec{j}_t = -\rho c_p \partial t/\partial \tau \qquad (20.2)$$

to obtain a general differential equation for thermal conduction. For an isotropic homogeneous medium, where σ_t, ρ, and c_p are constant and independent of direction, we obtain

$$\partial t/\partial \tau = (\sigma_t/\rho c_p) \, [\partial^2 t/\partial x^2 + \partial^2 t/\partial y^2 + \partial^2 t/\partial z^2]. \qquad (20.3)$$

The group of constants $\sigma_t/\rho c_p$ often is represented by D_t and was named thermal diffusivity by Kelvin.

As one example of an application of Eq. (20.3) let us solve for the variations of temperature within the Earth's crust as a result of diurnal and annual temperature changes at its surface. For a given locality this problem may be considered essentially one dimensional. From experience we know that

---

[1] Actually, Biot enunciated this law as early as 1804 and Fourier began applying it in 1811 (Jakob, M., *Heat Transfer*, Vol. I, p. 2, Wiley, New York, 1949).

the smoothed-out profile consists mainly of two superposed terms with periods of 24 hours and one year. As a first approximation therefore we shall assume each term may be represented by a product $f(x) \exp(i\omega\tau)$, where $f(x)$ is a function of depth x, i equals $\sqrt{-1}$, and ω represents 2π divided by the appropriate period. We wish to find an explicit form of $f(x)$ for each term and thereby the equations for variations in temperature.

When $f(x) \exp(i\omega\tau)$ is substituted into the one-dimensional form of Eq. (20.3) we obtain

$$D_t d^2 f(x)/dx^2 = i\omega f(x), \qquad (20.4)$$

whose solution is

$$f(x) = Ae^{ax} + Be^{-ax}, \qquad (20.5)$$

where a equals $(i\omega/D_t)^{1/2}$. But the crust temperature becomes less dependent on surface conditions as depth increases, and therefore A must equal zero. The complete equation for t then is

$$t = Be^{i\omega\tau - ax}. \qquad (20.6)$$

Now $\sqrt{i}$ equals $(1 + i)/\sqrt{2}$, so Eq. (20.6) may be rewritten in the form

$$t = Be^{-kx}e^{i(\omega\tau - kx)}, \qquad (20.7)$$

whose real part is

$$t = t_0 e^{-kx} \cos(\omega\tau - kx), \qquad (20.8)$$

in which t_0 is the surface temperature at zero time. This is an equation for an attenuated plane wave of period $2\pi/\omega$ and of wavelength $2\pi/k$, where k equals $(\omega/2D_t)^{1/2}$. A wave of temperature, whose amplitude decreases exponentially with depth, is conceived to flow into the crust. The speed of this wave equals the quotient of wavelength and period, or $\omega/k = (2\omega D_t)^{1/2}$. Since D_t depends only on properties of the crust material and not on the wave form, it follows that the diurnal wave travels $\sqrt{365}$ or about 19 times as fast as the annual one, but penetrates only $\frac{1}{19}$ as far before its amplitude is reduced to half the surface value.

In Fig. 20.1 the curve represents the exponentially decreasing

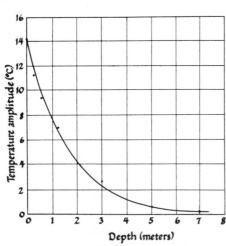

Figure 20.1.   The amplitude of a temperature wave decreases exponentially with depth.

amplitude in Eq. (20.7) for an annual temperature wave with D_t equal to 0.0027 cm²sec⁻¹. The points are observed values compiled from measurements taken underground in Japan.[2] From measurements to depths of 3 m at Bozeman, Montana, Fitton and Brooks[3] found a value of 0.009 cm²sec⁻¹ for the thermal diffusivity. In ordinary moist soil D_t equals approximately 0.005 cm²sec⁻¹.

From Eq. (20.8) we see that a variation in temperature at the surface of the Earth does not appear at depth x until a time kx/ω later. Thus a minimum of temperature at x for which $\omega\tau - kx$ equals π occurs at time $x(2\omega D_t)^{-(1/2)}$ after its occurrence at the surface. From these relations a maximum depth of penetration for freezing temperatures may be computed, provided the latent heat for freezing of water is taken into account.

Ordinarily, the complete solution of Eq. (20.3) for a time-dependent conduction problem consists of two parts: a steady-state solution and a transient. The steady-state solution applies not only at the start but also after a long period of time, and it may be either constant or periodic. The transient appears only initially and usually dies out rather rapidly. As an illustration consider the following problem. A large slab of material of uniform thickness l and at an elevated temperature t_0 suddenly is immersed in a rapidly circulating liquid bath maintained at 0°C. The surfaces are assumed to come to 0°C immediately, and thereafter heat flows from the interior through the surfaces into the bath where it is carried away by the circulating liquid. After sufficient time has elapsed the slab temperature is reduced to a uniform 0°C, and conduction ceases. Actually, as we shall discover in the next section, the temperature of the surfaces remains slightly higher than 0°C during the flow process, but we shall neglect this small effect. What is the temperature at each point in the slab at any instant as it cools down?

If the length and width of the slab are much greater than its thickness, edge effects may be disregarded, and the problem becomes essentially one-dimensional. We shall therefore orient the x-axis so it is normal to the slab with the origin in one surface, as shown in Fig. 20.2. A solution for the one-dimensional form of Eq. (20.3) is found by separation of variables; thus

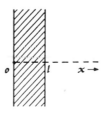

Figure 20.2. The x-axis is normal to the slab.

$$t = e^{-b\tau}[A' \sin (b/D_t)^{1/2}x + B' \cos (b/D_t)^{1/2}x], \qquad (20.9)$$

[2] Tamura, S. T., *Monthly Weather Rev.*, **33**, 296 (1905).
[3] Fitton, E. M., and C. F. Brooks, *Monthly Weather Rev.*, **59**, 6 (1931).

in which A', B', and b are constants to be evaluated by means of given initial and boundary conditions in the problem. [Note that Eq. (20.7) is obtained from Eq. (20.9) by setting b equal to $-i\omega$.] Since the temperature of both surfaces of the slab remains at 0°C throughout the flow process, it follows that B' must vanish and $(b/D_t)^{1/2}l$ must equal an integral number n of π radians for a nontrivial solution. Let t_n be the partial temperature and A'_n the coefficient corresponding to integer n; then

$$t_n = A'_n e^{-k_n{}^2 D_t \tau} \sin (k_n x), \qquad (20.10)$$

where k_n equals $\pi n/l$. The general solution for t now consists of the sum of all n solutions like Eq. (20.10). Sums of this kind were first introduced by Fourier; hence they are called Fourier series.

The coefficients A'_n are evaluated from the initial temperature distribution by the standard method. Here,

$$t_0 = \Sigma_n A'_n \sin (k_n x). \qquad (20.11)$$

Both sides of this equation are multiplied by $\sin (k_n x)dx$ and then integrated between the limits 0 and l. All terms on the right vanish except one, and from this we find

$$A'_n = 2t_0(1 - \cos \pi n)/\pi n. \qquad (20.12)$$

We conclude therefore that the temperature at a point in the slab at any instant is represented by a series of terms like Eq. (20.10) in which A'_n equals $4t_0/\pi n$, where n is odd.

Other time-dependent conduction problems can easily become more involved than the foregoing. For instance, for heat flow through cylindrical structures Eq. (20.3) is transformed to cylindrical coordinates, and then, even for the simplest situation of radial heat flow, the solution comes out in terms of Bessel functions. Furthermore, usually a conducting system is surrounded by a convecting fluid which modifies the surface temperature markedly. This effect we shall consider briefly in the next section.

20.2. Thermal Convection

The convective process is more complex than conduction, for it involves the mass movement of the medium which is transferring thermal energy from one region to another. This process, first described by Count Rumford in 1797, was named convection by William Prout in 1834. The simplest arrangement for convection to take place is made by connecting the source and sink of thermal energy with a tube of liquid or gas, as in Fig. 20.3. At the warm end the fluid rises to give place to cooler fluid flowing in along the

bottom of the tube from the cold
end. Meanwhile the warmed fluid
flows along the top from the warm
to the cold end where it delivers
thermal energy to the sink as it

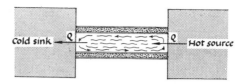

falls to the bottom of the tube.
Once circulation is established the
fluid acts as a conveyer of energy
from source to sink. Even though

Figure 20.3.   Convection process transports
thermal energy rapidly from
a source to a sink.

the fluid normally is a poor thermal conductor it may carry away large
quantities of energy very rapidly by the convective process.

Within a thin film of convecting fluid next to a source or sink of thermal
energy the speeds are so low that the flow is streamlined. Outside this thin
film, where the speeds are sufficiently high, the fluid is turbulent. The thickness of the thin film and depth of the transition zone depend on the geometry
and structure of the surface, the physical properties of the fluid, and the
extent of the turbulence. When a steady state has been reached a more or
less constant temperature distribution is maintained in the outer region,
and heat is transferred between this region and the source or sink through
the thin low-speed film essentially by conduction. The one-dimensional law
of thermal convection therefore is a modified form of Fourier's law in which
the film thickness is included in the coefficient:

$$dQ/d\tau = hA\Delta t, \qquad (20.13)$$

where A is the surface area, Δt is the difference between the temperature of
source or sink and the turbulent part of the fluid, and h is the coefficient of
thermal convection or simply film transfer coefficient.

By dimensional methods[4] Nusselt (1915) derived the relation

$$hl/\sigma_t = C(l^3\rho^2\beta g\Delta t/\eta^2)^m(\eta c_p/\sigma_t)^n \qquad (20.14)$$

for natural convection near a vertical surface of height l. In this equation
σ_t is the thermal coefficient of conduction, ρ the density, β the volume expansivity, η the coefficient of viscosity, and c_p the specific heat at constant
pressure of the fluid; g is the gravitational acceleration, and Δt is the difference in temperature between the surface and the bulk fluid. The constants
C, m, and n are determined from experiments or from a direct analysis of the
problem by the laws of fluid dynamics. As early as 1881 Lorenz had solved
the differential equations for fluid flow near a vertical surface under steady-
state conditions and found 0.548 for C and $\frac{1}{4}$ for m and n. By a somewhat

[4] Jakob, M., and G. A. Hawkins, *Elements of Heat Transfer and Insulation*, 2nd ed., p. 99
(Wiley, New York, 1950).

more elaborate analysis and carefully controlled experiments Schmidt and Beckmann (1930) showed that C should be about 6% lower in value. Equations similar to Eq. (20.14) have been obtained for horizontal surfaces and cylindrical tubes.

For convection in the atmosphere often it is convenient to lump the fluid parameters in Eq. (20.14) together with constant C. For a vertical wall of height l less than 0.3 m we get 1.37 $(\Delta t/l)^{1/4}$ for h in mks units. If the wall height exceeds 0.3 m, the coefficient may be considered nearly independent of height and is given by 1.97 $(\Delta t)^{1/4}$. Similarly, for a flat horizontal slab the relation is $2.49(\Delta t)^{1/4}$ at the upper surface and $1.31(\Delta t)^{1/4}$ at the lower surface; for a horizontal pipe it is $1.07(\Delta t/D)^{1/4}$, in which D is the external diameter in meters.

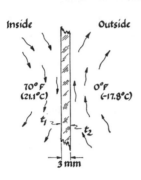

Figure 20.4. The window pane problem.

As an example, consider the flow of heat through a vertical window pane of 3 mm thickness and 1 m² area. The thermal conductivity of window glass equals approximately 1 watt/m-deg Celsius. Let the mean temperature of room and outside air be 70°F (21.1°C) and 0°F (−17.8°C). As illustrated in Fig. 20.4, convection occurs at both the inside and outside surfaces while conduction takes place through the glass. Under steady-state conditions all three current densities have the same value; hence

$$j_t = 1.97(21.1 - t_1)^{5/4}$$
$$= (1000/3)(t_1 - t_2)$$
$$= 1.97(t_2 + 17.8)^{5/4},$$

in which t_1 and t_2 are the temperatures of the inside and outside surfaces. From these equations we get

$$t_1 + t_2 = 3.3,$$

where

$$t_1 - 1.65 = 0.002955(21.1 - t_1)^{5/4}.$$

One of three common methods may be applied to solve the last equation for t_1, and then both t_2 and j_t are calculated.

In the trial and error method a series of values for t_1 are tried until one is found to satisfy the equation. In the graphical method the right and left sides of the equation are plotted separately on the same graph, and the point of intersection of the two curves gives the desired temperature. Finally, in the method of successive approximations a reasonable estimate of t_1 is substituted in the right side of the equation, and a value of t_1 on the left is computed. This new t_1 now is inserted on the right, and another value of t_1 on the left is computed. This cycle is repeated until the computed value on the left equals the inserted value on the right. In practice usually not more than two or three cycles are needed to obtain an answer of sufficient accuracy.

For the window pane let the initial value of t_1 equal the average of the air temperatures, namely $\frac{1}{2}(21.1 - 17.8)$ or 1.65°C. In two successive cycles the computed values of t_1 equal 1.771°C and 1.770°C. We conclude that t_1 equals 1.7_7°C, and therefore t_2 equals 1.5_3°C. The rate of heat loss through the window pane may be calculated from any one of the equations for j_t; thus from the second we get $(1000/3)(1.77 - 1.53)$ or 80 watts/m². Convection losses through a window may be reduced substantially by inclosing thin layers of dry air between glass. This is the principle behind storm windows and the multiglazed sash. The optimum separation of the panes appears to be approximately 1 cm.

Convective processes are encountered at every turn. Cyclones and anticyclones, fronts, hurricanes and little whirlwinds, cloud formations, updrafts, and nearly all disturbances that influence weather are the result of convection in the atmosphere. We wear clothes in cold regions on the Earth largely for protection from the weather, not so much to reduce losses by conduction and radiation as to reduce them by convection. Houses are heated by convection of the fluid in the heating system and of the air in the room. They are ventilated by convective processes too. A fan is a simple device for producing convective currents. A household kettle or an industrial boiler of water is heated rapidly primarily because of convection in the water. From the flow of great ocean currents to the act of blowing across a spoonful of hot soup the convective process plays a dominant role in the life of man.

On examining all the foregoing situations we conclude that convection is a thermomechanical process in which heat exchange occurs because of a pressure difference in addition to a temperature difference between regions of a fluid. The pressure difference may arise naturally, as an unbalanced hydrostatic pressure in the atmosphere or in a kettle of water, or it may arise by forced circulation, as in fanning or in blowing across hot soup. These two types are said to be natural and forced convection. Forced convection usually is more effective than natural convection.

We may conclude from our study of radiation (Chapter 16), conduction, and convection that a system and its near-surround, which are in mechanical and chemical equilibrium, will exchange thermal energy until a state of dynamic equilibrium is established where as much heat enters the system as leaves it by these processes. This may be called the universal law of heat exchange. Only if the temperature of the system differs from that of the near-surround will there be a net flow of heat, and, from a macroscopic point of view, this always takes place in such a direction as to bring about a state of equilibrium.

20.3. Temperature and Entropy of Conductors During Flow Processes

We have learned that temperature is a meaningful concept only for a system in thermal equilibrium, namely one whose temperature is uniform throughout as determined by means of the zeroth law of thermodynamics (Chapter 2). A system which experiences a thermal process, however, is not in equilibrium, and therefore we may properly ask: What does "temperature" mean in this situation? Clearly, a specific operational definition can be formulated in terms of prescribed thermometers and procedures to satisfy any one of the empirical equations for heat transfer. But this would give us several different and seemingly unrelated "temperatures," none of which would necessarily agree with the fundamental one from equilibrium thermodynamics.

Only if the thermal flow process is so slow that the thermophysical state of the system supporting it can be considered almost stationary is it possible to assign a temperature in the thermodynamic sense to each small region of the system. In other words, the macroscopic flow should not disrupt equilibrium in a small region faster than it can be reestablished at the molecular level. For heat conduction through a linear system in a stationary state as much thermal energy enters at one end as leaves at the other (Fig. 20.5). It is convenient to imagine the system divided into a large number of thin contiguous wafers.

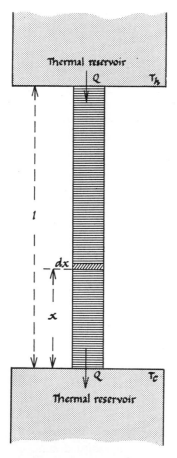

Figure 20.5. Computing the entropy of a heat conductor.

Each wafer then is assumed to be in thermal equilibrium and therefore to have a uniform temperature. Moreover, the wafers are arranged in a sequence of monotonically increasing temperature from the cold (T_c) to the hot (T_h) end, such that the temperature at distance x from the cold end is given by the equation

$$T = T_c + (T_h - T_c)x/l, \qquad (20.15)$$

in which l is the length of the conductor. From this we find the average temperature equals $\frac{1}{2}(T_h + T_c)$. If the system were suddenly cut from the source and sink of thermal energy and were surrounded by an adiabatic wall, we surmise that conduction would occur between its parts until the system comes to thermal equilibrium at this average temperature.

The entropy of a system supporting a thermal flow process is as difficult to establish as its temperature, for entropy and temperature are conjugate to one another with respect to energy. Only for reversible processes, and therefore for systems in quasistatic equilibrium, can we equate the heat exchange with the near-surround $d'Q$ to the product TdS. For the conducting rod of Fig. 20.5 we suppose each wafer is raised from an initial temperature T_c to its steady-state temperature T by placing it in contact with a continuous series of thermal reservoirs having temperatures between T_c and T. This process is isobaric and quasistatic. The wafer at distance x from the cold end has thickness dx, cross-sectional area A, density ρ, and specific heat c_p. For it the increase in entropy is given by the integral

$$d(\Delta S) = \int_{T_c}^{T} d'Q/T = \int_{T_c}^{T} (c_p\rho A dx)(dT/T)$$
$$= c_p\rho A dx \ln (T/T_c). \qquad (20.16)$$

We substitute for T its value from Eq. (12.15) and integrate with respect to x between the limits 0 and l. Thus the total entropy of the rod relative to its state at uniform temperature T_c is found to be

$$\Delta S = C_p[(1 - T_c/T_h)^{-1} \ln (T_h/T_c) - 1], \qquad (20.17)$$

where C_p is the heat capacity of the entire rod at constant pressure.

This value of entropy should be compared with that obtained when the rod is allowed to come to equilibrium at its average temperature $\frac{1}{2}(T_h + T_c)$. For this situation

$$\Delta S' = C_p \int_{T_c}^{T_{av}} dT/T$$
$$= C_p \ln \frac{1}{2}(1 + T_h/T_c), \qquad (20.18)$$

which exceeds ΔS for all values of T_h/T_c greater than unity. The difference $\Delta S - \Delta S'$ may be considered the negative entropy (negentropy) associated with the ordered arrangement of wafers within the conducting rod. It is a measure of information regarding the temperature distribution in the rod system.

The temperature of a system which supports any *isothermal* flow process, such as diffusion of particles, conduction of electricity, or streaming of liquids, really is a function of the gradient that maintains the flow, as we shall learn in Section 20.6. Consequently, neither the temperature nor the entropy of such a system is sharply defined. On the other hand, the total entropy of the conducting system is believed to be less than its equilibrium value when isolated. Again the difference is a measure of the information associated with the flow process. Negative entropy of flow no doubt exists even for such complex systems as those possessing life. Over short intervals of time, living systems may be thought to exist in a steady state as matter is conveyed through them and metabolism occurs. The entropy of this matter is increased during the flow process, while the system maintains nearly a constant total entropy of value less than it would have if it were dead and disintegrated. Here, as in all the other conducting systems, entropy appears to be created during the irreversible flow process.

20.4. Creation of Entropy During Flow Processes

Again consider the rod of Fig. 20.5 in a steady state as heat $d'Q$ passes through it in time $d\tau$. The cold end of the wafer at x is at temperature T, while the hot end is at temperature $T + dT$; therefore the increase in entropy of the local universe as heat $d'Q$ enters and leaves the wafer is given by the equation

$$dS_{\text{irr}} = d'Q/(T + dT) - d'Q/T$$
$$= -d'Q \cdot dT/T^2 \qquad (20.19)$$

in which dT is intrinsically negative. The rate of increase of entropy resulting from the irreversible heat flow equals $dS_{\text{irr}}/d\tau$, and the rate per unit volume is found by dividing by the volume of the wafer $A dx$, where A is the cross-sectional area. Let this rate of increase of entropy per unit volume be represented by θ_{irr}; then we get

$$\theta_{\text{irr}} = (d'Q/Ad\tau)(-dT/T^2 dx), \qquad (20.20)$$

which is the product of the thermal current density into the negative temperature gradient divided by the square of the temperature. For thermal conduction in a three-dimensional system three terms like Eq. (20.20) enter into θ_{irr}; consequently,

$$\theta_{\text{irr}} = -\vec{j_t} \cdot \nabla T/T^2. \qquad (20.21)$$

For other flow processes we may obtain similar equations for the rate of production of entropy per unit volume. As another example, let us determine an equation for θ_{irr} resulting from the isothermal passage of a mixture of fluids through a capillary of a porous membrane at constant pressure.

First we shall work out the general equation for the rate of entropy increase during any irreversible flow process at constant pressure and temperature, then we shall apply it to our problem. Suppose heat $d'Q = dU + PdV$ flows into a system to maintain constant temperature T during the irreversible flow process. Then

$$dS_{irr} = dS - d'Q/T$$

or

$$TdS_{irr} - TdS - dU - PdV$$
$$= -d(U + PV - TS) = -dG,$$

since both P and T are constant, and therefore

$$TdS_{irr}/d\tau = -dG/d\tau. \tag{20.22}$$

Consider now an element of the capillary or porous membrane of length dx and cross-sectional area A. Let the chemical potentials of the ith species of fluid be μ_i and $\mu_i + (\partial\mu_i/\partial x)dx$ on the two sides of the element. The increase in the Gibbs function G as a result of flow through it is given by the equation

$$dG = \Sigma_i[\mu_i + (\partial\mu_i/\partial x)dx]dn_i - \Sigma_i\mu_i dn_i$$
$$= \Sigma_i(\partial\mu_i/\partial x)dxdn_i, \tag{20.23}$$

for all i species in the fluid at constant temperature and pressure. We insert this value of dG into Eq. (20.22) and divide throughout by $TAdx$ to get the rate of increase in entropy per unit volume:

$$\theta_{irr} = -T^{-1}\Sigma_i(\partial\mu_i/\partial x)(dn_i/Ad\tau). \tag{20.24}$$

If we represent the current density of fluid flow $dn_i/Ad\tau$ for the ith species by j_i, then for a three-dimensional system we find

$$\theta_{irr} = -T^{-1}\Sigma_i\vec{j}_i \cdot \nabla\mu_i. \tag{20.25}$$

If a temperature gradient also exists, the rate of production of entropy per unit volume by the fluid flow alone is given by the more inclusive equation,

$$\theta_{irr} = -\Sigma_i\vec{j}_i \cdot \nabla(\mu_i/T), \tag{20.26}$$

which reduces to Eq. (20.25) under isothermal conditions.

For electrical conduction, particle diffusion and other irreversible flow processes equations for θ_{irr} similar to the foregoing ones may be derived. They all show that $T\theta_{irr}$ equals the product of a current density and a gradient. Suppose, however, more than one of these processes exist in a system simultaneously. What then is the expression for the rate of production of entropy? For this situation the principle of superposition is found to apply, so $T\theta_{\mathrm{irr}}$ equals the sum of the product terms for each of the separate processes. We shall not give a general proof here; the original papers and books in the bibliography should be consulted.

20.5. Energy Transfer During Flow Processes

A system which supports an isothermal flow process is open to its environment. For simplicity let us consider it to possess only one inlet and one outlet through which matter passes, and furthermore let us suppose its total internal energy either fluctuates about a constant mean value or does not change at all. As a matter of fact, for this discussion and all that follows we shall restrict the flow process to one which is time invariant, so the total internal energy is constant; the results, however, usually may be extended to periodic and other fluctuating situations. What is the energy equation for transformations within the system as matter flows through it?

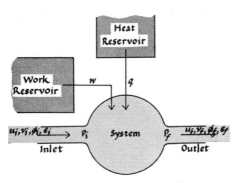

Figure 20.6.   Energy flow through an open system.

As suggested in Fig. 20.6, at the inlet a unit mass of the flowing substance carries in specific internal energy u_i, potential φ_i, and kinetic energy per unit mass ϵ_i. The corresponding $P\text{-}V$ work equals $P_i v_i$, in which P_i is the pressure and v_i is the specific volume. Hence the total energy per unit mass entering the system by this process is $u_i + P_i v_i + \epsilon_i + \varphi_i$. Similarly, the total energy per unit mass carried out of the system at the outlet is $u_f + P_f v_f + \epsilon_f + \varphi_f$. Meanwhile, heat q and work w per unit mass may enter the system from the near-surround by other means than the flow process. The algebraic sum of all these energies must equal the change in internal energy of the system, but this equals zero for the time invariant condition. Thus we get

$$q + w = h_f - h_i + \epsilon_f - \epsilon_i + \varphi_f - \varphi_i, \qquad (20.27)$$

where h_i and h_f are the specific enthalpies at the inlet and outlet. In order for this equation to apply, the flow process must not be too rapid, which means the system should be close to its state of thermodynamic equilibrium.

Applications of Eq. (20.27) can be made to a number of well-known systems. For the flow of fluid through a porous plug or throttling valve no net work is done, and the process is adiabatic, so both w and q equal zero. Also, the inlet and outlet are nearly on the same level, whence φ_i equals φ_f, and the speed of flow is so slow that the kinetic energy terms are negligible. Consequently, we find from Eq. (20.27) that the final and initial values of enthalpy are equal, in agreement with the analysis in Section 8.3. For a rigid tube surrounded by an adiabatic wall and passing an incompressible fluid, both q and w again equal zero. Furthermore, because the fluid is incompressible and no heat exchange takes place, u_f equals u_i, and therefore Eq. (20.27) reduces to Bernoulli's equation for the flow of a nonviscous fluid through a tube. In a similar manner, Eq. (20.27) may be applied to any idealized engine or turbine, nozzle or diffuser. It is the general energy equation for isothermal flow processes.

20.6. Secondary Flow Processes

Energy is conceived to flow through an open system, whose steady state is time invariant, and thereby it becomes degraded in accordance with the second law of thermodynamics. Flow takes place in the direction of negative gradient in pressure, temperature, concentration, electrical potential, and so on. The fundamental phenomenological law for each of these primary flow processes is a direct proportion between a current density and a gradient. In the diagonal boxes of the chart in Fig. 20.7 are entered several of the primary processes, the name of the man who formulated the law, and the date of its publication.

Often a primary flow process is accompanied by secondary or cross-effects. These are entered in the off-diagonal boxes of the chart. Several of these secondary effects have many names, but we have selected those which we believe fit into a fairly consistent nomenclature. Under each is given the discoverer of the effect, if known, and the date of his discovery. Curiously, the oldest known of these secondary processes are filtration (which probably goes back to prehistoric times), and its inverse, osmosis. Thermo-osmosis was observed in gases by Reynolds[5] in 1879 and in liquids by Lippmann[6] in 1907.

We have retained the term thermoelectricity for the production of an electrical potential along a conductor which supports a temperature gradi-

---

[5] Reynolds, O., *Papers I*, p. 257 (The University Press, Cambridge, 1900).
[6] Lippmann, M. G., *Comptes Rendus*, **145**, 104 (1907).

Current Densities J_i	Gradients X_j			
	Temperature	Electrical potential	Fluid pressure	Particle concentration
Thermal	Thermal conduction (*Fourier, 1822*)	Electropyrosis (*Benedicks, 1918*)	Flow temperature (*Joule-Thomson, 1852*)	Diffusion temperature (*Dufour, 1873*)
Electrical	Thermo-electricity (*Thomson, 1856*)	Electrical conduction (*Ohm, 1826*)	Flow potential (*Quinke, 1859*)	Diffusion potential (*Dorn, 1878*)
Fluid	Thermo-osmosis (*Reynolds, 1879*) (*Lippmann, 1907*)	Electro-osmosis (*Reuss, 1808*)	Capillary flow (*Poiseuille, 1846*)	Osmosis (*Nollet, 1748*)
Particle	Thermodiffusion (*Soret, 1879–1880*)	Electrophoresis (*Reuss, 1808*)	Filtration	Diffusion (*Fick, 1855*)

Figure 20.7.   Primary (on diagonal) and secondary flow processes.

ent, in spite of a possible confusion with thermoelectric effects at junctions. The inverse of this effect, electropyrosis, has not been firmly established, although Benedicks[7] claimed to have detected it in 1918.

From Fig. 20.7 it is clear that each current density depends not only on the primary gradient but also on several secondary gradients. From experimental observations we find each term is directly proportional to the appropriate gradient, provided the system is not too far from equilibrium, and therefore the current density is assumed to be a linear function of all possible gradients. Thus

$$J_i = \Sigma_j L_{ij} X_j, \qquad (20.28)$$

in which J_i is the ith current density, X_j is the jth gradient, L_{ij} is the cross-coefficient for the ij term, and the summation extends over all j gradients. The term for which j equals i corresponds to a primary flow process; all others in Eq. (20.28) are terms for secondary effects. Of course, any of the coefficients L_{ij} may equal zero.

Equations like Eq. (20.28) have been called phenomenological relations or thermodynamic equations of motion. In them, the J_i's are said to be "fluxes," "flows," or "currents," and the X_j's are called "forces." In general there exists a wide choice of conjugate fluxes and forces which satisfy Eq.

[7] Benedicks, C., *Comptes Rendus*, **167**, 296 (1918); *Ann. Physik*, **55**, 1, 103 (1918).

(20.28) and are suitable for the analysis of a flow problem. Consequently, the J_i's and X_j's need not be the experimentally observed current densities and gradients. This freedom of choice is discussed rather fully by de Groot.

If a proper choice is made for the fluxes J_i and the forces X_j, the matrix of the cross-coefficients L_{ij} is symmetric; that is

$$L_{ij} = L_{ji}. \qquad (20.29)$$

This is a statement of Onsager's fundamental theorem in which Eqs. (20.29) are called reciprocal relations. By "proper choice" here we mean the fluxes and forces are chosen such that the sum of their products equals $T\theta_{irr}$:

$$T\theta_{irr} = \Sigma_i J_i X_i. \qquad (20.30)$$

For the sake of completeness we should add that if the system is in an applied magnetic held or has a uniform rotation, Eq. (20.29) must be modified to the form

$$L_{ij}(H, \omega) = L_{ji}(-H, -\omega). \qquad (20.31)$$

From a macroscopic point of view this theorem may be considered an extension to the second law of thermodynamics. On the other hand, Onsager showed that it stems directly from the principle of microscopic reversiblity in operation at the molecular level of the system. We shall not digress to give this statistical "proof" here, but shall accept the theorem much as we accept the second law of thermodynamics. An excellent discussion of this proof may be found in Denbigh's small monograph.

The easiest way to obtain relations for the fluxes and forces is to solve for $T\theta_{irr}$ and then to abstract therefrom equations for J_i and X_i. Thus from Eq. (20.21) we see that if J_t equals the thermal current density j_t, then

$$X_t = -T^{-1}\nabla T; \qquad (20.32)$$

and similarly from Eq. (20.26) if J_i equals the current density for the flow of the ith species j_i, then

$$X_i = T\nabla(\mu_i/-T). \qquad (20.33)$$

Applying the same method to electric currents we find that if J_e is the current density, then X_e is the negative gradient of electrical potential.

20.7. *Thermo-osmosis*

As a first application of Onsager's theorem we shall determine the equation for the coefficient of thermo-osmosis which applies to the unidirectional flow of a pure fluid through a membrane, as illustrated in Fig. 20.8. This treatment is modeled after that of Denbigh. We imagine the regions on either

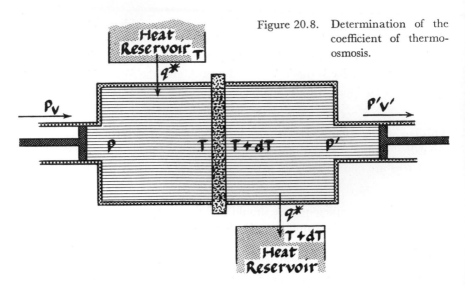

Figure 20.8. Determination of the coefficient of thermo-osmosis.

side of the membrane are maintained at temperatures T and $T + dT$ in the steady state. For this system we need only two equations like Eq. (20.28),

$$J_1 = L_{11}X_1 + L_{12}X_2 \qquad (20.34)$$

and

$$J_2 = L_{21}X_1 + L_{22}X_2. \qquad (20.35)$$

Here J_1 represents the flow of thermal energy resulting from both a gradient of chemical potential and a gradient of temperature, and J_2 represents the concomitant flow of fluid which equals zero for the steady-state condition. The forces X_1 and X_2 are

$$X_1 = -T^{-1}dT/dx \qquad (20.36)$$

and

$$X_2 = -Td(\mu/T)/dx, \qquad (20.37)$$

as determined from Eqs. (20.32) and (20.33).

We now eliminate X_1 and X_2 from Eq. (20.35) by means of Eqs. (20.36) and (20.37) and equate J_2 to zero. Thus we find

$$T^2 d(\mu/T)/dT = -(L_{21}/L_{22}), \qquad (20.38)$$

which may be a function of temperature. In order to interpret the ratio L_{21}/L_{22} consider an isothermal flow of fluid through the membrane. The temperatures on the two sides then are equal and X_1 vanishes; hence

$$L_{12}/L_{22} = (J_1/J_2)_{X_1=0}.$$

But by the reciprocal relation $L_{12} = L_{21}$, and therefore

$$L_{21}/L_{22} = (J_1/J_2)_{X_1=0}; \qquad (20.39)$$

that is, the ratio L_{21}/L_{22} equals the energy transported per mole of fluid through the membrane when there is no temperature gradient. We would expect this energy to consist of the specific internal energy u plus the P-V energy per mole of fluid. Actually, we find it is a little greater by an amount q^*, so

$$L_{21}/L_{22} = u + Pv + q^* = h + q^*. \qquad (20.40)$$

The additional term q^* is called the heat of transport, for it is characteristic of an irreversible flow of matter and equals zero under reversible flow conditions.

Consider an *isothermal* transfer of one mole of fluid from one side of the membrane to the other by a constant pressure head. Energy $h + q^*$ is lost from the high-pressure side by the flow process, and therefore to maintain constant pressure and temperature on that side work w and heat q per mole are supplied quasistatically from work and heat reservoirs. The algebraic sum of these energies $-(h + q^*) + w + q$ must equal $-u$, the change in internal energy on the high-pressure side. Since w equals Pv it follows that q^* equals q. In other words, q^* equals the heat absorbed on the high-pressure side of the membrane per mole of fluid transported through it. This excess energy is delivered to the low-pressure side.

From the general equation for an infinitesimal increase in internal energy of an open system,

$$dU = TdS - PdV + \Sigma_i \mu_i dn_i,$$

which applies to any thermophysical process, reversible or not, we see that

$$U = TS - PV + \Sigma_i \mu_i n_i, \qquad (20.41)$$

where

$$SdT - VdP + \Sigma_i n_i d\mu_i = 0. \qquad (20.42)$$

For one mole of a single species of matter (the pure fluid) Eqs. (20.41) and (20.42) reduce to the forms

$$u + Pv = Ts + \mu = h$$

and

$$vdP/dT = s + d\mu/dT.$$

These may be combined by eliminating s between them:

$$vTdP/dT = h - \mu + Td\mu/dT$$
$$= h + T^2 d(\mu/T)/dT. \qquad (20.43)$$

Finally, from Eqs. (20.38) and (20.40) we see that the right side of this equation equals $-q^*$; hence

$$dP/dT = -q^*/vT. \qquad (20.44)$$

This is the relation for the coefficient of thermo-osmosis. It was first derived by Eastman[8] through pseudo-thermodynamic reasoning and later by Meixner[9] from the Onsager theory. It is the equation which applies to the fountain effect in helium II.

20.8. Thermo-electricity

Consider next a heat conductor connected between two thermal reservoirs, as in Fig. 20.5. Let us imagine a steady state exists in which heat flows through the conductor at a constant rate and there is developed between its ends an emf. Here Eqs. (20.34) and (20.35) apply, where J_1 and X_1 have the same meaning as before, but now J_2 is the electrical current density and X_2 is the negative of the potential gradient:

$$J_1 = -L_{11}T^{-1}dT/dx - L_{12}dE/dx \qquad (20.45)$$

and

$$J_2 = -L_{21}T^{-1}dT/dx - L_{22}dE/dx. \qquad (20.46)$$

For the steady state J_2 equals zero, and therefore

$$TdE/dT = -(L_{21}/L_{22}). \qquad (20.47)$$

Under isothermal conditions we note that L_{12}/L_{22} equals $(J_1/J_2)_{X_1=0}$, and when the reciprocal relation $L_{12} = L_{21}$ is introduced we get

$$L_{21}/L_{22} = (J_1/J_2)_{X_1=0}. \qquad (20.48)$$

Thus L_{21}/L_{22} is the energy per unit charge transferred through the conductor when there is no temperature gradient.

Ordinarily, under isothermal conditions we would expect a unit charge to dissipate E units of energy such that J_1 would equal $-J_2E$; but for a steady state the unit charge takes on additional energy φ^*, so J_1 actually equals $(-E + \varphi^*)J_2$. Consequently, we find from Eqs. (20.47) and (20.48)

$$TdE/dT = E - \varphi^*. \qquad (20.49)$$

The energy φ^* per unit charge, the Thomson emf, is found to be directly proportional to the difference in temperature between the two ends of the conductor; thus

$$\varphi^* = \sigma\Delta T, \qquad (20.50)$$

in which the proportionality constant σ is the coefficient of thermo-electricity, commonly known as the Thomson coefficient.[10] A relation for σ may be obtained by differentiating both Eqs. (20.49) and (20.50):

[8] Eastman, E. D., *Jour. Am. Chem. Soc.*, **48**, 1482 (1926).
[9] Meixner, J., *Ann. d. Physik*, **39**, 333 (1941).
[10] Thomson, W., *Phil. Mag.*, **11**, 379 (1856); *Trans. Roy. Soc. Edin.*, **21**, 153 (1887).

$$\sigma = d\varphi^*/dT = -Td^2E/dT^2. \tag{20.51}$$

Experimental values of σ equal a few microvolts per degree, as suggested by the data in Table 20.1. Ordinarily it is difficult to measure φ^*, and thereby σ, directly. Instead a known temperature gradient is set up along the wire,

TABLE 20.1.   *Values of σ in Microvolts per Degree for a Few Metals.*

Metal	0°C	20°C	100°C
Cu	1.6	1.6	2.0
Fe	7.2	—	16.4
Pt	12.3	12.3	13.1

and then a measured current is passed either up or down the gradient. The difference between the rates of dissipation of electrical energy and of conduction of heat, both of which can be measured, equals the rate of transfer of Thomson heat, namely $\sigma J_2 \Delta T$. Since J_2 and ΔT are known, a value for σ may be computed.

20.9. The Thermocouple

The thermocouple consists of two dissimilar metallic or semiconducting wires connected at their ends to form a closed loop, as illustrated in Fig. 2.7. When the two junctions are held at different temperatures five thermal and electrical phenomena exist in the system simultaneously. The primary Seebeck effect was discovered in 1821, within a year of Ampere's work and several years before Ohm's law was established. Seebeck[11] found that there is developed in the thermocouple an emf whose value depends on the wire materials and on the temperature difference of the junctions. By 1834 Peltier[12] had found the reciprocal effect. When a current is passed through a thermojunction by applying an external emf its temperature is changed to differ more or less from that due to Joule heating. This effect occurs even for a current generated by the thermocouple itself. The rate at which Peltier heat is transferred is proportional to the current through the junction. The proportionality constant, called the Peltier coefficient, depends only on the materials and the temperature of the junction.

In addition to the foregoing strictly junction effects, Joule heating occurs if the Seebeck thermal emf produces a current in the thermocouple circuit,

[11] Seebeck, T. J., *Pogg. Ann.*, **6**, 133, 263 (1826).
[12] Peltier, A., *Ann. Chim. et Physique*, 2nd ser., **56** (1834); *Comptes Rendus*, **1**, 360 (1835).

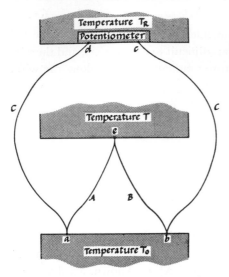

Figure 20.9. A thermocouple circuit.

Fourier heat conduction takes place between the hot and cold junctions along the two wires, and a Thomson heat exchange necessarily exists. Both the Joule and Thomson heat effects occur transversely to the wires, whereas heat conduction takes place along them. On the other hand, the Thomson effect is reversible, whereas the other two are not.

Figure 20.9 is a schematic diagram of the thermocouple circuit of Fig. 2.8. The probe junction e is at temperature T which is to be measured against the reference junctions a, b at temperature T_0 (often in an ice-point cell). Copper wires C, C connect junctions a, b with the potentiometer terminals c, d at room temperature T_R. When the potentiometer is balanced there is no flow of electrical current in the circuit, and therefore Eq. (20.49) can be applied to each of the wires A, B, C, C. We shall introduce the definition

$$\pi = E - \varphi^* \qquad (20.52)$$

and then apply the equation to each wire by integrating from one end of it to the other; thus

$$E_a - E_d = -\int_{T_0}^{T_R} (\pi_C/T)dT,$$

$$E_e - E_a = \int_{T_0}^{T} (\pi_A/T)dT,$$

$$E_b - E_e = -\int_{T_0}^{T} (\pi_B/T)dT,$$

$$E_c - E_b = \int_{T_0}^{T_R} (\pi_C/T)dT. \qquad (20.53)$$

When these equations are added together the left side reduces to $E_c - E_d$, the Seebeck difference in potential developed in the thermocouple, which we shall represent by E_t. We get

$$E_t = \int_{T_0}^{T} (\pi_A - \pi_B)dT/T, \qquad (20.54)$$

which may be differentiated holding T_0 constant in order to solve for $\pi_t = \pi_A - \pi_B$:

$$\pi_t = TdE_t/dT. \qquad (20.55)$$

To show that π_t in Eq. (20.55) is the
Peltier coefficient as defined earlier,
consider in detail the several currents
at junction e of Fig. 20.9 as depicted
in Fig. 20.10. An electrical current of
density J_2 passes through the junction
and thermal current density J_q leaves
it while Thomson thermal current
densities J_{1A} and J_{1B} are generated in
wires A and B. From Eqs. (20.47),
(20.48), (20.49), and (20.52) we observe that the heat current density in a

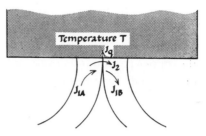

Figure 20.10.   Electrical and thermal
currents at the test
junction of the ther-
mocouple.

wire under steady-state conditions is given by the equation

$$J_1 = -(E - \varphi^*)J_2 = -\pi J_2. \qquad (20.56)$$

Hence J_{1A} equals $-\pi_A J_2$, and J_{1B} equals $-\pi_B J_2$. The rate with which heat
leaves the junction therefore is given by the conservation equation

$$\begin{aligned}
J_q &= J_2^2 R_j - J_{1A} + J_{1B} \\
&= J_2^2 R_j + (\pi_A - \pi_B)J_2 \\
&= J_2^2 R_j + \pi_t J_2, \qquad (20.57)
\end{aligned}$$

in which R_j is the resistance of the junction and $J_2^2 R_j$ equals the rate of heat
loss per unit area due to the Joule effect. By definition, the rate of heat loss
over and above Joule heating equals the Peltier heat, and this is proportional
to the current through the junction; hence from Eq. (20.57) we see that π_t
is the coefficient of the Peltier heat term.

Equation (20.55) is the first of two well-known thermocouple equations
derived by Thomson[10] in 1856 by pseudo-thermodynamic reasoning, that is,
by neglecting all irreversible processes in the argument. The other may be
obtained from Eq. (20.51):

$$\sigma_A - \sigma_B = -Td^2(E_A - E_B)/dT^2 = -Td^2E_t/dT^2. \qquad (20.58)$$

From these equations the Peltier coefficient of a junction and the difference
of the Thomson coefficients of the two wires at any temperature may be
computed once the temperature dependence of the thermal emf is known.

From some data published by Zemansky[13] the measured value of π_t/T for
a copper-nickel thermocouple at 100°C equals 24.4 μvolt/deg, whereas the
measured value of dE_t/dT equals 24.9 μvolt/deg. Similarly, for an iron-mercury
thermocouple at 100°C these values are 13.9 and 13.74 μvolt/deg, respectively. From the data in Table 20.1 we find that $(\sigma_{Cu} - \sigma_{Fe})/373°$ equals

---

[13] Zemansky, M., *Heat and Thermodynamics*, p. 309 (McGraw-Hill, New York, 1957).

-0.039 μvolt/deg^2 and $(\sigma_{Cu} - \sigma_{Pt})/373°$ equals -0.030 μvolt/deg^2. The corresponding values of $-d^2E_t/dT^2$, as given by Zemansky, are -0.033 μvolt/deg^2 for the copper-iron thermocouple and -0.036 μvolt/deg^2 for the copper-platinum thermocouple. We conclude that the equations we have derived give a satisfactory description of the phenomena in a thermocouple.

Bibliography

Bosworth, R. C. L., *Heat Transfer Phenomena* (Wiley, New York, 1952).

Davies, R. O., "The Macroscopic Theory of Irreversibility," *Reports on Progress in Physics*, vol. XIX (The Physical Society, London, 1956), pp. 326–367.

de Groot, S. R., *Thermodynamics of Irreversible Processes* (Interscience, New York, 1951).

Denbigh, K. G., *The Thermodynamics of the Steady State* (Wiley, New York, 1951).

Engineering Research Institute, *Heat Transfer, a Symposium* (University of Michigan Press, Ann Arbor, 1953).

Grew, K. E., and T. L. Ibbs, *Thermal Diffusion in Gases* (The University Press, Cambridge, 1952).

Ingersoll, L. R., O. J. Zobel, and A. C. Ingersoll, *Heat Conduction with Engineering, Geological and Other Applications* (University of Wisconsin Press, Madison, 1954).

Jakob, M., *Heat Transfer*, vol. I (Wiley, New York, 1949).

Langhaar, H. L., *Dimensional Analysis and Theory of Models* (Wiley, New York, 1951).

Prigogine, I., *Introduction to Thermodynamics of Irreversible Processes* (Blackwell, Oxford, 1955).

Problems

1. (a) A thin-walled steam pipe of radius r is sheathed with insulation. How thick should this insulation be in order to reduce the loss of heat by thermal conduction from length b of the pipe to K? Let the thermal conductivity of the insulating material be σ_i and suppose the temperature of the inside and outside surfaces are t_1 and t_2.

   (b) If the steam pipe is 5 cm in diameter and is covered with asbestos for which the thermal conductivity equals 0.085 watt/m-deg Celsius, how thick should the insulation be to have a rate of loss not exceeding 40 watt/m length of pipe, where the temperature on the inside and outside surfaces of the insulation are 100°C and 20°C?

2. Heat flows along a cylindrical rod of uniform cross-section A, density ρ, and specific heat capacity c_p, as illustrated in Fig. 20.11. Show that the net amount of heat leaving an element of volume $A dx$ per unit time equals $A(\partial j_x/\partial x) dx$, where j_x is the thermal current density. Then apply the definition of heat capacity at constant pressure to obtain

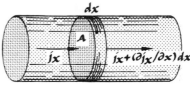

$$\partial j_x/\partial x = -\rho c_p(\partial t/\partial \tau),$$

in which $\partial t/\partial \tau$ is the time rate of change of temperature for the element of volume. (This is the one-dimensional form of the equation of continuity.) Finally, develop the equation for three dimensions.

Figure 20.11.   Deriving the equation of continuity.

3. Show how to obtain Eq. (20.7) from Eq. (20.9).

4. Solve the one-dimensional form of Eq. (20.3) by separation of variables to obtain the result in Eq. (20.9). To do this let $t = TX$, in which T is a function of time only and X is a function of x only.

5. A slab with parallel surfaces initially is at temperature t_i. If one surface is suddenly brought in contact with a thermal reservoir at temperature $0°$ while the other is maintained at t_i, find an expression for the temperature at any point within the slab at subsequent times.

6. From a number of temperature readings in sandy loam at New Haven, Connecticut, the mean daily temperature range was found to be 7.5 times greater at a depth of 7.5 cm than at 30.5 cm. From these data show that the thermal diffusivity of sandy loam equals 0.0047 cm² sec⁻¹.

7. (a) Show that the thickness x of the ice on a pond is related to the time of freezing τ by the equation

$$x^2 = 2\sigma_t t\tau/\rho l,$$

where the thermal conductivity, density, and latent heat of fusion for ice are σ_t, ρ, and l, and the upper surface of the ice is at $-t$ degrees.

(b) Convection actually takes place, so if the air were at t degrees, then x is given by the relation

$$x/h + x^2/2\sigma_t = -t\tau/\rho l,$$

where h is the convection coefficient for air over a flat horizontal surface. Derive this equation.

8. Often in practice a wall at a constant temperature t_w is covered with insulation of thickness x and of thermal conductivity σ_t. The outer surface of the insulation is in contact with air at atmospheric pressure and temperature t_a. If conduction takes place through the insulation and convection at the outside surface, show that the effective or overall coefficient of heat transfer h' is given by the relation

$$1/h' = x/\sigma_t + 1/h,$$

where h is the convective coefficient at the outside surface.

9. By dimensional analysis show that

$$hD/\sigma_t = C(\rho D \mathcal{V}/\eta)^m (\eta c_p/\sigma_t)^n$$

for forced convection through circular pipes of diameter D, where $\mathcal{V}$ is the mean velocity of the fluid and the other symbols have the same meaning as in Eq. (20.14). From experiments on turbulent flow of fluids through pipes, m and n are found to have the values 0.8 and 0.4 and the dimensionless coefficient C has the value 0.023.

10. Derive Eq. (20.14) by dimensional analysis. Here it is convenient to consider heat Q, time T, length L, mass M, and temperature Θ as independent dimensions. Note that in natural or free convection buoyancy is an important factor. If a unit volume of fluid with a density ρ_1 at temperature t_1 is heated to temperature t_2, its density decreases to a new value ρ_2, and therefore it is lifted by a buoyant force of value $(\rho_1 - \rho_2)g$. But since $\rho_1 - \rho_2$ equals $\rho_2\beta(t_2 - t_1)$, from thermal expansion we see that β and g would enter into the equations for natural convection as the product βg.

11. Show that the rate of production of entropy per unit volume in a linear electrical conductor under steady-state conditions is

$$dS/Vd\tau = -j_e\Delta E/Tl,$$

where j_e is the current density, l is the length of the conductor, T is its temperature, and ΔE is the applied emf. Generalize this result to three-dimensional flow.

CHAPTER 21

Very High Temperatures

As a pure substance is heated it undergoes a series of phase transformations. Consider a spicule of ice in a chamber with walls of carbon. When the chamber is heated its temperature rises, the ice first melts and then vaporizes, and finally the molecules of water dissociate. Meanwhile some of the molecules and atoms become ionized, thermionic emission occurs, chemical reactions with the walls take place, and near 4000°K the remaining carbon sublimates. This sequence of events takes us from low temperatures within a few hundred degrees of 0°K into the high-temperature region beyond 3000°K. During the process new thermophysical phenomena appear and matter becomes difficult to confine. In this chapter we shall investigate the behavior of matter and its interaction with radiation at very high temperatures.

21.1. Thermodynamic and Kinetic Temperatures

The enormous range of temperatures from 1°K to 10^9 degrees Kelvin may be displayed advantageously on a logarithmic scale, as in Fig. 21.1. For comparison we have entered natural phenomena associated with several of these temperatures. Thus the upper end of the scale extends from low temperatures at the surfaces of cool type-M stars to ultrahigh temperatures at the center of hot type-O stars. Virtually all atoms are ionized beyond 20,000°K and their nuclei are disintegrated above 2×10^{10}°K. At these ele-

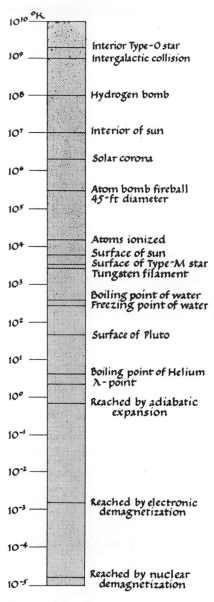

Figure 21.1.   Temperature chart.

vated temperatures only gravitational and magnetic fields have been found suitable for confining matter.

Although the *word* "temperature" has been introduced in the foregoing paragraphs, we should pause to ask if it really has an operationally meaningful definition in extremely hot systems. We recall that "temperature" is defined for systems which are in thermodynamic equilibrium. Consider a closed gaseous system in a state of equilibrium at 1000°K. The molecules in it maintain their normal statistical distributions of translational, rotational, and vibrational energies through random intermolecular and wall collisions. In addition, the system contains blackbody radiation arising from these collisions and satisfying the Planck distribution law. Since the system is in thermodynamic equilibrium, the parameter T in the several distribution laws is assumed to have a common numerical value. This T then is said to be the thermodynamic temperature of the system.

As the gas system is heated the mean energy per molecule and the radiation density increase such that T must have higher values. At sufficiently high temperatures some of the thermal energy enters the excitation and ionization processes. If thermodynamic equilibrium still prevails, however, the number of excited atoms and the number of ionized atoms at any instant each satisfy a Boltzmann form of distribution law with the same parameter T in it. Throughout the system the rate of production of excited atoms by impact equals the number of collisions of the second kind per unit time, and, similarly, the rate of ionization by molecular interaction equals the rate of recombination through three-body collisions. Furthermore, absorption and emission of radiation occur at equal rates in all parts of the electromagnetic spectrum. Here temperature appears to have a perfectly good physical meaning.

The actual situation in real hot-gas systems usually is not one of thermodynamic equilibrium. Thus we may have a system in a steady-state where as much energy enters it from thermal reservoirs as leaves it by the several thermal processes. But if this exchange is very slow, as in the Sun, the system may be treated as though each small part of it were in quasistatic equilibrium with a characteristic temperature. At very low pressures—less than a few millimeters of mercury—molecular collisions in a hot gas may be so infrequent that a Boltzmann distribution cannot be established quickly enough to allow the application of thermodynamic methods. On the other hand, at pressures of an atmosphere or more, where radiation losses are low, as in flames outside the reacting zone and in plasmas of electrical arcs, each small region of the system may be considered in quasistatic equilibrium at a characteristic temperature.

Sometimes the molecular energies in a system may satisfy the Boltzmann distribution, even though the radiant energy in it does not satisfy the Planck distribution. The system is said to be "optically thin." It has a kinetic temperature but not a thermodynamic one. Although a system possesses a very high kinetic temperature it may radiate far less thermal energy than a similar system at a much lower thermodynamic temperature. Thus the Sun's corona, at a kinetic temperature of approximately two million degrees Kelvin, emits radiation of much less intensity than does its photosphere, which is at a thermodynamic temperature of only 6000°K. Although the particles in the corona move at much higher speeds than those in the photosphere, they suffer far fewer radiative collisions per unit time because their number per unit volume is so low.

21.2. Law of Mass Action

At very high temperatures a system contains not only molecules but atoms, ions, electrons, and electromagnetic radiation. Physical and chemical reactions are conceived to occur continually at rates which depend on the temperature of the system and on the physical characteristics of the reacting components. Even so, under equilibrium conditions the molar concentration of each kind of material particle remains constant. This situation implies that there exists a dynamic balance in which the rate of formation of a single component equals the rate of its dissociation. By applying this principle to chemical reactions at low temperatures Guldberg and Waage of Norway discovered the law of mass action in 1867. This law applies at high temperatures as well, and even to the ionization process, as was demonstrated by Saha in 1920.

For simplicity consider the formation and dissociation of a substance AB in the reversible reaction

$$AB \rightleftharpoons A + B, \qquad (21.1)$$

as illustrated by the decomposition and reformation of ammonium chloride,

$$NH_4Cl \rightleftharpoons NH_3 + HCl,$$

or the ionization of calcium and the reverse process,

$$Ca \rightleftharpoons Ca^+ + e.$$

If the system is in dynamic equilibrium, the rate of dissociation equals the rate of recombination. But the rate of dissociation must be proportional to the molecular concentration of AB, thus,

$$\Re_1 = K_1 n_{AB}; \qquad (21.2)$$

and the rate of recombination must be proportional to the molecular concentrations of both A and B, thus

$$\Re_2 = K_2 n_A n_B, \qquad (21.3)$$

where the proportionality constants K_1 and K_2 depend on the reacting substances and on the temperature of the system. These relations arise because the number of interactions per unit time must depend upon the rate of collision events, and these in turn are directly proportional to the molecular concentrations. Under equilibrium conditions $\Re_1$ equals $\Re_2$, and therefore

$$n_A n_B / n_{AB} = K_1/K_2 = f(T), \qquad (21.4)$$

which is constant under conditions of thermal equilibrium. This is one form of the law of mass action.

Because molecular concentrations are directly proportional to partial pressures, Eq. (21.4) may be written in terms of partial pressures. On the other hand, if n represents the total number of particles of all reacting substances in a unit volume, then

$$x_A x_B / x_{AB} = f(T)/n, \qquad (21.5)$$

in which x_A, x_B, and x_{AB} are the relative molecular concentrations. This equation tells us that if a gaseous system were allowed to expand isothermally and thus reduce n, the ratio $x_A x_B / x_{AB}$ would increase. This can happen only by the reaction in Eq. (21.1) going from left to right to increase the concentrations of A and B and decrease the concentration of AB. The energy for dissociation comes from the heat supplied to maintain a constant temperature in the expanding gas. We know that dissociation also occurs when the temperature of the system is raised. Consequently, we would expect to find almost complete decomposition and eventually ionization of a gas at high temperatures and low densities.

21.3. The Equilibrium Constant

The equilibrium constant in Eq. (21.4) may be evaluated explicitly in terms of temperature T by applying the condition that the total Gibbs function has a minimum value for a system in isothermal and isobaric equilibrium. For a virtual displacement of the reaction in Eq. (21.1) from left to right, in which one molecule of AB disappears when two new molecules A and B are formed, it follows that

$$\Delta G_A + \Delta G_B - \Delta G_{AB} = 0. \qquad (21.6)$$

But from the definition of the Gibbs function we find

$$\Delta G = \Delta U + \Delta(PV) - \Delta(TS). \qquad (21.7)$$

The terms in this equation are now evaluated for each of the reactants by introducing the state and other thermophysical equations for U, V, and S. This computation is especially simple if the constituents of the system are assumed to approximate ideal gases.

For an ideal monatomic gas of N molecules the state equation is $PV = NkT$, and its internal energy equals $U_0 + \frac{3}{2}NkT$, in which U_0 represents the value of U at 0°K. For the virtual reaction therefore,

$$\Delta(PV) = kT, \qquad (21.8)$$

and

$$\Delta U = \Delta U_0 + \tfrac{3}{2}kT. \qquad (21.9)$$

A value of S is obtained by means of statistical thermodynamics as discussed in Section 13.3. From Eq. (13.32) we see that

$$\Delta(TS) = kT(\tfrac{5}{2} + \tfrac{3}{2}\ln kT - \ln n + \ln b), \qquad (21.10)$$

in which b equals $c(2\pi m)^{3/2}$ and n represents the number of molecules per unit volume. Eq. (21.7) now is written in the form

$$\Delta G = \Delta U_0 - kT(\ln b + \tfrac{3}{2}\ln kT - \ln n), \qquad (21.11)$$

and then values of ΔG_A, ΔG_B, and ΔG_{AB} are inserted into Eq. (21.6).

We represent the zero-point heat of reaction by Q_0, where

$$Q_0 = \Delta U_{0A} + \Delta U_{0B} - \Delta U_{0AB}, \qquad (21.12)$$

and we replace the quantity $b_A b_B / b_{AB}$ by a single symbol K. Thus we find

$$\ln \left(n_A n_B / n_{AB} \right) = \ln K + \tfrac{3}{2} \ln kT - Q_0 / kT, \qquad (21.13)$$

from which

$$f(T) = K(kT)^{3/2} \exp \left(-Q_0 / kT \right). \qquad (21.14)$$

Here we see that $f(T)$ increases with temperature and that it reduces to a three-halves power function at very high temperatures.

Equilibrium constants for more complex reactions may be evaluated in the same way. Furthermore, if the gases are not ideal, then the appropriate state functions and equations for entropy and internal energy should be applied.

21.4. Determination of High Gas Temperatures

The temperature of a hot gaseous system ordinarily is determined from measurements on its emission or absorption spectrum of electromagnetic radiation. If the system is in thermodynamic equilibrium, its temperature T_g may be found by measuring the absolute intensities of the spectral lines (provided they are not self-reversed) or the spectral energy distribution of the continuous radiation and then by applying the Planck law to these data. The parameter T in this law and the gas temperature T_g are assumed to have the same value. This method is limited, however, to gases with optically thick layers; that is, with layers in which the radiation and material particles are in thermal equilibrium. At very high temperatures this condition is not likely to occur, as we have already pointed out in Section 21.1, and therefore we must apply more elaborate and often less direct procedures.

If a hot gas contains undissociated molecules, its temperature may be evaluated from intensity measurements on its molecular band structure, for the intensity distribution over the rotational structure of a single band from thermally excited molecules corresponds to the Boltzmann law. This method requires a spectrograph of high resolving power and large dispersion, and it is limited to gas temperatures of only a few thousand degrees at which large numbers of molecules can exist in an undissociated state.

High temperatures may be determined by measurements of Doppler broadening in spectral lines. Atoms in a hot radiating gas are in rapid thermal motion with speeds distributed according to the Maxwell-Boltzmann law. As an atom approaches or recedes along the line of sight its emitted radiation experiences a Doppler shift in frequency; the cumulative effect from all the atoms produces broadening of the spectral lines. The width of a line due to this effect depends on the gas temperature; thus

$$\Delta\lambda = (8 \ln 2)^{1/2}(\lambda_0/c)(RT_g/M)^{1/2}, \qquad (21.15)$$

where c is the speed of light, R is the universal gas constant, M is the molecular weight of the gas, and λ_0 is the wavelength of the line (see Problem 21.5). In this way, Burhorn[1] demonstrated that the gas temperature T_g in a free-burning iron arc equals the electron temperature T_e as determined by an independent method and thereby proved that the electrons and atoms within the arc were in thermal equilibrium. This method of measuring T_g is useful only if the lines are sharp and if pressure and other line-broadening effects are negligible or can be accounted for.

A hot gas at temperature T_g absorbs energy from transmitted continuous radiation of temperature $T > T_g$ at those frequencies where it normally emits. Consequently, many equations for absorption spectra are similar to those for emission spectra. Thus temperature measurements have been made by means of x-ray and microwave absorption experiments. Similarly, temperatures of hot gases have been measured successfully from observations on the scattering of alpha particles. Absorption and scattering processes are useful only if the source and detector of the radiation can be located on either side of the system.

Since the temperature of a gas is related to pressure and density through a state equation, measurement of gas densities at known pressures constitutes still another method for determining gas temperatures. At very high temperatures, however, the gas contains large numbers of electrons and ions for which the state equation is complex and often unknown.

21.5. Plasma Temperatures

A plasma is a highly ionized gas consisting of electrons, ions, and only a few neutral atoms. A gas becomes a plasma not only at very high temperatures but also at very low densities, as described in Section 21.2, so a plasma really may have almost any temperature. If it is in thermal equilibrium, the law of mass action applies:

$$n_+ n_e/n_o = f(T_p). \qquad (21.16)$$

The number densities n_A, n_B and n_{AB} in Eq. (21.4) have been replaced by n_+, n_e and n_o for the ions, electrons, and neutral atoms, respectively, and T_p is the desired plasma temperature. Since Eq. (21.16) contains four unknown quantities, we need three additional relations between them if we wish to determine their values. Two can be set down immediately, provided the

---

[1] Burhorn, F., *Zeits. Physik*, **140**, 440 (1955).

plasma is electrically neutral and the pressure in the plasma, or, what amounts to the same thing, the total number of material particles per unit volume n, is known. They are

$$n_+ = n_e \qquad (21.17)$$

and

$$n = n_+ + n_e + n_o. \qquad (21.18)$$

The fourth equation ordinarily comes from measurements on a specific property of the gas; for example, its temperature from the intensities of lines of known transition probabilities or its electron and ion densities from line widths and profiles.

For a plasma in thermal equilibrium the number of atoms per unit volume in an excited state s is given by the Boltzmann distribution Eq. (13.16) in the form

$$n_s = n_o g_s Z^{-1} \exp\left(-E_s/kT\right), \qquad (21.19)$$

where n_o is the number density of neutral atoms in the system, g_s is the statistical weight of state s, E_s ($= h\nu$) is the energy of transition between the s and ground state, and Z is the partition sum of the system. The intensity of the emitted radiation resulting from the transition is $A_{s,o} n_s h\nu$, in which $A_{s,o}$ is the transition probability, and therefore we find

$$I_{s,o} = A_{s,o} g_s n_o h\nu Z^{-1} \exp\left(-h\nu/kT\right). \qquad (21.20)$$

Temperature T in this equation not only is the electron temperature T_e but also, because thermal equilibrium exists, the plasma temperature T_p.

Temperatures T_e and T_p may be obtained from other kinds of measurements. Instead of determining the absolute intensity of a spectral line, the intensity ratio of two lines of known transition probabilities may be measured. Likewise, the absolute intensity of the continuous radiation or the intensity ratio of the continuous radiation at two different wavelengths produces satisfactory results. Once T_p has been measured, values of n_o, n_e, and n_+ may be computed by means of the foregoing equations.

The other rather general procedure for evaluating n_e, n_+, n_o, and T_p is to determine the concentration of electrons n_e or ions n_+ from measurements on the width, profile, or shift of a spectral line in radiation from the hot gas and then to compute the other unknown quantities by means of Eqs. (21.16), (21.17), and (21.18).

We know from quantum mechanical studies that an energy level in an atom is not infinitesimally narrow but actually is a band of energies. Consequently, a spectral line has a natural breadth determined by the widths of the energy levels between which transitions occur. Superposed on this is a Doppler broadening, as described in the preceding section. These effects are independent of interactions between particles. On the other hand, the radiating atoms may be so perturbed by collisions and by the electrical fields of neighboring ions and electrons that they give rise to additional line broadening and a red shift. These effects are simply related to the concentrations of the perturbing particles.

When a radiating atom suffers a collision its emitted frequency is altered by an amount $\Delta\nu$ which depends on the nature of the collision. A study of all physically possible situations shows that $\Delta\nu$ is an inverse function of the radial distance r between the radiating atom and perturbing particle; namely

$$\Delta\nu = C/r^\epsilon, \qquad (21.21)$$

where ϵ is a small integer and C is a constant for each type of collision and transition. The minimum value of r is the collision parameter for the two particles. The integrated effect over all possible collision parameters of interacting particles indicates not only a line broadening of half-width δ but also a line displacement D toward lower frequencies for the principal collision processes in plasmas at high temperatures.

Perhaps the most common collision process in plasmas at elevated temperatures is that between a radiating atom and a charged particle. For this process $\epsilon = 4$,

$$\delta = 38.8(C^2\bar{v})^{1/3}n_e, \qquad (21.22)$$

and

$$D = 33.4(C^2\bar{v})^{1/3}n_e. \qquad (21.23)$$

In these equations $\bar{v}$ represents the mean value of the relative velocity of the perturbed and perturbing particles and n_e is the number of electrons (or ions) in a unit volume.

A radiating atom also is perturbed by an electrical field; the resulting splitting of spectral lines is called the Stark effect. If the splitting is proportional to the first power of the field intensity, as in an external applied field, the effect is said to be linear; if the splitting is proportional to the square of the field intensity, as between interacting atoms and ions, the effect is said to be quadratic. The ions and electrons around a radiating atom produce a randomly variable electrostatic field whose net effect is to cause a quadratic Stark shift in frequency. If this effect is averaged over all radiating atoms in a plasma, it is found that here too Eq. (21.22) applies. This statistical broadening adds to the foregoing collision broadening to produce the overall line profile and to cause the red shift.

The constant C can be determined from quantum mechanical calculations or from laboratory measurements. For the quadratic Stark effect

$$|\Delta\nu| = c\Delta\lambda/\lambda^2 = C/r^4 = CE^2/e^2, \qquad (21.24)$$

in which e/r^2 has been replaced by field intensity E. Thus by measuring splitting $\Delta\lambda$ and the corresponding applied electrical field E a value for C may be determined experimentally.

From a careful analysis of the width and shift of spectral lines values of δ and D may be found, and from them values for n_+ and n_e can be computed by means of Eqs. (21.22) and (21.23). Finally, n_0 and T_p are evaluated by means of Eqs. (21.16) and (21.18).

Other types of collisions which produce line broadening involve mutually interacting neutral atoms of the same kind ($\epsilon = 3$) and the interaction of neutral atoms through van der Waals forces ($\epsilon = 6$). At very high temperatures, however, these effects are negligible.

Values of n_e and n_+ also may be estimated from the apparent limit of the Balmer series in hydrogen-like spectra or from the distribution of intensities in the continuous radiation beyond the series limit. The shift of the series limit towards longer wavelengths suggests that the ionization potential within the plasma is lowered. This diminution of the ionization potential was shown by Unsöld to be proportional to the cube root of the electron concentration, and therefore it too is suitable for evaluating n_e. On the other hand, it represents an important correction for the ionization potential in the Saha equation and in equations for line intensities.

21.6. Ionic Composition of Plasmas

The electrostatic forces between charged particles in a plasma are much larger than van der Waals or gravitational forces, and therefore they should exert a measurable influence on the thermophysical properties of the plasma. If the pressure is low enough and the temperature is high enough that the thermal energy per particle is far greater than the average electrical potential energy of two adjacent charged particles, then insofar as the composition of the plasma is concerned the effect of the electrostatic forces may be disregarded, and the plasma may be treated as an ideal hot gas. For this computation we assume the mean distance between adjacent charged particles is $n^{-1/3}$, and therefore the corresponding electrostatic potential energy equals $e^2 n^{1/3}/4\pi\epsilon_0$, where e is the elementary charge, 1.60×10^{-19} coulomb, and ϵ_0 is the permittivity of free space, 8.854×10^{-12} farads/m. If we suppose the thermal energy per particle equals nearly $\frac{3}{2}kT$ and n is approximately P/kT, where P is the pressure in the gas, then the ratio of these energies is

$$\text{Ratio} = 6\pi\epsilon_0(kT)^{4/3}/e^2 P^{1/3}. \qquad (21.25)$$

At a pressure of one atmosphere
and a temperature of 20,000°K
this ratio comes out to be 25.
Even at 5000°K it equals 4. We
conclude therefore that the equations for an ideal gas may be
applied to a plasma at low pres-

Figure 21.2.   Particle concentrations
in nitrogen at high
temperatures and at
one atmosphere of pres-
sure. [Adapted from
W. Lochte-Holtgreven,
"Production and Meas-
urement of High Tem-
peratures," *Reports on
Progress in Physics*, vol.
XXI, p. 312, 1958.]

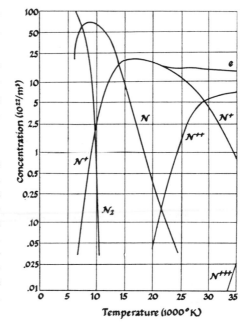

sures and at temperatures greater than about 5000°K.

The ionic composition of a plasma at temperatures greater than 6000°K
may now be computed by means of the Saha equilibrium equation, Eq.
(21.16), in which $f(T_p)$ is expressed explicitly in terms of ionization potential,
temperature, and partition function as in Eq. (21.14). These computations
have been carried out for nitrogen
at a pressure of one atmosphere,
and from them the mass density of
the plasma has been determined.
The curves in Figs. 21.2 and 21.3,
which show the results, are repro-

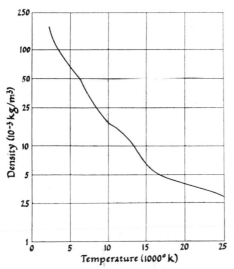

Figure 21.3.   Effect of temperature on
the mass density of a
nitrogen plasma at a
pressure of one atmos-
phere. [Adapted from
W. Lochte-Holtgreven,
"Production and Meas-
urement of High Tem-
peratures," *Reports on
Progress in Physics*, vol.
XXI, p. 312, 1958.]

duced from the summary article by Lochte-Holtgreven. The irregularities in the density curve arise from ionization effects. Note that the number concentrations of electrons and singly ionized nitrogen atoms are identical until doubly ionized and later triply ionized nitrogen atoms appear in the plasma.

21.7. Transport Phenomena in Plasmas

The transport properties of a plasma at very low densities or at high temperatures usually have markedly different values from those of a conventional nonionized gas. We recall from Section 12.6 that the coefficient of viscosity for a pure dilute gas is given by

$$\eta = (5/16\Omega_\eta)(MkT/\pi N_0)^{1/2}, \qquad (21.26)$$

in which M is the molecular weight of the gas, N_0 is the Avogadro number, k is the Boltzmann constant, and Ω_η is an effective collision cross-section for viscosity. In the rigid-sphere model of atoms Ω_η equals $\pi\sigma^2$, where σ is a collision diameter. In general, however, Ω_η depends on the interatomic potential energy function and on the temperature of the gas.

Since a pure gas at very high temperatures is nearly completely ionized, the interatomic potential energy for it is predominantly coulombic and strongly repulsive. For this reason an ion suffers many small deflections produced by long-range encounters as it travels from one close collision to the next. An effective cross-section must be worked out therefore by a suitable averaging process. When this is done in the theory of Enskog and of Chapman for nonuniform gases as it applies to a completely ionized plasma, the effective cross-section for viscosity to a first approximation is found to have the form

$$\Omega_\eta = \tfrac{1}{2}(e^2/2kT)^2[\ln(1+\beta^2) - \beta^2/(1+\beta^2)], \qquad (21.27)$$

where $\beta = 4dkT/e^2$. Here, e is the ionic charge and d is the maximum distance over which an ion experiences an effective interatomic force. Chapman and Cowling[2] assumed d equals the mean distance between ions $n_+{}^{-(1/3)}$. Persico,[3] however, suggested that it should equal the Debye distance h at which the electron-ion plasma shields a charged particle. For a plasma consisting of electrons with a particle density n_e and of ions with an average charge Ze,

$$h^2 = kT/4\pi n_e e^2(1+Z). \qquad (21.28)$$

[2] Chapman, S., and T. G. Cowling, *The Mathematical Theory of Non-uniform Gases*, p. 179 (The University Press, Cambridge, 1939).

[3] Persico, E., *Monthly Notices, R.A.S.*, **86**, 294 (1926).

Actually the value of h differs by only a few percent from the mean distance between ions. Maeker, Peters, and Schenk, on the other hand, concluded from their experimental study of the problem that d should be much smaller than this; and they obtained good agreement with d set equal to $\frac{1}{4}n_+^{-(1/3)}$. Fortunately, all these values of d give the same order of magnitude for the value of Ω_η. For this discussion we shall adopt for d one-quarter of the mean distance between ions. Whereas in the classical rigid-sphere model of an ideal gas the viscosity is independent of pressure, here a definite relation exists between them, for n_+ is a function of pressure.

As a specific illustration let us compute a value for the coefficient of viscosity of a plasma consisting of singly ionized nitrogen atoms at a pressure of one atmosphere and at a temperature of 20,000°K. From Fig. 21.2 we see that n_+ is approximately 2×10^{17} ions per cubic centimeter, so

$$\beta = \frac{1.38 \times 10^{-16} \times 20{,}000}{(2 \times 10^{17})^{1/3} \times (4.80 \times 10^{-10})^2} = 20.5,$$

and from Eq. (21.27) we get $\Omega_\eta = 4.39 \times 10^{-15}$ cm². Finally,

$$\eta = \frac{5}{16 \times 4.39 \times 10^{-15}} \left(\frac{14 \times 1.38 \times 10^{-16} \times 20{,}000}{\pi \times 6.03 \times 10^{23}} \right)^{1/2}$$

$$= 3.2 \times 10^{-4} \text{ gm-cm}^{-1} \text{ sec}^{-1},$$

or 320 micropoise. This value may be compared with 419 micropoise for molecular nitrogen at 1100°K.

The collision cross-section for thermal conduction among ions is identical to that for viscosity. Consequently, Eq. (12.20) for thermal conductivity,

$$\sigma_t = \tfrac{5}{2} c_v \eta, \tag{21.29}$$

applies here, in which the specific heat capacity at constant volume c_v is constant if the plasma is an ideal gas. But energy transport along a thermal gradient at elevated temperatures is much more complicated than the simple kinetic theory treatment suggests. Molecules diffusing into hot regions of the plasma absorb energy as they dissociate, and atoms moving into cool regions give up energy as they recombine. Similarly, at high temperatures atoms absorb energy as they ionize in hot regions, and they give up energy during recombination in cool regions. The rapid diffusion of thermal energy from the dissociation and ionization processes causes large increases in thermal conductivity. Lochte-Holtgreven has shown that the calculated thermal conductivity of air reaches a maximum value of nearly 0.075 w/deg at 7000°K if transport of dissociation energy is taken into account. This is more than fifteen times its value from simple theory without dissociation of molecules.

The effect of the heats of dissociation and ionization on the specific internal energy of nitrogen gas is depicted in Fig. 21.4. Since the slope of this curve equals the specific heat capacity at constant volume, c_v is far from constant. Thus in this respect the plasma is unlike an ideal gas.

The coefficient of self-diffusion for ions may be computed from Eq. (12.19),

$$D = (3/8\rho\Omega_D)(MkT/\pi N_0)^{1/2}, \tag{21.30}$$

where ρ is the mass density of the plasma and Ω_D is the collision cross-section for diffusion,

$$\Omega_D = \tfrac{1}{4}(e^2/2kT)^2 \ln(1 + \beta^2), \tag{21.31}$$

in which β has the same significance as in Eq. (21.27). From the foregoing

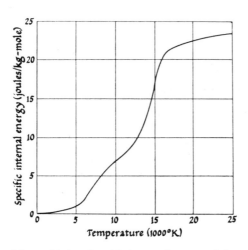

value of β and the value of ρ at 20,000°K as read from Fig. 21.3, the diffusivity of nitrogen ions is computed to equal 160 cm²/sec. The self-diffusion of nitrogen gas at 293°K and one atmosphere of pressure is only 0.20 cm²/sec. Thus although diffusion of particles in a gas increases roughly as the $\tfrac{5}{2}$ power of temperature, this effect is greatly reduced in a completely ionized plasma where strong interatomic forces exist.

Figure 21.4.   Specific internal energy of the nitrogen plasma.

An additional transport phenomenon in a plasma is that of electrical conductivity, which arises primarily from the large concentration of free electrons. To a high degree of approximation the coefficient of electrical conductivity in a neutral plasma consisting of singly charged ions (hydrogenic gas) and electrons is

$$\sigma_e = n_e e^2 D_e/kT, \tag{21.32}$$

where n_e is the number concentration and D_e is the diffusivity of electrons in the plasma. We shall not reproduce the derivation of this equation here; it may be found elsewhere.[4] The diffusivity D_e is given by an equation like Eq. (21.30); namely

$$D_e = (\pi/4Q_e n_e)(2kT/\pi m_e)^{1/2}, \tag{21.33}$$

in which m_e is the mass of an electron and Q_e is the electron-ion collision

---

[4] See, for example, *The Mathematical Theory of Non-Uniform Gases* by Chapman and Cowling (Cambridge: The University Press, 1939).

cross-section for diffusion of electrons through a hydrogenic gas. Specifically,

$$Q_e = (e^2/kT)^2 \ln (kT/e^2 n_+^{1/3}). \qquad (21.34)$$

These equations may now be combined to obtain an explicit relation between the electrical conductivity and temperature. As shown in Fig. 21.5, the theoretical curve derived from it fits the experimental data obtained by Maecker, Peters, and Schenk on a water plasma rather

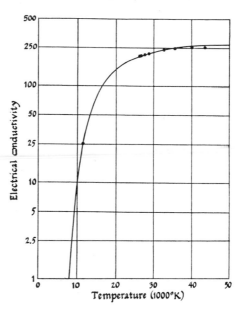

Figure 21.5.   Electrical conductivity of a water plasma. Curve, theoretical; points, experimental. [Adapted from H. Maecker, T. Peters, and H. Schenk, "Ionen und Atomquerschnitte im Plasma verschiedener Gase," *Zeits. f. Physik*, **140**, p. 119, 1955.]

well. These several thermophysical properties of plasmas are especially significant in devices which are designed to produce controlled thermo-nuclear reactions.

21.8. *The Production of High-temperature Plasmas*

In Table 21.1 are listed several methods by which very high temperatures may be attained. Perhaps the most widely exploited of these is the electric arc. Generally, the arc column is at a higher temperature than the electrodes. Thus in a free-burning, low-current (5–10 amp) arc between carbon rods temperatures of 6000–7000°K are obtained while the cathode is at 3200–3600°K and the anode is at 4000°K. Still higher temperatures can be realized in low-voltage, high-current arcs, such as between water-cooled electrodes of tungsten (cathode) and copper (anode) which carry several hundred amperes at a potential difference of only a few volts. Temperatures of 5000–30,000°K have been obtained in this way. When the arc is confined as in the Maecker water-pipe arc sustained temperatures of more than

TABLE 21.1. *Ranges of High Temperatures as Obtained by Several Methods.*

Method	Condition	Temperature range (°K)
Solar furnace	ideal sky	up to 4900
Chemical reaction		3000–6000
Plane shock wave	condensed spark	7000–17,500
	shock tube	5700–25,000
Electric arc	free-burning	3200–30,000
	confined	20,000–50,000
Exploded wire	unconfined	10,000–100,000
	confined	much higher
Pulsed discharge and spark		30,000–5,000,000
Detonation shock wave	chemical explosion	5500–41,000
	nuclear explosion (fission)	50,000–300,000
	thermonuclear explosion	up to 10^8
Nuclear reaction	nonexplosive	up to 10^{10}

50,000°K are possible. A practical limit to higher temperatures is reached when large changes in current are required to produce relatively small increases in temperature. Unfortunately, the position of the arc column within the guiding tube is rather unsteady, but attempts have been made to reduce this effect by means of water-cooled copper diaphragms.

Pulsed discharges from large transformers or charged low-inductance capacitors can produce very high temperatures. At several thousand amperes the magnetic field of the discharge current squeezes the discharge into a smaller volume, increasing the charge density and thereby the temperature of the plasma. Stability is maintained by suitable externally applied magnetic fields. In this way temperatures of 0.2–5×10^6 °K have been obtained.

When stored electrical energy is suddenly discharged through a fine wire (or a liquid jet) an explosion occurs, and the resulting plasma in the shock wave may reach a temperature of 10,000–100,000°K. Even higher temperatures are believed possible if the wire is confined. The details of the exploding-wire phenomenon are being actively investigated.

High temperatures are associated with shock waves however they may be produced. As suggested in Table 21.1, in detonation shock waves, especially from nuclear fission and fusion explosions, temperatures of 50,000–100,000,000°K are possible. But even higher temperatures are believed to come from nonexplosive nuclear reactions such as those which take place in the interior of stars.

Bibliography

Ambartsumyan, V. A. (ed), J. B. Sykes (trans.), *Theoretical Astrophysics* (Pergamon, New York, 1958).

Chapman, S., and T. G. Cowling, *The Mathematical Theory of Non-uniform Gases* (The University Press, Cambridge, 1939).

Cohen, R. S., L. Spitzer, Jr., and P. M. Rontly, "The Electrical Conductivity of an Ionized Gas," *Phys. Rev., 80,* 230–238 (1950).

Fischer, H., and L. C. Mansur (ed), *Conference on Extremely High Temperatures* (Wiley, New York, 1958).

Hirschfelder, J. O., C. F. Curtiss, and R. B. Bird, *Molecular Theory of Gases and Liquids* (Wiley, New York, 1954).

Lochte-Holtgreven, W., "Production and Measurement of High Temperatures," *Reports on Progress in Physics,* vol. XXI (The Physical Society, London, 1958), pp. 312–383.

Maecker, H., T. Peters, and H. Schenk, "Ionen-und Atomquerschnitte im Plasma verschiedener Gase," *Zeits. f. Physik,* **140,** 119–138 (1955).

Saha, M. N., and B. N. Srivastava, *A Text-book of Heat* (Indian Press, Ltd., Allahabad, India, 1931).

Shankland, R. S., *Atomic and Nuclear Physics* (Macmillan, New York, 1955).

Spitzer, L., Jr., *Physics of Fully Ionized Gases* (Interscience, New York, 1956).

Problems

1. (a) Show that for the reaction

$$2H_2O \rightleftharpoons 2H_2 + O_2$$

the law of mass action has the form

$$n_{H_2}^2 n_{O_2} / n_{H_2O}^2 = f(T).$$

(b) In the same way set down the equation of reaction, and derive the law of mass action for the double ionization of helium and also for the bimolecular reaction between hydrochloric acid HCl and calcium oxide CaO.

(c) Generalize these results by deriving the law of mass action for any reaction between components A, B, C, $\cdots$,

$$\nu_1 A + \nu_2 B + \nu_3 C + \cdots = 0$$

in which some of the numerical coefficients ν_1, ν_2, $\cdots$ are negative.

2. Evaluate $f(T)$ explicitly in terms of T for the dissociation of water vapor.

3. Show that $f(T)$ for the process $A \rightleftharpoons A^+ + e$ has the form

$$f(T) = KT^{5/2} \exp{(-E_i/kT)},$$

in which E_i is the ionization potential of atom A.

4. Consider the reaction between lithium and neon

$$\text{Li} + \text{Ne}^+ \rightleftharpoons \text{Li}^+ + \text{Ne},$$

in which lithium has a much smaller ionization potential than neon and therefore is more electropositive. Show that the equilibrium constant is given by the equation

$$f(T) = K \exp{\left[\frac{E_i(\text{Li}) - E_i(\text{Ne})}{kT} \right]},$$

and that lithium is nearly completely ionized while neon is not, in a mixture of lithium vapor and neon at very low temperatures.

5. The width of a spectral line is defined as the width of its intensity curve at half the maximum intensity. If the atoms were not in rapid thermal motion, the line would be very sharp and narrow. But because of these motions a Doppler broadening occurs. Now the probability that an atom has a velocity component between v and $v + dv$ along an arbitrary axis is given by the maxwellian distribution law

$$dw = (\beta/\pi)^{1/2} \exp{(-\beta v^2)}dv,$$

where $\beta = m/2kT$, and the change in frequency $\Delta \nu$ due to the motion of a source in the direction of the observer equals $\nu v/c$, where   is the speed of light. Show that the intensity distribution for a spectral line is

$$I_\nu = I_0 \exp{[-\beta(c^2/\nu^2)(\nu - \nu_0)^2]},$$

and from this show that the Doppler width in wavelength units is

$$(2\lambda_0/c)[(2kT/m)\ln 2]^{1/2}.$$

6. Suppose a hot plasma is composed of air and vaporized carbon, as in the column of a free-burning carbon arc. Here the relative amount of oxygen and nitrogen is known, but the amount of carbon is not. Set down the six equations which apply, and thus show that the evaluation of the eight unknown quantities necessitates independent measurements of two of them.

7. Construct the curve for the electrical conductivity of nitrogen plasma consisting of singly charged ions as a function of temperature up to 20,000°K.

8. Table 21.2 shows values of particle densities in an argon plasma at atmospheric pressure. From these data compute the mass density, viscosity, and diffusivity of the argon plasma at 10,000°K, 15,000°K, and 20,000°K.

9. Compute values for the electrical conductivity σ_e in an argon plasma at atmospheric pressure, and construct a curve to show how σ_e varies with temperature.

TABLE 21.2.   *Particle Densities in an Argon Plasma at Atmospheric Pressure**

T (°K)	n_e	n_o	n_+	n_{++}	n_{+++}
5 000	1.324(12)†	1.468(18)	1.324(12)		
6 000	2.944(13)	1.224(18)	2.944(13)		
7 000	2.715(14)	1.048(18)	2.715(14)	5.607(1)	
8 000	1.442(15)	9.150(17)	1.442(15)	2.130(4)	
9 000	5.282(15)	8.053(17)	5.282(15)	2.217(5)	
10 000	1.481(16)	7.047(17)	1.481(16)	9.285(7)	
11 000	3.378(16)	6.000(17)	3.378(16)	2.006(9)	
12 000	6.476(16)	4.824(17)	6.476(16)	2.635(10)	
13 000	1.057(17)	3.534(17)	1.057(16)	2.355(11)	
14 000	1.478(17)	2.289(17)	1.478(16)	1.557(12)	8.651(1)
15 000	1.792(17)	1.312(17)	1.792(17)	8.017(12)	4.002(3)
16 000	1.947(17)	6.949(16)	1.947(17)	3.398(13)	1.274(5)
17 000	1.975(17)	3.700(16)	1.973(17)	1.223(14)	5.281(6)
18 000	1.936(17)	2.105(16)	1.929(17)	3.828(14)	1.562(7)
19 000	1.872(17)	1.307(16)	1.851(17)	1.064(15)	4.114(8)
20 000	1.806(17)	8.834(15)	1.752(17)	2.575(15)	6.050(9)
21 000	1.746(17)	6.363(15)	1.628(17)	5.919(15)	4.900(10)
22 000	1.704(17)	4.781(15)	1.468(17)	1.181(16)	3.068(11)
23 000	1.682(17)	3.634(15)	1.264(17)	2.092(16)	1.534(12)
24 000	1.680(17)	2.716(15)	1.026(17)	3.265(16)	6.177(12)
25 000	1.685(17)	1.961(15)	7.811(16)	4.517(16)	2.033(13)
26 000	1.688(17)	1.316(15)	5.594(16)	5.634(16)	5.656(13)
27 000	1.681(17)	8.844(14)	3.813(16)	6.475(16)	1.385(14)
28 000	1.662(17)	5.612(14)	2.524(16)	7.000(16)	3.044(14)
29 000	1.633(17)	3.472(14)	1.641(16)	7.253(16)	6.162(14)
30 000	1.599(17)	2.126(14)	1.063(16)	7.286(16)	1.165(14)

* From "Thermal and Electrical Properties of an Argon Plasma," Olsen, H. N. (*Phys. Fluids 2*, pp. 614–623, 1959).
    † Power of 10.

INDEX

Abbot, 241
Absolute scale, 29
Absorption spectrum, 347
Absorptivity, 239
Accessible microstates, 196
Adiabatic, definition, 7
Air conditioning, 74
Allen, 116, 290, 291
Andrews, 139
Andronikashvili, 299
Antimony point, 25, 28
Atomic spectra, 249, 346–347
Aubert, 116
Average speeds of gas molecules, 181
Avogadro, 160
Avogadro number, 160, 209, 213, 232, 265
Avogadro's hypothesis, 160
Azizia, 242

Bacon, 4
Balmer series, 350
Bardeen, 313, 314
Beattie, 23, 35
Beau de Rochas, 67
Beckmann, 322
Becquerel, 10
Benedicks, 330
Bernoulli, 9
Bernoulli's equation, 329
Berthelot, 35
Bessel function, 320
Biot, 317
Bismuth, 147, 168, 303
Black, 4
Blackbody, 28, 238, 239
Blackbody radiation, 243–250
Bleaney, 218, 278
Bohr magneton, 233
Boiling point, effect of pressure, 88
Bolometer, 243
Bolton, 3
Boltzmann, 10, 185, 197, 199, 239
Boltzmann constant, 37, 160, 200, 253; factor, 220, 231, 281
Born, 227
360

Bose-Einstein distribution law, 258–260, 267
Bots, 296
Boyle, 4, 34
Boyle's law, 23
Brayton cycle, 71
Bridgman, 1, 35, 125, 147
Brightness temperature, 28, 241
Brillouin, 234, 251
Brillouin cycle, 251, 252; equation, 235
British Thermal Unit, 8
Brooks, 319
Brown, 10, 156
Brownian motion, 10, 156, 207, 212, 253; in gases, 209; linear, 209; of colloidal suspensions, 209; of galvanometer coil, 210; rotational, 210
Buchdahl, 83
Bulk modulus, 135
Bureau of Standards, 17
Burhorn, 347

Callendar, 31
Caloric theory, 4
Calorie, 8
Calorimeter, 241; adiabatic, 53
Canonical distribution, 197
Capacitor, state equation, 44
Capillary flow, 330
Carathéodory, 83
Carbon 12, 51
Carbon dioxide: P-V diagram, 139–140
Carbon monoxide, specific heat, 161
Carnot, 63
Carnot cycle: electric cell, 64; gas, 63–64; paramagnetic substance, 63, 64; stretched wire, 63, 64
Carnot engine, 65; refrigerator, 66
Carnot's theorem, 81; corollary, 82
Casimir, 313
Cells in item-space, 215; in phase space, 197
Celsius, 3
Celsius scale, 30
Cerium magnesium nitrate, 282
Cesium, 169

Chapman, 185, 352
Chapman-Enskog theory, 185
Charge fluctuations, 213
Charles, 34
Chemical equilibrium, 33
Chemical potential, 153, 203
Chemical process, 5
Christy, 121
Chromium potassium alum thermometer, 278
Clapeyron, 86
Clapeyron equation, 95, 150; generalized form, 85
Clark, 122
Claude's gas-liquefying machines, 270
Clausius, 10, 86, 159
Clausius' theorem, 93
Clearance volume, 67, 70
Clement, 120
Clusius, 286
Coblenz, 248
Coefficient of performance, 66, 74
Cohen, 301
Coin systems, statistics, 193–195
Collins helium-liquefying system, 271
Collision cross-section: 178, 186; parameter, 349; probability, 189; frequencies, table, 181
Collisions, 349
Comet tail, 132
Complexion, 193
Compressibility: adiabatic, 42, 123, 135; isothermal, 41, 135
Compressibility factor, 34; critical value, 142
Compressional wave, speed, 123, 227
Compression ratio, 67, 70
Compressor, axial flow, 71
Condensation, 55
Condensation, Bose-Einstein gas, 260
Condensation: Smoluchowski, 219; mean square value, 221
Conduction electrons, 230
Conductor, heat, 317, 324–325
Convection, 320; coefficient, 322; forced, 323; natural, 323
Cooling curve, 54
Cooper, 31
Corak, 312
Corresponding isotherms, 15
Count Rumford, 4, 320
Cowling, 352
Crank-end dead center, 67
Critical isotherm, 140
Critical point, 140, 142, 144, 220, 221, 287; data table, 143
Critical temperature for Einstein condensation, 293

Curie constant, 38, 126, 235; law, 38, 126, 232, 235
Current fluctuations, 212

Dalton's law, 124
Daunt, 291, 294, 301
Davy, 4
Dead space, 23
Death Valley, 242
de Boer, 301
de Broglie, 209
Debye, 227
Debye distance, 352; equation, 228, 232; temperature, 228–229
Degradation of energy, 102
Degree of freedom, 161, 246
de Groot, 331
de Klerk, 272
Delsaulx, 156
Demagnetization, 271, 272
Denbigh, 116, 331
Density fluctuation, 218
Density in phase, 201
Desormes, 120
Diathermic wall, 7
Dielectric constant, helium, 285
Diesel, 69
Diesel engine, 67–70
Dieterici equation of state, 152
Diffraction, 10
Diffusion: 330; coefficient, 185, 186; entropy production, 327; potential, 330; rate, 184; temperature, 185, 330; thermal energy, 353
Diffusivity of electrons, 354
Dipole, magnetic, 37, 126, 232
Dipole moment: electric, 232; electron, 233; magnetic, 232; mean value per molecule, 231; nitrous oxide, 233; oxygen, 233; paramagnetic gas, 234; silver, 234
Disorder, 103
Displacement law, radiation, 243, 249
Dissociation energy, 344, 345, 353
Distribution law, radiation, 243
Doppler broadening of spectral lines, 346, 348
Doppler effect, 174, 244, 346
Dorn, 330
Drebbel, 2
Dry-air lapse rate, 127
Dual cycle, 70
Dufour, 330
Dulong, 132, 225

Earth, radiation, 241, 254; surface temperature, 242–243

Earth's crust, penetration of freezing temperatures, 319; temperature variations, 317–318
Eastman, 334
Effective temperature, 240
Efficiency, thermal, 65
Ehrenfest's equations, 151
Ehrenhaft, 209
Einstein, 10, 156, 203, 207, 210, 226, 293
Einstein: condensation temperature, 262; equation for Brownian motion, 208; quantum condensation, 293
Elastic continuum, 227; moduli, 41, 235; systems, 36
Elastomers, 133–134
Eldridge, 167
Electric arc, 356; dipoles, 231, 232
Electric conduction, 330
Electrolytic cell: Carnot cycle, 63; state equation, 37
Electromagnetic radiation, 10; spectrum, 237–238
Electron emission, 171; gas, 173; temperature, 173, 348
Electronic specific heats, 264–266
Electron-volt, 8
Electro-osmosis, 330
Electrophoresis, 330
Electropyrosis, 330
Elvins, 3
emf, 37
Emissivity, 238
Energy: availability, 101; density, 36, 260; equation, 130; fluctuation, 207; gap, 300; tranfer (flow), 328
Enlarged system, 97
Ensemble, 193
Enskog, 185, 352
Enthalpy, 52, 129, 328
Entropy, 49, 129; change, 96, 97, 252; creation, 326, 327; of conductor, 325; of gas mixture, 124; in living systems, 326; statistical, 199, 200; thermodynamic, 93; zero, 94
Equation of continuity, 317
Equation of state, 15, 34, 36, 37
Equilibrium constant, 345–346
Equipartition of energy, 161, 213, 246
Ergodic hypothesis, 192
Estermann, 169
Eucken, 184
Evaporation, 55
Exact differential, 43
Expansion ratio, 70
Expansivity: linear, 40; volume, 41
Exploding wire phenomenon, 356
Extensibility, long range, 133

Extension-in-phase, 201
Extensive quantities, 47

Fahrenheit, 3
Fahrenheit scale, 29, 30
Fairbank, 299
Far-surround, 1
Fermi-Dirac distribution law, 262, 263
Fermi energy, 265; of sodium, 264
Fermi oscillator, 203
Feynman, 301
Fick, 330
Fick's law, 185, 317, 330
Film transfer: coefficient, 321, 322; rate, 290
Filtration, 330
Fitten, 319
Fixed point, 16; basic, 24, 25; primary standard, 16; secondary, 24, 25; standard pair, 16
Flow equation, 317
Flow processes: creation of entropy, 326; energy transfer, 328
Flow potential, 330; temperature, 330
Fluctuation: density, 218; electron number, 217; emf, 213; energy, 207; momentum, 207; potential energy, 219, 220; power dissipation, 214, 215; volume, 218
Foot-pound, 8
Fountain effect, 116, 290, 334
Fourier, 317, 320, 330
Fourier: analysis, 212; heat conduction, 336; law, 183, 317; series, 320
Fourth-power law, 36, 239, 249
Fowler, 84, 192
Frandsen, 109
Fraunhofer, 10
Free energy, 152
Free expansion, 107, 110
Free path, 177, 186
Free-path volume, 178
Freezing point, effect of pressure, 88
Freezing process, 55
Fröhlich, 313
Fuel-air engine, 69
Fusion, curves, 144; nuclear, 356

Gadolinium sulfate, 272
Galileo, 2
Galvanometer: rotational Brownian motion, 210; sensitivity, 210
Gamma, 136; measurement, 120; table of values, 123
Gamma function, 221
Gas: absorption, 23; Carnot cycle, 63; liquefication, 112; pressure in kinetic theory, 159; universal constant, 34, 160

Gas thermometer, 22; corrections, 23
Gasoline engine, 66–69
Gaussian distribution, 217
Gay-Lusac, 34, 108
Generalized displacement, 47; force, 47
Gerlach, 233
Giauque, 16, 272
Gibbs, 193
Gibbs function, 129, 148, 152; law of partial entropies, 124; paradox, 125
Gold point, 24, 25, 29
Gorter, 272, 296, 299, 313
Gough, 37, 134
Gough-Joule effects, 133
Gouy, 156
Graham's law, 163
Grand Duke of Tuscany, 3
Guggenheim, 84
Guldberg, 344
Guth, 37

Halliday, 239
Harmonic oscillators, 202
Head-end dead center, 67
Heat, 5, 49, 280
Heat of crystallization, 57
Heat of discharge, 57
Heat of formation, 57
Heat of mixture, 57
Heat of reaction, 57
Heat of relaxation, 57
Heat of solution, 57
Heat of transport, 163, 333
Heat of transformation, 311
Heat of vaporization, 87, 169, 285
Heat capacity: Black's discovery, 4; definition, 50; measurement, 53–55; related to enthalpy, 52; related to internal energy, 52; symbols, 51
Heat conduction rate, 183; current density, 292
Heat engine, 65; pump, 74; reservoir, 57
Heat exchange: universal law, 323–324; Prevost's law, 237
Heat flow: cylinder, 320; Earth, 317–319; in He II, 295; slab, 320
Heat reservoir, 57–58
Heat-work cycle, 62
Heisenberg's uncertainty principle, 257
Helium: data for melting, 154; first triple point, 146; internal convection, 292; λ-point, 146, 286; liquid I and II, 286; physical properties, 145, 288, 284–301; second sound, 297; second triple point, 146; separated from nitrogen, 163; solid, 146, 284; two liquid phases, 145

Helium 3: physical properties, 288; production, 288
Helium 4: physical properties, 284–301
Helium vapor-pressure thermometer, 32
Helmholtz function, 60, 129, 198
Henshaw, 300
Hertz, 10
Heylandt, 270
Hooke, 3, 4, 9
Hooke's law, 36, 41
Household heating, 74
Hull, A., 218
Hull, G., 132
Hydrogen, 162, 275

Ice, heat of sublimation, 87, 148
Ice point, 16, 23
Ideal crystalline solid, 225
Ideal elastomer, state equation, 137
Ideal gas, 23, 39, 156–157, 250; adiabatic equation, 119; definition, 34, 156–157; entropy, 200; Helmholtz function, 200; in kinetic theory, 156; internal energy, 110, 200; molar heat capacity, 161; partition sum, 200; values of γ, 123, 161
Ideal gas temperatures equivalent to Kelvin temperature, 84
Indicator diagram, 67
Inexact differential, 48
Information, 251, 253, 326
Inner melting, 18
Integrating factor, 48
Intensity of radiation, 36, 238
Intensive quantities, 47
Interdiffusion, 125
Intermediate state, 307
Internal convection, 292, 295
Internal energy, 5, 49, 128, 131, 156, 198; of ideal gas, 110, 200; of paramagnetic substance, 132
Internal pressure, 129
International Conference on Weights and Measures, 3, 8, 29
Inversion point, 113
Ionization potential, 350
Irradiancy, 238; of Earth, 241, 254
Irreversibility, 102–103
Irreversible process, 38; change of entropy, 94, 97
Isenthalpic curve, 113
Isentropic process, 50
Isobaric process, 40
Isochoric process, 40
Isodynamic process, 40
Isometric coefficient, 134; process, 40
Isotherm for water, 142, 143

Isotope effect, 304
Item space, 215

James, 37
James-Guth equation, 37, 134
Jeans, 180, 245
Jet engine, 71
Jet-propulsion, 72
Johnson, 213
Johnson emf, 214; noise, 214
Jones, H., 116, 290, 291
Jones, R., 211
Joule, 4, 16, 108, 111, 134, 159
Joule (unit), 8
Joule coefficients, 108; cycle, 71; heating, 335
Joule-Thomson coefficient, 113, 114, 115; effect, 111, 290, 330

Kapitza, 270
Kappler, 211
Katz, 122
Keesom, 284, 286, 312
Kelvin, 16, 102, 317
Kelvin temperature, 82; equivalent to ideal gas temperature, 84
Kepler, 132
Khalatnikev, 300
Kilowatt-hour, 8
Kinetic temperature, 343
Kinetic theory, 9, 156, 157; distribution law, 165
Kirchhoff, 10
Kirchhoff-Stewart law, 239, 240
Knudsen effect, 23
Ko, 167, 168
Kramers, 299
Kurti, 272
Kusch, 167, 168-169

Lagrange's method of undetermined multipliers, 164, 197
λ-point, 146, 286
Landau, 299
Lane, 299
Langen, 67
Langevin, 37, 207
Langevin function, 231, 235
Langley, 241, 243
Laplace, 9, 123
Latent heat, 4, 150; definition, 55
Lavoisier, 9
Law of heat exchange, Prevost, 237; universal, 323-324
Law of mass action, 343-344, 347
Laws of thermodynamics: first, 7, 49, 280; second, 78-79, 97, 99-100; third, 83-84, 94-95, 280; zero, 14

Lebedew, 132
Leverton, 122
Lewis log-log plot, 302-303
Life, 253, 326
Lindemann, 135
Line broadening, 349; profile, 349; width, 345, 347
Linnaeus, 3
Liouville theorem, 192, 201
Lippmann, 116, 329, 330
Liquid saturation curve, 140, 144; surfaces, 89; tension, 141
Liter-atmosphere, 8
Lithium chloride, 169
Living systems, 326
Local universe, 96
Lochte-Holtgreven, 352, 353
Locke, 4
Logarithmic temperature, 31
London, 262, 292, 293, 313
Lorenz, 321
Lummer, 10, 120, 132, 240

Macroscopic variables, 13
Macrosystem, 193
MacDougal, 272
Maeker, 353, 355
Maeker water-pipe arc, 355
Magnetic dipole, 230-235; moment, 37, 232; temperature, 273, 277
Magnetization, 132
Magnetocaloric coefficient, 271, 282
Maneuvier, 120
Massieu, 118
Massieu function, 118, 137
Matthais, 305
Mayer, 7, 8
Maxwell, 10, 131, 163, 197, 250
Maxwell's distribution law, 163-167, 202, 247
Maxwell's identities, 129, 130, 134
Maxwell's sorting demon, 250-251
McCombie, 211
Mean collision frequency, 187, 188
Mean distance of travel, 189
Mean fluctuation in current, 217
Mean free paths, 177-178, 181, 187
Mean potential energy, 220
Mean square condensation, 221
Mean square deviation, 205-206
Mechanical equilibrium, 33
Mechanical process, 5
Meissner, 307
Meissner effect, 307-309
Meixner, 334
Melting, 55
Mendelssohn, 291, 294

Mental experiments, 38
Mercury superconductivity, 285
Metallic vapors, 170
Method of successive approximations, 322
Microscopic reversibility, 331
Microstates, 191, 192
Microsystem, 191, 192
Miller, 167
Millikan, 209
Molar dipole moment, 232
Molar heat capacity, 183, 186
Molar volume, definition, 34, 51
Mole, definition, 51
Molecular band structure, 346; beam apparatus, 167–168; chains, 134; diameters, 182; distribution of speeds, 165; effusion, 162; heat, 226; random flight, 207
Monochromatic energy density, 246, 248
Monochromatic radiancy, 239
Monomolecular film, state equation, 44
Moon, 241; surface temperature, 242
Munters, 74

Natural convection, 321
Natural processes, 102
Near-surround, 1
Negative temperature, 278–281
Negentropy, 253, 325
Nernst, 84, 135, 275
Nerst-Lindemann equation, 135
Neumann, 226
Neutron-scattering experiments, 300
Newton, 123, 180
Nichols, 132, 248
Nitrogen, distribution of speeds, 166; Joule-Thomson effect, 111
Noise spectrum, 213
Nollet, 330
Nordlund, 209
Normal boiling point, definition, 140
Normal distribution, 192
Normal modes of vibration, 227
Nuclear demagnetization, 272
Nuclear paramagnetic thermometer, 278
Nuclear reaction temperatures, 356
Nuclear reactor, 178
Nuclear spin systems, 279
Nusselt, 321
Nyquist, 213

Ochsenfeld, 307
Occupation number, 196, 216
Ohm, 330
Ohm's law, 317, 330
Olsen, 359

Onnes, 35, 284, 305
Onsagner's theorem, 331
Opalescence, 221
Operational definition, 2
Opportunity, 101
Optical pyrometers, 26–28, 240–241; disappearing filament, 27, 241; total radiation, 27, 240
Osmosis, 330
Osterberg, 111
Otto, 67
Otto cycle, 67–69
Oxygen point, 25, 28, 30
Oxygen, susceptibility, 236

Palevsky, 300
Paramagnetic salt thermometer, 276
Paramagnetic substance, 37, 132; Carnot cycle, 65
Partial derivative, definition, 40, 42
Partial pressure, 124, 344
Partition sum, 198, 348; for harmonic oscillator, 202; for ideal gas, 199–200
Paschen, 240, 248
Pauli exclusion principle, 262
Peltier, 335
Peltier coefficient, 335, 337
Peltier heat, 335, 337
Periodic table, 304
Permeability of free space, 232
Permittivity of free space, 232
Perrin, 10, 156, 209, 210
Persico, 352
Persistence of velocities, 180
Persistent currents, 309
Peshkov, 298, 299
Peters, 353, 355
Petit, 132, 225
Phase space, 192, 258
Phase transformation: Gibbs function, 148, 149
Phase transformation of first kind, 40, 95, 138, 149; of second kind, 138, 149
Phase velocity, 36
Phonon field, 300, 314
Phonons, 300, 301
Photoelectric cell, 241
Photoelectric effect, 10, 249
Photoelectrons, velocity distribution, 256
Photomultiplier tube, 241
Photosphere, 343
Pinch effect, 356
Planck, 10, 115, 155, 243, 247, 256
Planck function, 115, 137
Planck's law, 27, 29, 137, 247, 248, 342
Planckian oscillator, 202, 226–228

Plasma, 347, 350; argon, 359; collision cross-section, 353, 354; electrical conductivity, 354–355; ionic composition, 350; nitrogen, 351, 353; self-diffusion, 354; temperature, 347–348, 355–356; transport phenomena, 352–354; viscosity, 352, 353
Plate-current fluctuations, 218
Platinum resistance thermometers, 19–20, 275
Poiseille's law, 317, 330
Poisson distribution law, 216
Polymer dissociation energies, 169
Potassium, 168
Pound, 278
Precession of magnetic dipoles, 231
Pre-ignition, 69
Pressure dilation, 23
Prevost's theory of exchanges, 237
Principle of detailed balance, 201
Principle of superposition, 328
Pringsheim, 10, 120, 132, 240
Probability, 193–194, 266–267
Probe, 173
Prout, 320
Pulsed discharge, 356
Purcell, 278
P-V-T surface, 144–145
Pyrometer, 26–28, 240–41
Pyrometry, 240

Quantum, 243, 247–248
Quantum of energy, 249, 252, 256
Quantum theory of dipole moment, 233–235
Quasistatic process, definition, 38
Quinke, 330

Radiancy: definition, 238; of sun, 242
Radiant energy density, 240
Radiation constant, 36, 240
Radiation pressure, 132, 137, 240
Radiation temperature, 240
Radiative systems, 36, 203
Ram-jet, 72
Ramsey, N., 278, 280
Ramsey, W., 163
Random currents, 212
Random flight, 188, 208
Rankine, 29, 30
Rankine scale, 30
Rapid evaporation, 271
Raumann, 116
Rayleigh, 245
Rayleigh-Jeans law, 246
Rayleigh's law of scattering, 219
Reciprocal relations, 331

Reciprocal temperature scale, 280
Red shift, 349
Reference junction, 26, 27
Reflectancy, 238
Refractive index, 219
Refrigerants, 73
Refrigeration cycle, 66; reversible, 62
Refrigerator: vapor absorption, 74–76; vapor compression, 66
Regnault, 226
Renaldini, 3
Resistance thermometers, 19–20
Retarding potential, 173
Reuss, 330
Reynolds, 116, 163, 329, 330
Richardson-Dushmann equation, 172
Richardson plot, 172
Riemann zeta-function, 261
Rieser, 121
Rinkel, 122
Robinson, 272
Rockets, 72
Roebuck, 111
Roemer, 3
Roentgen, 10
Root mean square displacement of molecules, 188
Root mean square speed, 157
Rossini, 109
Rotational Brownian motion, 210
Rotons, 300
Rubber, state equation, 37, 133–134
Rubens, 248
Rüchardt, 120, 121
Rumford, 4, 320
Rutger's formula, 311

Saha, 23, 344
Satterthwaite, 312
Sawl, 7
Scattering of light, 219
Schenk, 353, 355
Schmidt, 322
Schottky, 217
Schrieffer, 314
Schrödinger, 253
Sears, 101
Secondary emission, 241
Secondary flow processes, 329–331
Second displacement law, 245
Second law of thermodynamics: Clausius' statement, 80; Kelvin-Planck statement, 80; Kelvin-Planck-Ramsey statement, 280
Second sound, 297
Seebeck, 26, 335
Seebeck effect, 26, 335

Seguin, 8
Self-diffusion coefficient, 354
Sensitivity of galvanometer, 210
Shock wave, 356
Shoenberg, 306
Silver, Debye temperature, 230
Simon, 272
Simpson, 169
Sizos, 305
Small-shot effect, 217
Smithsonian Institute, 241
Smoluchowski, 207, 219
Sodium, electronic energy, 265
Sodium chloride, Debye temperature, 230
Solar constant, 241
Solar furnace, 356
Sommerfeld, 230, 263
Soret, 330
Sound speed in dry air, 127
Space charge, 171; smoothing factor, 218
Space quantization, 233
Species of matter, definition, 55
Specific charge, 47
Specific dipole moment, 230
Specific enthalpy, 53, 113, 119, 328
Specific entropy: change in, 108, 310; of helium II, 296
Specific Gibbs function, 152, 296; magnetic system, 309
Specific heat, 9, 47, 51; air, 51; Debye's theory, 227; difference $c_p - c_v$, 117 118; Einstein's theory, 226; electrons, 264; helium, 285, 286; hydrogen, 161–162; magnetic, 126, 277; molar at low temperatures, 104; solid, 228; water, 9, 51, 105
Specific Helmholtz function, 152
Specific internal energy, 45, 47, 53, 228, 287; helium, 287; nitrogen, 354
Specific volume, 47; water, 127, 148
Spectral energy distribution, 243
Spohr, 272
Srivastava, 23
Standard pair of fixed points, 16
Standard thermometer features, 274
Stark effect, 349
State, definition, 1
Statistical entropy of ideal gas, 200
Steady state, 61
Steam point, 16, 25, 28
Steenland, 272
Stefan, 36, 132, 239
Stefan's constant, 36, 249
Stefan's law, 36, 131
Stern, 169, 233
Stern-Gerlach experiment, 233
Stimson, 18

Stirling's approximation, 194
Stokes law, 208
Sublimation, 55, 144
Subscript notation, 41
Sulfur, normal boiling point, 24, 25
Sulfur point, 25, 28
Sun, 241; surface temperature, 242, 244; radiancy, 242
Superconductivity, 301; intermediate state, 307; Meissner effect, 307; shielding currents, 307; specific heat, 311; theories, 312–314
Superconductors: alloys and compounds, 305; distribution in periodic table, 304; effect of pressure, 305; elements, 302, 304; isotope effect, 304; magnetic properties, 305–309; threshold field, 305–306
Supercooling, 141
Superfluidity, 289–291; BCS theory, 314; two-fluid model, 313
Super heat conduction, 292, 294
Superheating, 141
Supersaturation, 141
Surface energy, 89
Surface heat, 89
Surface tension, 44, 89
Surface work, 89
Survival equation, 189
Susceptibility, 277
Sutherland, 190
Sutherland equation, 189
Swenson, 287
System, symbol, 58
Szilard, 251

Tamura, 319
T-cube law, 228
Tektites, 254
Temperature, 3, 13–32, 274–278, 346–350; absolute, 49; basic concept, 2; chart, 342; ideal gas, 24, 84; in kinetic theory, 160; in statistics, 279; integrating factor, 49; Kelvin, 82, 84; of heat conductors, 324; operational definition, 2; parameter, 15; speed of sound method of measurement, 123; wave, 318
Thallium, 168
Thermal capacity, 50
Thermal conductivity, 183, 186, 292, 317, 353
Thermal conduction, 101, 317, 319, 324, 330; production of entropy, 326, 327
Thermal convection, 320–324
Thermal current density, 317
Thermal diffusivity, 317, 319
Thermal efficiency, 65
Thermal effusion, 117

Thermal emf, 27
Thermal equilibrium, 14, 33
Thermal expansion: linear, 40; volume, 41
Thermal noise, 212, 213
Thermal process, definition, 5
Thermal transpiration, 116, 163
Thermionic current, 217
Thermionic emission, 55, 171
Thermionic work function, 172
Thermobaroscope, 2
Thermocouple, 26, 27, 335–338; circuit, 27, 336; copper-constantan, 275; in pyrometer, 240; standard, 29
Thermodiffusion, 185, 330
Thermodynamic equations of motion, 330
Thermodynamic equilibrium, 33
Thermodynamic potential, 152
Thermodynamic process, 5, 33, 39–40
Thermodynamic surface, 39, 144–145
Thermoelastic properties of elastomers, 133
Thermo-electricity, 330, 334–335
Thermometers: gas, 21–24; liquid-in-glass, 18–19; paramagnetic salt, 276; pyrometers, 27, 240–241; resistance, 19–21, 276; semi-conductor, 275–276; thermocouple, 26, 27, 335; vapor pressure, 275
Thermometric property, 16
Thermonuclear reactions, 355
Thermo-osmosis, 116, 290, 329, 330, 331–333
Thermophysical coefficients, 40–42
Thermophysical probability, 193–196
Thermopile, 27, 240
Thompson, 4
Thomson coefficient, 334
Thomson curves, 141
Thomson heat, 335, 336
Thomson isotherm, 141, 151
Thomson, J., 140, 155
Thomson, W. (Lord Kelvin), 16, 83, 86, 111, 140, 330, 334, 337
Thoriated tungsten, 172
Threshold field, 306
Threshold field curve, 306, 309, 310
Throttling process, 73, 112–113, 270
Throttling valve, 73, 329
Tisza, 291, 293, 294, 297
Tolman, 192
Total radiation pyrometer, 240
Transit times, 187
Transition probability, 348
Transport phenomena in plasma, 352–353
Transverse waves, 227, 228
Trial and error method, 322
Triple line, 144
Triple point, 144–148; bismuth, 147; definition, 16; helium, 286; water, 16, 146, 148
Triple point cell, 17–18
Turbine, 71
Turner, 83
Two-fluid theory: of helium II, 292; of superconductivity, 313
Tyndal, 4, 239

Unavailable work, 102
Unsöld, 350
Unswept volume, 67
Uranium, 163

Van der Waals, 35
Van der Waals constants, table, 35
Van der Waals equation, 35, 143
Van der Waals fluid, 35, 127, 142
Van Laer, 312
Vapor absorption refrigerator, 74–76
Vapor-compression refrigerator, 66, 73–74
Vapor pressure, 140, 153; equation, 87
Vapor saturation curve, 140, 144
Velocity distribution function, 165, 167
Verwiebe, 147
Virial coefficients, 36
Virial equation, 35–36
Viscosity, 353; coefficient, 179–180, 186, 352; gas, 179–180; helium II, 290; measurement by capillary tube, 291; measurement by oscillating disk, 291; Sutherland equation, 190
Viscus drag, 180
Volume fluctuations, 218
von Kármán, 227
von Platen, 74

Waage, 344
Warburg, 248
Wasscher, 299
Water: heat of fusion, 105; heat of vaporization, 87, 88; P-V-T surface, 145, 147; surface energy, 89; surface tension, 89; triple points, 146, 148
Weiss, 38
Weiss constant, 38
Westgren, 209
Weston cell, 37
Wheatstone bridge, 243
Wien, 243, 246
Wien displacement law, 245
Wien distribution law, 245
Wiener, 156
Williams, 218
Wire: Carnot cycle, 63–64; equation of state, 36; isothermal extension, 36

Wolfke, 286
Wollaston, 10
Woods, 122
Work: adiabatic, 50; external, 46; graphical representation, 47–48; integrals, 48; internal, 46; sign convention, 7
Work capacity, 60
Work function, 152, 172
Working substance, 65
Work reservoir, 57
Worthing, 2, 239

X-Rays, 10

Yarnell, 300
Young, 10
Young's modulus, 37, 41; adiabatic, 41; common definition, 44; isothermal, 41

Zartmann, 167
Zeeman effect, 233
Zemansky, 337
Zero-point energy of electrons, 265
Zustandsumme, 198